GRADE

4

Curriculum Units

1 | Factors, Multiples, and Arrays
Multiplication and Division 1

2 | Describing the Shape of the Data
Data Analysis and Probability

3 | Multiple Towers and Division Stories
Multiplication and Division 2

4 | Size, Shape, and Symmetry
2-D Geometry and Measurement

5 | Landmarks and Large Numbers
Addition, Subtraction, and the Number System

6 | Fraction Cards and Decimal Squares
Fractions and Decimals

7 | Moving Between Solids and Silhouettes
3-D Geometry and Measurement

8 | How Many Packages? How Many Groups?
Multiplication and Division 3

9 | Penny Jars and Plant Growth
Patterns, Functions, and Change

Multiple Towers and Division Stories

Multiplication and Division 2

UNIT 3

Polished Spiral Karin Kuhlmann

"Although the creation of fractals is bounded to strict mathematical rules, the results are always very inspiring."– **Karin Kuhlmann**

GRADE 4

Multiple Towers and Division Stories

Multiplication and Division 2 UNIT 3

Investigations

IN NUMBER, DATA, AND SPACE®

Glenview, Illinois • Boston, Massachusetts
Chandler, Arizona • Upper Saddle River, New Jersey

The Investigations curriculum was developed by TERC, Cambridge, MA.

This material is based on work supported by the National Science Foundation ("NSF") under Grant No. ESI-0095450. Any opinions, findings, and conclusions or recommendations expressed in this material are those of the author(s) and do not necessarily reflect the views of the National Science Foundation.

ISBN-13: 978-0-328-60031-1
ISBN-10: 0-328-60031-8

5 6 7 8 9 10 V064 16 15 14 13

Co-Principal Investigators

Susan Jo Russell

Karen Economopoulos

Authors

Lucy Wittenberg
Director Grades 3–5

Karen Economopoulos
Director Grades K–2

Virginia Bastable
(SummerMath for Teachers, Mt. Holyoke College)

Katie Hickey Bloomfield

Keith Cochran

Darrell Earnest

Arusha Hollister

Nancy Horowitz

Erin Leidl

Megan Murray

Young Oh

Beth W. Perry

Susan Jo Russell

Deborah Schifter
(Education Development Center)

Kathy Sillman

Administrative Staff

Amy Taber
Project Manager

Beth Bergeron

Lorraine Brooks

Emi Fujiwara

Contributing Authors

Denise Baumann

Jennifer DiBrienza

Hollee Freeman

Paula Hooper

Jan Mokros

Stephen Monk
(University of Washington)

Mary Beth O'Connor

Judy Storeygard

Cornelia Tierney

Elizabeth Van Cleef

Carol Wright

Technology

Jim Hammerman

Classroom Field Work

Amy Appell

Rachel E. Davis

Traci Higgins

Julia Thompson

Note: Unless otherwise noted, all contributors listed above were staff of the Education Research Collaborative at TERC during their work on the curriculum. Other affiliations during the time of development are listed.

Collaborating Teachers

This group of dedicated teachers carried out extensive field testing in their classrooms, met regularly to discuss issues of teaching and learning mathematics, provided feedback to staff, welcomed staff into their classrooms to document students' work, and contributed both suggestions and written material that has been incorporated into the curriculum.

Bethany Altchek
Linda Amaral
Kimberly Beauregard
Barbara Bernard
Nancy Buell
Rose Christiansen
Chris Colbath-Hess
Lisette Colon
Kim Cook
Frances Cooper
Kathleen Drew
Rebeka Eston Salemi
Thomas Fisher
Michael Flynn
Holly Ghazey
Susan Gillis
Danielle Harrington
Elaine Herzog
Francine Hiller
Kirsten Lee Howard
Liliana Klass
Leslie Kramer
Melissa Lee Andrichak
Kelley Lee Sadowski
Jennifer Levitan
Mary Lou LoVecchio
Kristen McEnaney
Maura McGrail
Kathe Millett
Florence Molyneaux
Amy Monkiewicz
Elizabeth Monopoli
Carol Murray
Robyn Musser
Christine Norrman
Deborah O'Brien
Timothy O'Connor
Anne Marie O'Reilly
Mark Paige
Margaret Riddle
Karen Schweitzer
Elisabeth Seyferth
Susan Smith
Debra Sorvillo
Shoshanah Starr
Janice Szymaszek
Karen Tobin
JoAnn Trauschke
Ana Vaisenstein
Yvonne Watson
Michelle Woods
Mary Wright

Advisors

Deborah Lowenberg Ball,
University of Michigan

Hyman Bass, Professor of Mathematics and Mathematics Education
University of Michigan

Mary Canner, Principal, Natick Public Schools

Thomas Carpenter, Professor of Curriculum and Instruction,
University of Wisconsin-Madison

Janis Freckmann, Elementary Mathematics Coordinator,
Milwaukee Public Schools

Lynne Godfrey, Mathematics Coach,
Cambridge Public Schools

Ginger Hanlon, Instructional Specialist in Mathematics,
New York City Public Schools

DeAnn Huinker, Director, Center for Mathematics and
Science Education Research, University of Wisconsin-Milwaukee

James Kaput, Professor of Mathematics, University of
Massachusetts-Dartmouth

Kate Kline, Associate Professor, Department of Mathematics
and Statistics, Western Michigan University

Jim Lewis, Professor of Mathematics,
University of Nebraska-Lincoln

William McCallum, Professor of Mathematics,
University of Arizona

Harriet Pollatsek, Professor of Mathematics,
Mount Holyoke College

Debra Shein-Gerson, Elementary Mathematics Specialist,
Weston Public Schools

Gary Shevell, Assistant Principal,
New York City Public Schools

Liz Sweeney, Elementary Math Department,
Boston Public Schools

Lucy West, Consultant, Metamorphosis:
Teaching Learning Communities, Inc.

This revision of the curriculum was built on the work of the many authors who contributed to the first edition (published between 1994 and 1998). We acknowledge the critical contributions of these authors in developing the content and pedagogy of *Investigations*:

Authors

Joan Akers

Michael T. Battista

Douglas H. Clements

Karen Economopoulos

Marlene Kliman

Jan Mokros

Megan Murray

Ricardo Nemirovsky

Andee Rubin

Susan Jo Russell

Cornelia Tierney

Contributing Authors

Mary Berle-Carman

Rebecca B. Corwin

Rebeka Eston

Claryce Evans

Anne Goodrow

Cliff Konold

Chris Mainhart

Sue McMillen

Jerrie Moffet

Tracy Noble

Kim O'Neil

Mark Ogonowski

Julie Sarama

Amy Shulman Weinberg

Margie Singer

Virginia Woolley

Tracey Wright

Contents

UNIT 3

Multiple Towers and Division Stories

Overview of Program Components

FOR TEACHERS

The **Curriculum Units** are the teaching guides. (See far right.)

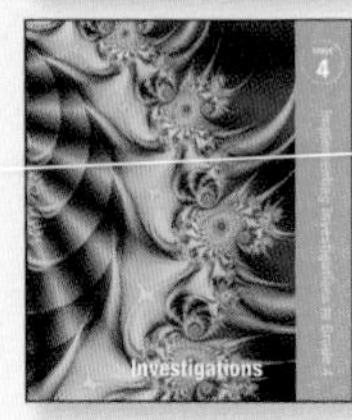

Implementing Investigations in Grade 4 offers suggestions for implementing the curriculum. It also contains a comprehensive index.

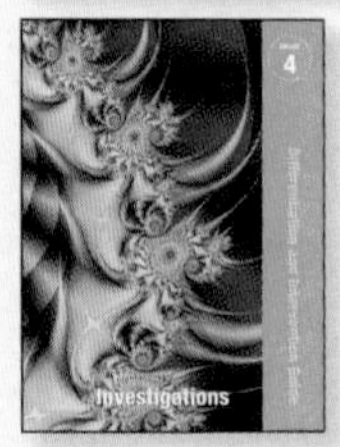

The **Differentiation and Intervention Guide** offers additional activities for each Investigation to support the range of learners.

Investigations for the Interactive Whiteboard provides whole-class instructional support to enhance each session.

The **Resource Masters and Transparencies CD** contains all reproducible materials that support instruction. The **LogoPaths CD** provides an environment in which students investigate a variety of geometric ideas.

FOR STUDENTS

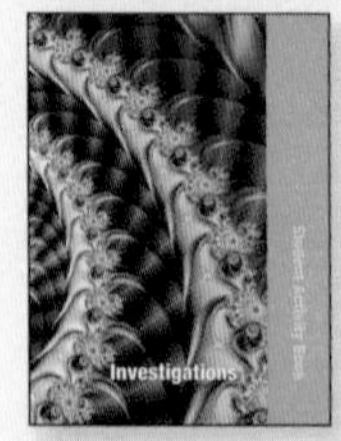

The **Student Activity Book** contains the consumable student pages (Recording Sheets, Homework, Practice, and so on).

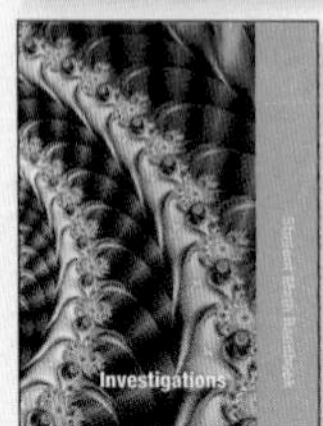

The **Student Math Handbook** contains Math Words and Ideas pages and Games directions.

The *Investigations* Curriculum

Investigations in Number, Data, and Space® is a K–5 mathematics curriculum designed to engage students in making sense of mathematical ideas. Six major goals guided the development of the *Investigations in Number, Data, and Space*® curriculum. The curriculum is designed to:

- Support students to make sense of mathematics and learn that they can be mathematical thinkers
- Focus on computational fluency with whole numbers as a major goal of the elementary grades
- Provide substantive work in important areas of mathematics—rational numbers, geometry, measurement, data, and early algebra—and connections among them
- Emphasize reasoning about mathematical ideas
- Communicate mathematics content and pedagogy to teachers
- Engage the range of learners in understanding mathematics

Underlying these goals are three guiding principles that are touchstones for the *Investigations* team as we approach both students and teachers as agents of their own learning:

1. *Students have mathematical ideas.* Students come to school with ideas about numbers, shapes, measurements, patterns, and data. If given the opportunity to learn in an environment that stresses making sense of mathematics, students build on the ideas they already have and learn about new mathematics they have never encountered. Students learn that they are capable of having mathematical ideas, applying what they know to new situations, and thinking and reasoning about unfamiliar problems.

2. *Teachers are engaged in ongoing learning* about mathematics content, pedagogy, and student learning. The curriculum provides material for professional development, to be used by teachers individually or in groups, that supports teachers' continued learning as they use the curriculum over several years. The *Investigations* curriculum materials are designed as much to be a dialogue with teachers as to be a core of content for students.

3. *Teachers collaborate with the students and curriculum materials* to create the curriculum as enacted in the classroom. The only way for a good curriculum to be used well is for teachers to be active participants in implementing it. Teachers use the curriculum to maintain a clear, focused, and coherent agenda for mathematics teaching. At the same time, they observe and listen carefully to students, try to understand how they are thinking, and make teaching decisions based on these observations.

Investigations is based on experience from research and practice, including field testing that involved documentation of thousands of hours in classrooms, observations of students, input from teachers, and analysis of student work. As a result, the curriculum addresses the learning needs of real students in a wide range of classrooms and communities. The investigations are carefully designed to invite all students into mathematics—girls and boys; members of diverse cultural, ethnic, and language groups; and students with a wide variety of strengths, needs, and interests.

Based on this extensive classroom testing, the curriculum takes seriously the time students need to develop a strong conceptual foundation and skills based on that foundation. Each curriculum unit focuses on an area of content in depth, providing time for students to develop and practice ideas across a variety of activities and contexts that build on each other. Daily guidelines for time spent on class sessions, Classroom Routines (K–3), and Ten-Minute Math (3–5) reflect the commitment to devoting adequate time to mathematics in each school day.

About This Curriculum Unit

This **Curriculum Unit** is one of nine teaching guides in Grade 4. The third unit in Grade 4 is *Multiple Towers and Division Stories.*

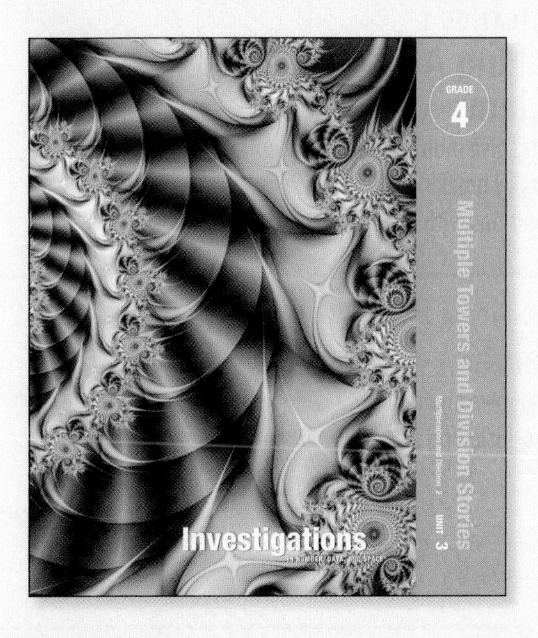

- The **Introduction and Overview** section organizes and presents the instructional materials, provides background information, and highlights important features specific to this unit.
- Each Curriculum Unit contains several **Investigations.** Each Investigation focuses on a set of related mathematical ideas.
- Investigations are divided into one-hour **Sessions,** or lessons.
- Sessions have a combination of these parts: **Activity, Discussion, Math Workshop, Assessment Activity,** and **Session Follow-Up.**
- Each session also has one or more **Ten-Minute Math activities** that are done outside of math time.
- At the back of the book is a collection of **Teacher Notes** and **Dialogue Boxes** that provide professional development related to the unit.
- Also included at the back of the book are the **Student Math Handbook** pages for this unit.
- The **Index** provides a way to look up important words or terms.

Overview

OF THIS UNIT

Investigation	Session	Day
INVESTIGATION 1 **Breaking Apart Multiplication Problems** Students solve multiplication problems with small 2-digit numbers by breaking the numbers apart and representing their solutions with arrays.	**1.1** Solving Multiplication Problems	1
	1.2 Making Big Arrays	2
	1.3 Small Array/Big Array	3
	1.4 Small Array/Big Array, *continued*	4
	1.5 Assessment: Solving 18×7	5
INVESTIGATION 2 **Division** Students solve and represent division problems in story contexts, including problems with remainders.	**2.1** Looking at Division	6
	2.2 Division with Remainders	7
	2.3 Division Stories	8
	2.4 Strategies for Division	9
	2.5 Related Multiplication and Division Problems	10
	2.6 Assessment: Writing and Solving a Division Problem	11
INVESTIGATION 3 **Multiplying 10s** Students solve and represent problems that involve multiples of 10. They examine the mathematical relationship that underlies the pattern they see when a number is multiplied by a multiple of 10.	**3.1** Building Multiple Towers	12
	3.2 Multiplying Groups of 10	13
	3.3 Multiplying 2-Digit Numbers	14
	3.4 Assessment: Multiplication Combinations	15
INVESTIGATION 4 **Strategies for Multiplication** Students develop strategies for solving multiplication problems with larger 2-digit numbers by breaking the problems apart in order to use number relationships that they know.	**4.1** Doubles and Halves	16
	4.2 Multiplicaton Cluster Problems	17
	4.3 Strategies for Multiplication	18
	4.4 Strategies for Multiplication, *continued*	19
	4.5 End-of-Unit Assessment	20

Each *Investigations* session has some combination of these five parts: **Activity, Discussion, Math Workshop, Assessment Activity,** and **Session Follow-Up.** These session parts are indicated in the chart below. Each session also has one **Ten-Minute Math** activity that is done outside of math time.

Ⓦ Interactive Whiteboard

Activity	Discussion	Math Workshop	Assessment Activity	Session Follow-Up	Ten-Minute Math: *Quick Images: Seeing Numbers*	Ten-Minute Math: *Counting Around the Class*
●●	Ⓦ			●	Ⓦ	
Ⓦ	Ⓦ			●	Ⓦ	
Ⓦ●				●	Ⓦ	
	Ⓦ	●		●		Ⓦ
		●	●	●		Ⓦ
●	Ⓦ			●		Ⓦ
●	Ⓦ			●		Ⓦ
	●	●		●		Ⓦ
Ⓦ	●	●		●	Ⓦ	
Ⓦ		●		●	Ⓦ	
	Ⓦ		●	●	Ⓦ	
●Ⓦ	Ⓦ			●		Ⓦ
Ⓦ		●		●		Ⓦ
	Ⓦ	●		●		Ⓦ
	Ⓦ	●	●	●		Ⓦ
Ⓦ●				●	Ⓦ	
Ⓦ●Ⓦ				●	Ⓦ	
	Ⓦ	●		●	Ⓦ	
	Ⓦ	●		●		Ⓦ
			●	●		Ⓦ

Mathematics

IN THIS UNIT

Multiple Towers and Division Stories, which focuses on the operations of multiplication and division, is the second Grade 4 unit in the numbers and operations strand of *Investigations.* These units concentrate on the meaning of operations with whole numbers, the development of computational fluency, the structure of place value and the base-ten number system, and generalizations about numbers and operations.

In early grades, students began thinking about ideas of multiplication as they counted by numbers other than 1 and solved problems involving equal groups. They worked with division situations as they solved problems about sharing a variety of objects equally and making equal-sized groups. In third grade, students learned that multiplication is used to combine a number of equal-sized groups and that division is used when an amount is divided into groups and either the number of equal-sized groups or the size of those groups must be determined. In the first Grade 4 unit, *Factors, Multiples, and Arrays,* students worked with arrays (rectangular arrangements of objects in rows and columns, such as 24 chairs arranged in 4 rows of 6 or 2 rows of 12) as a representation of multiplication. They built fluency with multiplication combinations to 12×12 and developed their understanding of the relationships between numbers and their factors and multiples in order to use these relationships to solve multiplication problems with greater numbers.

The work in this unit assumes that students understand that multiplication can be used in problems involving equal groups, that division is related to multiplication, and that division also involves making equal-sized groups. They should recognize arrays as a model for multiplication and should be able to represent both multiplication and division situations in a variety of ways, including arrays, story problems, and pictures or models of groups. It is also expected that students know most, if not all, of the multiplication combinations to 12×12. This unit builds directly on all of these ideas.

This unit focuses on 4 Mathematical Emphases:

1 Computational Fluency **Solving multiplication problems with 2-digit numbers**

Math Focus Points

- Developing strategies for multiplying that involve breaking apart numbers
- Reviewing multiplication combinations to 12×12
- Multiplying multiples of 10

When students solve multiplication problems, they most often use strategies that involve breaking numbers apart to create problems that are manageable and that make use of familiar number relationships. As they learn their basic multiplication combinations, they use such strategies to help with more difficult combinations. For example, to learn 7×8, students might think, "I know $5 \times 8 = 40$, and $2 \times 8 = 16$, so $7 \times 8 = 40 + 16$, which is 56."

Students can think of these problems in terms of groups (2 more groups of 8) or use arrays to visualize the relationship. As students solve problems involving 2-digit numbers in this unit, they develop more experience with breaking numbers apart in this way. Students might solve a problem such as 27×4, for example, by breaking it into more familiar parts, such as 20×4 and 7×4. For the numbers that they encounter in this unit, students typically break one of the factors apart, multiply each part by the other factor, and then combine the partial products.

Learning to multiply by multiples of 10 is a key component of this work. Although students may break numbers apart in different ways, the structure of our numbers in the base-ten number system makes it convenient and efficient to break numbers apart by place. As students learn how to break apart multiplication problems, they are applying an important property of multiplication, the *distributive property*. Although it is not important for fourth graders to identify the distributive property by name, it is important for you to understand how student strategies relate to this property in order to teach students how to keep track of which numbers must be multiplied when breaking numbers apart in a multidigit multiplication problem. The distributive property, $(a + b) \times c = (a \times c) + (b \times c)$, is a foundation for students' computational fluency in whole number multiplication and division and for later work in algebra. Read Algebra Connections in This Unit, page 16, for more about how students are using the distributive property in their work.

2 Whole Number Operations **Understanding and using the relationship between multiplication and division to solve division problems**

Math Focus Points

- Solving division story problems
- Using and interpreting division notation
- Solving division problems by making groups of the divisor
- Using known multiplication combinations to solve division problems

Multiplication and division are related operations. Both involve two factors and the product created by multiplying those two factors. For example, here is a set of linked multiplication and division relationships:

$14 \times 6 = 84$ $\quad$ $6 \times 14 = 84$

$84 \div 14 = 6$ $\quad$ $84 \div 6 = 14$

A problem situation that students identify as division can be solved by either multiplication or division. For example, if 84 apples are put in bags with 6 apples in each bag, how many bags are needed? The elements in this problem are: 84 apples, bags of 6, and the number of bags to be determined. In standard notation, this problem can be written as either $84 \div 6 =$ ____ or ____ $\times 6 = 84$. Many students learn to solve division problems by building up groups of the divisor or using multiplication (e.g., $10 \times 6 = 60$, that makes 10 bags and leaves 24 apples; $4 \times 6 = 24$ for another 4 bags, so that's 14 bags in all). In this unit, students work on using the multiplication relationships that they know in order to solve division problems. The inverse relationship between multiplication and division is one of the building blocks of later work in algebra. See "Understanding the Inverse Relationship Between Division and Multiplication" in Algebra Connections in This Unit, page 18.

3 Whole Number Operations **Reasoning about numbers and their factors**

Math Focus Points

- Understanding the effect of multiplying by a multiple of 10 (e.g., describing the relationship between 3×4 and 3×40)
- Finding multiples of 2-digit numbers
- Describing a sequence of multiples in order to predict other multiples
- Determining the effect on the product when a factor is doubled or halved

In this unit, students continue their investigation of the relationships between numbers and their factors. In Investigation 3, they create multiple towers—sequences of multiples of 2-digit numbers. In making these towers, they notice certain patterns in the 10th and 20th multiples in the sequence (e.g., the 10th multiple of 26 is 260, the 20th multiple is 520). This leads them to consider how the product of a pair of factors changes when one of the factors is multiplied by 10 (e.g., $2 \times 26 = 52$, $20 \times 26 = 520$). Understanding how multiplication by multiples of 10 works in our number system is critical to solving multidigit multiplication problems. See **Teacher Note:** Multiplying by Multiples of 10, page 167.

A fourth investigation about numbers and their factors focuses on what happens to the product when one of the factors in a multiplication expression is doubled (e.g., 3×3 and 6×3). Further, students examine what happens to the product when one factor is doubled and the other is halved (e.g., What is the relationship of 20×16 to 40×8?). This work gives students more tools for solving multiplication problems; some problems lend themselves to easy solutions when they are changed to an equivalent problem in this way. Just as important, this work emphasizes the development of mathematical justification. Students reason about why these relationships are true and, by doing so, engage in one of the most important processes of mathematics—identifying generalizations and developing logical justifications for why these generalizations are valid. See **Teacher Note:** Reasoning and Proof in Mathematics, page 168, for more information about mathematical generalization and justification.

4 Whole Number Operations **Representing the meaning of multiplication and division**

Math Focus Points

- Representing a multiplication or division problem with pictures, diagrams, or models
- Using arrays to model multiplication
- Making sense of remainders in terms of the problem context
- Creating a story problem to represent a division expression
- Comparing visual representations of multiplication situations

This unit includes work on relating multiplication and division expressions to story contexts that correspond to those expressions. Students both solve word problems and write their own word problems for given expressions. In a story context, students must make sense of the way a remainder affects the solution to the problem. For example, the number of vans needed to transport 44 students if each van holds 8 students and the number of balloons each person gets if 8 people share 44 balloons equally are not the same, even though both situations can be represented by $44 \div 8$. In the first case, 6 vans are needed to transport all of the students (one van will not be full). In the second case, the maximum number of balloons each person can get is 5 if each person is to get the same number of balloons. Neither vans nor balloons can be split in half. However, if we were dividing cookies, each person could get $5\frac{1}{2}$ cookies. See **Teacher Note:** What Do You Do with the Remainders?, page 162.

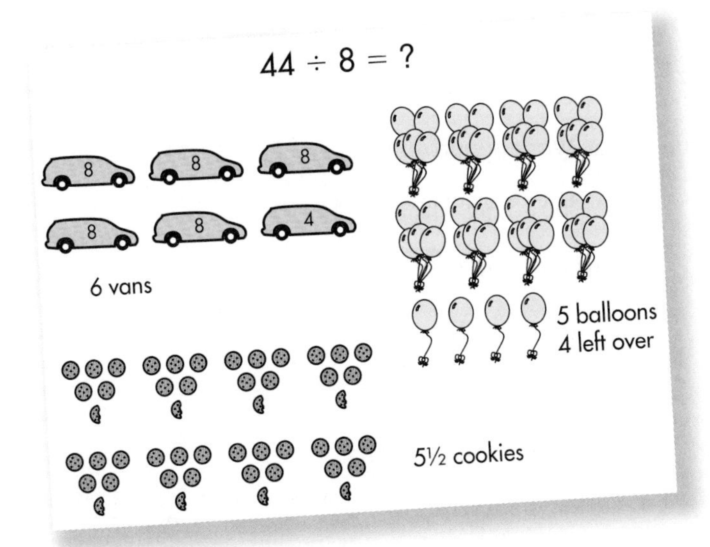

Throughout the unit, ask students to use representations, such as arrays, to explain how they break apart problems into subproblems. Talk through students' strategies and the way these strategies relate to story contexts. This work helps all students develop mental images of multiplication and division that are critical as they solve multidigit problems. See **Teacher Note:** Visualizing Arrays, page 154, and **Teacher Note:** Multiplying by Multiples of 10, page 167, for more about the use of arrays and other representations.

Students will continue the work of developing strategies for solving multiplication and division problems in a later unit on multiplication and division in Grade 4, *How Many Packages? How Many Groups?* This unit will emphasize multiplication and division with greater numbers and ways to keep track of all the parts of a problem that involves multidigit numbers. In Grade 5, students will consolidate their strategies for both multiplication and division as they continue to explore the properties of both operations.

Ten-Minute Math activities focus on

- Organizing and analyzing visual images
- Writing equations to represent the total number of dots in a pattern
- Finding the multiples of numbers through skip counting
- Becoming familiar with multiplication patterns
- Understanding the relationship between skip counting and multiplication

Technology Note

Getting Started with the *LogoPaths* Software Students are formally introduced to the *LogoPaths* software in the 2-D Geometry and Measurement unit *Size, Shape, and Symmetry,* the fourth unit in the Grade 4 sequence. However, if you plan to use the software this year, we recommend that students have access to the software **outside of math time** starting with this unit in order to return to *Feed the Turtle,* a *LogoPaths* activity from Grade 3, and to spend time with the *Free Explore* option. For information about the *LogoPaths* software and directions for *Feed the Turtle,* refer to the *Software Support Reference Guide* found on the CD. See **Part 5: Technology in *Investigations*** in *Implementing Investigations in Grade 4:* Introducing and Managing the *LogoPaths* Software in Grade 4.

ONGOING ASSESSMENT: Observing Students at Work

The following sessions provide **Ongoing Assessment: Observing Students at Work** opportunities:

- **Session 1.1, pp. 30 and 32–33**
- **Session 1.2, p. 38**
- **Session 1.3, p. 44**
- **Session 1.4, pp. 48 and 49**
- **Session 2.1, p. 63**
- **Session 2.2, p. 70**
- **Session 2.3, pp. 74–75**
- **Session 2.4, pp. 80–81**
- **Session 2.5, p. 86**
- **Session 3.1, p. 103**
- **Session 3.2, p. 108**
- **Session 3.3, pp. 113 and 114**
- **Session 3.4, p. 118**
- **Session 4.1, p. 127**
- **Session 4.2, pp. 131–132**
- **Session 4.3, pp. 142–143**

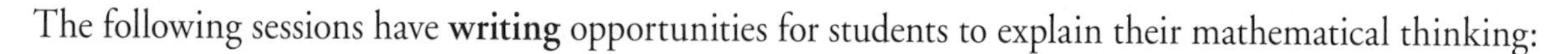

WRITING OPPORTUNITIES

The following sessions have **writing** opportunities for students to explain their mathematical thinking:

- **Session 2.3, p. 76**
  Student Activity Book, p. 28
- **Session 2.4, p. 83**
  Student Activity Book, p. 31
- **Session 2.6, p. 91**
  M46, *Assessment: Writing and Solving a Division Problem*
- **Session 3.1, p. 104**
  Student Activity Book, p. 39
- **Session 3.2, p. 110**
  Student Activity Book, p. 46
- **Session 3.3, p. 113**
  Student Activity Book, p. 47
- **Session 4.1, pp. 126–127**
  Student Activity Book, pp. 53–54

PORTFOLIO OPPORTUNITIES

The following sessions have work appropriate for a **portfolio:**

- **Session 1.4, p. 48**
  Student Activity Book, pp. 12–13
- **Session 1.5, p. 52**
  M43, *Assessment: Solving 18 × 7*
- **Session 2.3, p. 74**
  Student Activity Book, pp. 25–26
- **Session 2.6, p. 91**
  M46, *Assessment: Writing and Solving a Division Problem*
- **Session 3.1, p. 103**
  Student Activity Book, pp. 37–38
  M48–M49, *About Our Multiple Tower*
- **Session 3.2, pp. 108–109**
  Student Activity Book, pp. 42–43
- **Session 3.4, p. 117**
  M50, *Assessment: Multiplication Combinations*
- **Session 4.2, p. 131**
  Student Activity Book, pp. 57–58
- **Session 4.5, p. 149**
  M51–M52, *End-of-Unit Assessment*

Assessing the Benchmarks

Observing students as they engage in conversation about their ideas is a primary means to assess their mathematical understanding. Consider all of your students' work, not just the written assessments. See the chart below for suggestions about key activities to observe.

See the **Differentiation and Intervention Guide** for quizzes that can be used after each Investigation.

Benchmarks in This Unit	Key Activities to Observe	Assessment
1. Multiply 2-digit numbers by 1-digit and small 2-digit numbers (e.g., 12, 15, 20), using strategies that involve breaking the numbers apart.	**Sessions 1.4 and 1.5:** Solving Multiplication Problems **Session 3.2:** Multiplying by Multiples of 10 **Session 4.2:** Multiplication Cluster Problems	**Session 1.5 Assessment Activity:** Solving 18×7 **Session 4.5 End-of-Unit Assessment:** Problems 1 and 2
2. Solve division problems (2-digit and small 3-digit numbers divided by 1-digit numbers), including some that result in a remainder.	**Session 2.3:** More Division Stories **Session 2.5:** Related Multiplication and Division Problems	**Session 2.6 Assessment Activity:** Writing and Solving a Division Problem **Session 4.5 End-of-Unit Assessment:** Problem 3
3. Use story problems, pictures, or concrete models to represent division situations.	**Session 2.2:** Problems with Remainders **Session 2.4:** Strategies for Division **Session 2.5:** Related Multiplication and Division Problems	**Session 2.6 Assessment Activity:** Writing and Solving a Division Problem **Session 4.5 End-of-Unit Assessment:** Problem 3
4. Multiply by 10 and multiples of 10.	**Session 3.1:** Building Multiple Towers **Session 3.2:** Multiplying by Multiples of 10	**Session 4.5 End-of-Unit Assessment:** Problem 2
5. Demonstrate fluency with multiplication combinations up to 12×12.	**Sessions 2.4 and 2.5:** *Missing Factors*	**Session 3.4 Assessment Activity:** Multiplication Combinations

Relating the Mathematical Emphases to the Benchmarks

Mathematical Emphases	Benchmarks
Computational Fluency Solving multiplication problems with 2-digit numbers	**1, 4, and 5**
Whole Number Operations Understanding and using the relationship between multiplication and division to solve division problems	**2 and 3**
Whole Number Operations Reasoning about numbers and their factors	**1 and 4**
Whole Number Operations Representing the meaning of multiplication and division	**3**

Algebra Connections

IN THIS UNIT

In this unit, your students will have opportunities to work with ideas that lay a foundation for algebra. Fourth graders can and do think algebraically. Part of the work of fourth grade is helping students learn to verbalize and represent those thoughts both as a way to engage with generalizations about numbers and operations and as a foundation for meaningful use of algebraic notation in the future. At this point in the year, you are likely to notice that students are getting better at verbalizing their thinking and demonstrating their ideas about multiplication with skip counting, array arrangements, diagrams, and cube structures. Note that, although algebraic notation is not introduced in this unit, students will work with notation in *Penny Jars and Plant Growth.*

Using the Distributive Property

In this unit, students will articulate applications of the distributive property and make arguments illustrating how various strategies for multidigit multiplication call upon this property linking addition and multiplication. In formal terms, the distributive property is $(a + b) \times c = (a \times c) + (b \times c)$; however, your students are likely to express it through the use of representative examples such as: $12 \times 7 = (10 \times 7) + (2 \times 7)$ or $26 \times 25 = (20 \times 25) + (6 \times 25)$.

Consider this vignette.

A fourth-grade class is working on this problem:

Each of 14 children in the art class needs 12 crayons to draw with. How many crayons are needed?

Sabrina: I thought $14 \times 10 = 140$ crayons and $14 \times 2 = 28$ crayons, so $14 \times 12 = 168$ crayons.

Marisol: Sabrina renamed 12 and broke it down to two steps, 14×10 and 14×2.

Teacher: Why does that work?

Alejandro: She just said that 12 is the same as 10 and 2.

Teacher: What does that mean when Sabrina multiplied 14×12?

Alejandro: She multiplied 14×10 then 14×2 and added the two answers together.

Teacher: Why does that give us the answer to 14×12? Who can explain this by talking about the crayons and children in the story? If Sabrina started with 14×10, what do those numbers mean?

Jill: The 14 is the 14 kids.

Yuson: And it's like you gave every kid 10 crayons so far, like you're walking around giving them out, and you give 10 to every kid.

Teacher: So what part of the problem have you solved already? And what part do you still need to solve?

Steve: Everyone has 10, but they need 12, so you have to give 2 more to everyone.

Sabrina: So that's why I did 14 × 2 next because everyone got 2 more crayons.

Teacher: Can you draw something to show how that works?

Students work for a few minutes, then share their pictures. Derek has drawn the following:

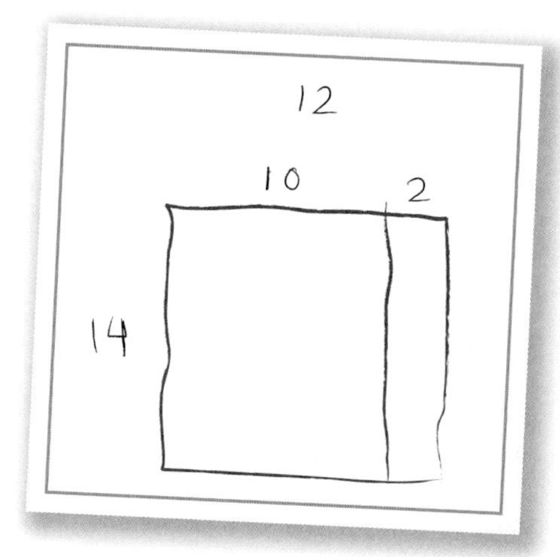

Derek's Work

Derek: The left side is 14 × 10 and the right side is 14 × 2. The whole thing is 14 × 12.

In this vignette, Sabrina, Alejandro, and Derek break apart the multiplication problem (14 × 12) into two parts (14 × 10 and 14 × 2). They use the story context and array diagrams to support their thinking. Their work is an example of the distributive property, which links multiplication and addition.

Throughout this unit, your students will have many opportunities to work with such ideas, both in solving multiplication problems and in playing *Small Array/Big Array.* Making connections among the number sentences, the story contexts, and the array diagrams is an important way for students to develop their reasoning skills.

Doubling and Halving

In solving the multiplication problems in this unit, students will also call upon other number relationships that they have noted about multiplication. For instance, in a multiplication problem, if you double one factor and halve the other, the product remains the same.

Consider this vignette.

Steve and Ramona are working on the multiplication problem 8 × 15.

Ramona: Here is what I did. I figured that 8 × 15 is the same as 4 × 30 and so the answer is 120.

Steve: I don't understand what you did. I broke up the 15 into 10 + 5 and did (8 × 10) + (8 × 5).

Ramona: We got the same answer. You did 80 + 40 and that is 120, too.

Steve: I see the answers are the same, but I still don't understand how yours works.

Ramona: It's like if you cut up an array. Look.

Ramona draws the following on grid paper:

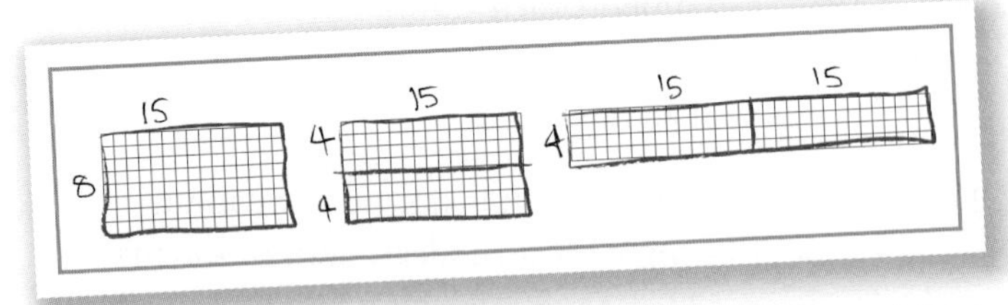

Ramona's Work

Ramona: Do you see what I mean?

Steve: You cut the 8 in half—and took 4 of the 15s and moved them so the eight 15s became four 30s. Is that right?

Ramona: Yes, it is still the same amount, 120.

Ramona is using the idea that you can halve one factor in a multiplication problem and double the other without changing the product. Expressed in symbols, this strategy is notated as $a \times b = (a \div 2) \times (b \times 2)$. Ramona expresses her reasoning using array diagrams. While most fourth graders think only about halving and doubling, some students might experiment with dividing and multiplying by other numbers. For example, 15×40 can be changed into the equivalent expression 5×120 by dividing the 15 by 3 and multiplying the 40 by 3. Expressed formally, the relationship can be seen as $a \times b = (a \div 3) \times (b \times 3)$ or, in the most general terms, $a \times b = (a \div c) \times (b \times c)$. The equivalence of these two expressions derives from the inverse relationship between multiplication and division; that is, multiplying by 3 and then dividing by 3 results in multiplying the product by 1.

When your students use multiplication strategies based on such number relationships, encourage them to use tools such as story contexts, cube structures, and array diagrams to explain why a strategy works. While doubling and halving is not always a good strategy for every problem, the focus on reasoning about relationships as part of learning helps to articulate and to justify properties of the operations.

Understanding the Inverse Relationship Between Division and Multiplication

Students also work on the inverse relationship between multiplication and division in other ways in this unit. Just as younger children often use addition to solve problems that adults might consider to be subtraction problems, so will your students sometimes use multiplication to solve what you might consider to be division problems.

Consider this vignette.

Cheyenne, Ursula, and Amelia are working on this problem.

There are 64 children in a class, and they are going to be placed into groups of 4. How many groups will there be?

Cheyenne: I know that 4×15 is 60, and then it's one more 4, so the answer is 16.

Ursula: First I thought $10 \times 4 = 40$, then that left 24 children, and that's 6 more 4s. That's 10 groups and then 6 more groups, which is 16.

Amelia: I knew that $8 \times 4 = 32$, and that's half of 64, so 8 and 8 is 16 groups.

In this vignette, Cheyenne, Ursula, and Amelia are using what they know about multiplication to solve a division problem. Their approaches are based on the inverse relationship between multiplication and division. In this vignette, since $16 \times 4 = 64$ then $64 \div 4 = 16$. In more general terms, if $a \div b = c$ then $b \times c = a$.

Encourage students to articulate their reasoning by asking questions.

"Why is it that a strategy using multiplication solves this problem?"

"When you say that $10 \times 4 = 40$, what part of the problem have you solved?"

"What does the 10 mean? The 4? The 40?"

Responding to such questions will help students articulate and clarify their own thinking about the relationship between multiplication and division and will form the basis for future work examining these operations.

Ten-Minute Math

IN THIS UNIT

Ten-Minute Math offers practice and review of key concepts for this grade level. These daily activities, to be done in ten minutes outside of math class, are introduced in a unit and repeated throughout the grade. Specific directions for the day's activity are provided in each session. For the full description and variations of each classroom activity, see *Implementing Investigations in Grade 4*.

Activity	Introduced	Full Description of Activity and Its Variations
Quick Images	Unit 1: *Factors, Multiples, and Arrays*	*Implementing Investigations in Grade 4*
Counting Around the Class	Unit 1: *Factors, Multiples, and Arrays*	*Implementing Investigations in Grade 4*

Quick Images

Students visualize and analyze images of dot patterns. After briefly viewing an image, students determine the number of dots in a pattern and write an equation to represent how they organized their count.

Math Focus Points

- Organizing and analyzing visual images
- Writing equations to represent the total number of dots in a pattern

Counting Around the Class

Students count around the class by a given number and discuss relationships between the chosen factor and its multiples. In a variation, they find the number of students who have counted, given the counting number and an ending number.

Math Focus Points

- Finding the multiples of numbers through skip counting
- Becoming familiar with multiplication patterns
- Understanding the relationship between skip counting and multiplication

Practice and Review

IN THIS UNIT

Practice and review play a critical role in the *Investigations* program. The following components and features are available to provide regular reinforcement of key mathematical concepts and procedures.

Books	Features	In This Unit . . .
Curriculum Unit	**Ten-Minute Math** offers practice and review of key concepts for this grade level. These daily activities, to be done in ten minutes outside of math class, are introduced in a unit and repeated throughout the grade. Specific directions for the day's activity are provided in each session. For the full description and variations of each classroom activity, see *Implementing Investigations in Grade 4.*	• **All sessions**
Student Activity Book	**Daily Practice** pages in the *Student Activity Book* provide one of three types of written practice: **reinforcement** of the content of the unit, **ongoing review,** or **enrichment** opportunities. Some Daily Practice pages will also have Ongoing Review items with multiple-choice problems similar to those on standardized tests.	• **All sessions**
	Homework pages in the *Student Activity Book* are an extension of the work done in class. At times they help students prepare for upcoming activities.	• **Session 1.1** • **Session 1.2** • **Session 1.3** • **Session 2.1** • **Session 2.2** • **Session 2.3** • **Session 2.4** • **Session 3.1** • **Session 3.2** • **Session 3.3** • **Session 4.1** • **Session 4.2** • **Session 4.3**
Student Math Handbook	**Math Words and Ideas** in the *Student Math Handbook* are pages that summarize key words and ideas. Most Words and Ideas pages have at least one exercise.	• **Student Math Handbook, pp. 18–21, 35–52**
	Games pages are found in a section of the *Student Math Handbook.*	• **Student Math Handbook, pp. G8, G10**

Supporting the Range of Learners

The **Differentiation and Intervention Guide** provides Intervention, Extension, and Practice activities for use within each Investigation.

Sessions	1.1	1.2	1.3	1.4	1.5	2.1	2.2	2.3	2.4	2.5	3.1	3.2	3.3	3.4	4.1	4.2	4.3	4.5
Intervention	•	•		•	•	•	•	•		•	•	•	•	•		•	•	•
Extension							•					•			•			
ELL			•				•		•		•							

Intervention

Suggestions are made to support and engage students who are having difficulty with a particular idea, activity, or problem.

Extension

Suggestions are made to support and engage students who finish early or may be ready for additional challenges.

English Language Learners (ELL)

As students work through the activities and games in *Multiple Towers and Division Stories,* classroom tools such as cubes, grid paper, and Array Cards will aid their understanding of multiplication and division. Before introducing games and activities to the class, you might preview them with English Language Learners. Encourage students to explain the steps in their own words to increase their fluency in discussing math.

One challenge for English Language Learners in this unit is the focus on story contexts for multiplication and division. While they may readily grasp the underlying math concepts, figuring out the story language adds an extra step to their work. To assess students' understanding, you can read the problems aloud and ask guiding questions to help them restate the problems in their own words. Help them see the language patterns in these story problems, and model the problems with actual objects or other visual aids and gestures. Follow up by helping English Language Learners find similar phrasing in the other story problems on the page.

In their work with remainders in division, students who are trying to decide how the remainders affect their solution must understand exactly what kind of objects are being divided. To support this understanding, display real examples of the objects, draw simple sketches, or encourage English Language Learners to use native language dictionaries to translate key words.

Working with the Range of Learners: Classroom Cases is a set of episodes written by teachers that focuses on meeting the needs of the range of learners in the classroom. In the first section, *Setting up the Mathematical Community,* teachers write about how they create a supportive and productive learning environment in their classrooms. In the next section, *Accommodations for Learning,* teachers focus on specific modifications they make to meet the needs of some of their learners. In the last section, *Language and Representation,* teachers share how they help students use representations and develop language to investigate and express mathematical ideas. The questions at the end of each case provide a starting point for your own reflection or for discussion with colleagues. See *Implementing Investigations in Grade 4* for this set of episodes.

INVESTIGATION 1

Mathematical Emphases

Computational Fluency Solving multiplication problems with 2-digit numbers

Math Focus Points

- Developing strategies for multiplying that involve breaking apart numbers
- Reviewing multiplication combinations to 12×12

Whole Number Operations Representing the meaning of multiplication and division

Math Focus Points

- Representing a multiplication problem with pictures, diagrams, or models
- Using arrays to model multiplication

Breaking Apart Multiplication Problems

Session	Student Activity Book	Student Math Handbook	Professional Development: Read Ahead of Time
SESSION 1.1 p. 28 **Solving Multiplication Problems** Students solve multiplication problems with smaller 2-digit numbers and consider ways to break apart the problems in order to make them easier to solve. Students discuss ways to represent their solutions.	1–4	20	• **Part 4: Ten-Minute Math** in *Implementing Investigations in Grade 4: Quick Images* • Mathematics in This Unit, p. 10 • Algebra Connections in This Unit, p. 16 • **Teacher Note:** Learning and Assessing Multiplication Combinations, p. 151
SESSION 1.2 p. 34 **Making Big Arrays** Students represent the breaking apart of multiplication problems by fitting smaller arrays together to construct a larger array. They discuss how many different combinations of smaller arrays they can use to make an 8×9 array.	5–6	18–19	• **Teacher Note:** Visualizing Arrays, p. 154
SESSION 1.3 p. 42 **Small Array/Big Array** Students discuss strategies for multiplying that involve breaking apart problems.	7–9	18–19; G10	• **Teacher Note:** Playing *Small Array/ Big Array,* p. 156

Ten-Minute Math See page 20 for an overview.

Quick Images: Seeing Numbers

- T34–T35, *Quick Images: Seeing Numbers* (overhead transparency)

Counting Around the Class

- No materials needed

Materials to Gather	Materials to Prepare
• **Connecting cubes** (as needed) • **Color tiles** (as needed)	• **M7, Centimeter Grid Paper** Make copies for use as a math tool. (as needed) • **M8, Practicing with Multiplication Cards** Make copies. (1 per student) • **M9–M14, Multiplication Cards** Students need their sets of cards from Unit 1: *Factors, Multiples, and Arrays.* If new sets are needed, make copies and cut apart the cards. (1 set per student) • **M15–M16, Family Letter** Make copies. (1 per student)
• **T2, Centimeter Grid Paper** (overhead transparency) (optional) • **Blank transparency** (optional)	• **M7, Centimeter Grid Paper** (as needed) • **M17–M37, Array Cards** Students need their sets of cards from Unit 1: *Factors, Multiples, and Arrays.* If new sets are needed, make copies on card stock and cut out the arrays. Write the product on the back of each card. Also, write one of the dimensions of the array, using smaller numbers, along one side of the card (sometimes the longer dimension, sometimes the shorter). Enlist the help of aides, parent volunteers, or students. (1 set per pair) • **Chart paper** (2 pieces, plus extras) Create two posters of unmarked arrays. On the first, draw a 4×9 rectangle with no grid lines, labeled 4×9 and 9×4. On the second, draw an 8×9 rectangle, also with no grid lines, labeled 8×9 and 9×8. (See illustrations, pages 36 and 39.)
• **Array Cards** (1 set per pair; from Session 1.2) • **T40, *Small Array/Big Array* Recording Sheet** (overhead transparency) (1 per student) • **Construction paper** (1 sheet per pair)	• **T3–T23** (overhead transparency), **Array Cards** Cut out the arrays. (optional, for game demonstration) • **M38–M39, *Small Array/Big Array*** Make copies. (as needed) Play a few rounds of the game to familiarize yourself with the rules, which are complex but become clearer through playing the game. • **M41–M42, Family Letter** Make copies. (1 per student)

Overhead Transparency

Breaking Apart Multiplication Problems, *continued*

	Student Activity Book	Student Math Handbook	Professional Development: Read Ahead of Time
SESSION 1.4 p. 46			
Small Array/Big Array, *continued* Students discuss strategies for multiplying that involve breaking apart problems.	7, 11–14	18–19; G10	• **Part 4: Ten-Minute Math** in *Implementing Investigations in Grade 4:* Counting Around the Class • **Dialogue Box:** Solving 17 × 6, p. 178
SESSION 1.5 p. 51			
Assessment: Solving 18 × 7 Students complete an assessment in which they solve a multiplication problem and represent one way to break apart the problem with arrays.	7, 11–13, 15	20; G10	• **Teacher Note:** Assessment: Solving 18 × 7, p. 158

	Materials to Gather	Materials to Prepare
	• **Array Cards** (1 set per pair; from Session 1.2) • **Construction paper** (1 sheet per pair) • **Connecting cubes** (as needed) • **Color tiles** (as needed)	• **M7, Centimeter Grid Paper** (as needed) • **M40, *Small Array/Big Array* Recording Sheet** (1 per student, or as needed)
	• **Array Cards** (1 set per pair; from Session 1.2) • **Construction paper** (1 sheet per pair) • **Connecting cubes** (as needed) • **Color tiles** (as needed)	• **M7, Centimeter Grid Paper** (as needed) • **M40, *Small Array/Big Array* Recording Sheet** (1 per student, or as needed) • **M43, Assessment: Solving 18 × 7** Make copies. (1 per student)

Solving Multiplication Problems

Math Focus Points

- Developing strategies for multiplying that involve breaking apart numbers
- Representing a multiplication problem with pictures, diagrams, or models
- Reviewing multiplication combinations to 12 × 12

multiplication

Today's Plan	Materials
ACTIVITY **1 Mr. Jones and the Bagels** — 20 MIN, CLASS, INDIVIDUALS	• *Student Activity Book,* p. 1 • M7* • Connecting cubes; color tiles
DISCUSSION **2 Showing Your Solution** — 15 MIN, CLASS	• *Student Activity Book,* p. 1
ACTIVITY **3 Multiplication Story Problems** — 25 MIN, INDIVIDUALS, PAIRS	• *Student Activity Book,* p. 2 • M7* • Connecting cubes; color tiles
SESSION FOLLOW-UP **4 Daily Practice and Homework**	• *Student Activity Book,* pp. 3–4 • M8*; M9–M14*; M15–M16*; Family Letter* • *Student Math Handbook,* p. 20

*See *Materials to Prepare,* p. 25.

Ten-Minute Math

Quick Images: Seeing Numbers Show *Quick Images: Seeing Numbers* (T34), Images 1 and 2, one at a time. For each pattern, ask students to write several different equations to find the total number of dots. For the first two viewings, give students 3 seconds to look at the pattern; the third time, leave the image displayed. Have two or three students explain how they saw the images (including any revisions they made) and their equations, showing how their numbers match the patterns. For example, Image 1 is an arrangement showing 9 groups of 4. Students might say $(4 \times 3) \times 3 = 36$, $9 \times 4 = 36$, and $12 \times 3 = 36$.

ACTIVITY

Mr. Jones and the Bagels

Let students know that they are returning to work on multiplication problems, building on the work they did in *Factors, Multiples, and Arrays.*

The last time you worked on multiplication, we talked about using what you already know to help solve harder problems. You practiced and learned the multiplication combinations, and you thought about the way arrays, pictures, and stories can help you visualize what's happening in a problem. Let's keep all that in mind as we work on some new problems.

Students work individually on *Student Activity Book* page 1. The story problems ask them to solve 14 × 12 and to consider two possible ways to break apart that problem: breaking the 14 into either 10 and 4 or 7 and 7. Let students know that they may use math tools such as Centimeter Grid Paper (M7) to represent these problems.①

Students should have access to math tools such as connecting cubes, color tiles, and grid paper at all times during this unit.

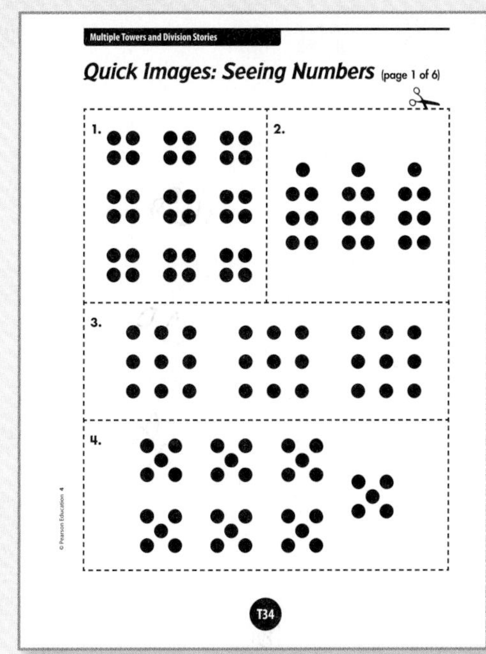

Multiple Towers and Division Stories

Quick Images: Seeing Numbers (page 1 of 6)

1.

2.

3.

4.

T34

▲ Transparencies, T34

Algebra Note

① **Distributive Property** The work students do in this unit is, in large part, related to the distributive property of multiplication, which is discussed more fully in Algebra Connections in This Unit, p. 16. Basic strategies for multiplication that involve breaking apart the numbers in a multiplication expression, computing partial products, and then adding those partial products together are based on this property. Students are not expected to name or articulate this property, but they learn to apply it as they represent and develop strategies for solving the problems in this unit.

Name Date

Multiple Towers and Division Stories

Mr. Jones and the Bagels

Solve these story problems. Show your thinking.

1. Mr. Jones needs to buy 14 dozen bagels for a big party. How many bagels does he need to buy? (Remember that a dozen is 12.)

   168

2. Mr. Jones goes to the bagel shop. They have only 10 dozen left! So he buys them all. How many bagels does he buy at the bagel shop?

   120

3. Mr. Jones goes to the supermarket to buy the rest of the bagels. How many more bagels does Mr. Jones need to buy? How do you know?

   48

4. What if the bagel shop had only 7 dozen bagels left? How many bagels would Mr. Jones have to buy at the supermarket then?

Session 1.1 Unit 3 1

▲ Student Activity Book, p. 1

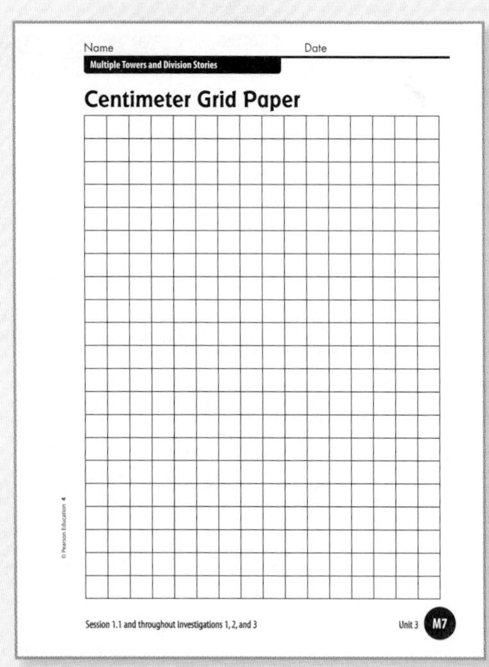
Name Date

Multiple Towers and Division Stories

Centimeter Grid Paper

Session 1.1 and throughout Investigations 1, 2, and 3 Unit 3 M7

▲ Resource Masters, M7

ONGOING ASSESSMENT: Observing Students at Work

Students solve 2-digit multiplication problems that help them consider different ways to break apart a problem.

- **How do students solve 14 × 12?** Do they consider breaking apart one of the factors and multiplying both parts by the other factor? Do they recombine the partial products accurately?
- **Do students represent the problem in some way (pictures, diagrams on grid paper, or cubes)?**
- **Do students' responses to Problems 3 and 4 show that they can interpret the relationship of 10 × 12 to 14 × 12 and the relationship of 7 × 12 to 14 × 12 in the story context?**

DIFFERENTIATION: Supporting the Range of Learners

Intervention At this point in the year, you can expect to see a range of strategies for solving a multiplication problem with 2-digit numbers. Although many students can solve a problem with smaller 2-digit numbers, breaking factors apart and using multiplication combinations that they know, some students may need to represent the problem to solve it. Encourage students who rely on counting or repeated addition to look for more efficient ways to combine groups within the representations that they make.

I see that you have made 14 towers of 12 cubes each. Can you group some of these towers together and tell me how many there are without counting all of the cubes? How many are there in 2 towers? 4 towers? 10 towers?

15 MIN CLASS

2 DISCUSSION

Showing Your Solution

Math Focus Points for Discussion

- Developing strategies for multiplying that involve breaking apart numbers

Bring the class together and hold a discussion about the strategies that students used to solve the first problem on *Student Activity Book* page 1.

Did anyone break apart 14 × 12 into easier problems before you solved it? What easier problems did you use?

Collect a few examples of the ways that students broke apart the problem, including some that involve breaking apart 14 and others that involve breaking apart 12, if possible. These might include the following:

Breaking Apart 14

$14 \times 12 = (10 \times 12) + (4 \times 12)$

$14 \times 12 = (12 \times 12) + (2 \times 12)$

$14 \times 12 = (7 \times 12) + (7 \times 12)$

Breaking Apart 12

$14 \times 12 = (14 \times 10) + (14 \times 2)$

$14 \times 12 = (14 \times 4) + (14 \times 4) + (14 \times 4)$

Students who broke 14 into either 10 plus 4 or 7 plus 7 may point out that this is also what happened in Problems 2 and 4. If not, bring up this similarity yourself.

What did you have to do to figure out how many more bagels Mr. Jones needs after he buys 10 dozen? Is there a picture or diagram you could draw to show how you know how many more he needs to buy? Talk about that with someone sitting next to you for a minute.

Give students time to talk and quickly sketch something if they haven't already. Call them back together and take students' suggestions for ways to represent what is happening in the problem. Include both a picture of groups and an array representation.

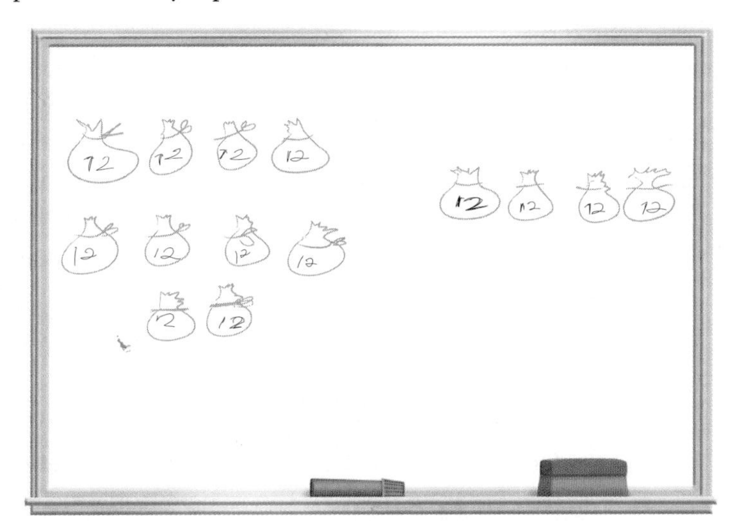

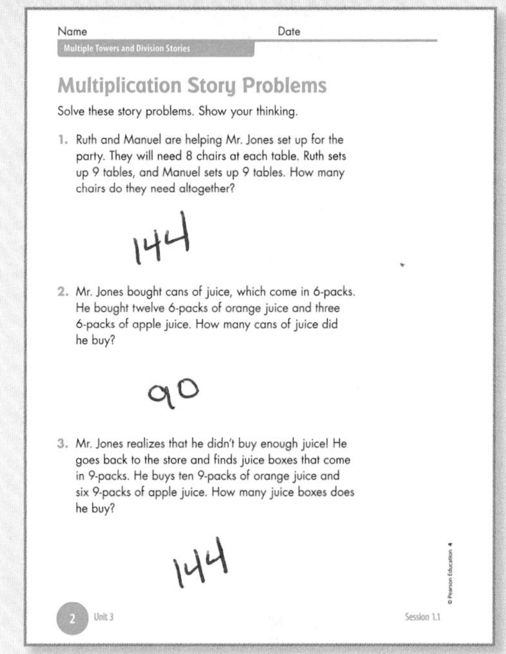

Name Date

Multiple Towers and Division Stories

Multiplication Story Problems

Solve these story problems. Show your thinking.

1. Ruth and Manuel are helping Mr. Jones set up for the party. They will need 8 chairs at each table. Ruth sets up 9 tables, and Manuel sets up 9 tables. How many chairs do they need altogether?

144

2. Mr. Jones bought cans of juice, which come in 6-packs. He bought twelve 6-packs of orange juice and three 6-packs of apple juice. How many cans of juice did he buy?

90

3. Mr. Jones realizes that he didn't buy enough juice! He goes back to the store and finds juice boxes that come in 9-packs. He buys ten 9-packs of orange juice and six 9-packs of apple juice. How many juice boxes does he buy?

144

2 Unit 3 Session 1.1

▲ Student Activity Book, p. 2

* Stack vertically to connect to algorithm

Name Date

Multiple Towers and Division Stories

Practicing with Multiplication Cards

1. Look at the front of each Multiplication Card. If you have a helper, that person can show you one card at a time.
2. Your job is to say the answer to the problem as quickly as you can. If you get the answer right away, put the card in a pile of combinations that you "just know." If you have to stop and figure it out, put it into a different pile of combinations that you are still "working on."
3. Paper clip your "just know" cards together, and set them aside.
4. Look at each card in your "working on" pile. Think of an easy multiplication combination, one that you already know, that can help you remember this one. Write it on the line that says "Start with ____."

   Example: "For 6 × 7, I know that 7 × 7 = 49, so it must be one 7 less—that's 42."

   6 × 7
   7 × 6
   Start with 7 × 7

5. Go through each of the cards in your "working on" pile at least 3 times, using your "start with" combinations to help you find the answers.
6. Put all of your cards back together, both "just know" and "working on," and go through them again.
7. Over the next few weeks, keep practicing until you have no more cards in your "working on" pile! Practice at school when you have extra time and practice at home with a family member.

M8 Unit 3 Sessions 1.1, 2.1, 3.1, 4.1

▲ Resource Masters, M8

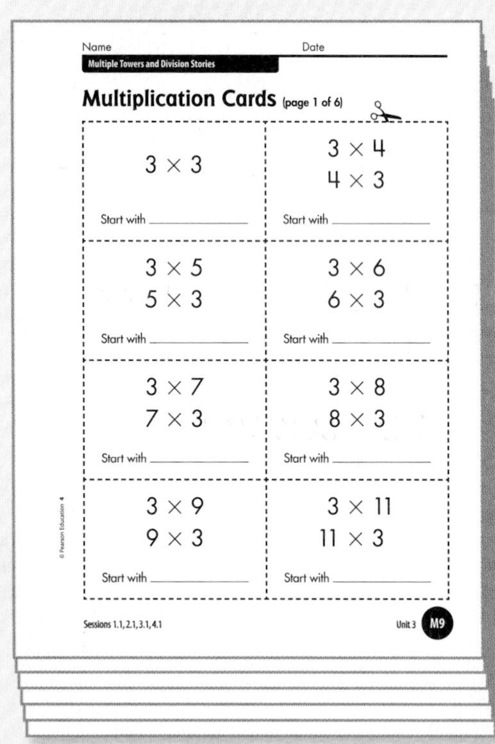
Name Date

Multiple Towers and Division Stories

Multiplication Cards (page 1 of 6)

3 × 3 Start with ____	3 × 4 4 × 3 Start with ____
3 × 5 5 × 3 Start with ____	3 × 6 6 × 3 Start with ____
3 × 7 7 × 3 Start with ____	3 × 8 8 × 3 Start with ____
3 × 9 9 × 3 Start with ____	3 × 11 11 × 3 Start with ____

© Pearson Education 4

Sessions 1.1, 2.1, 3.1, 4.1 Unit 3 M9

▲ Resource Masters, M9–M14

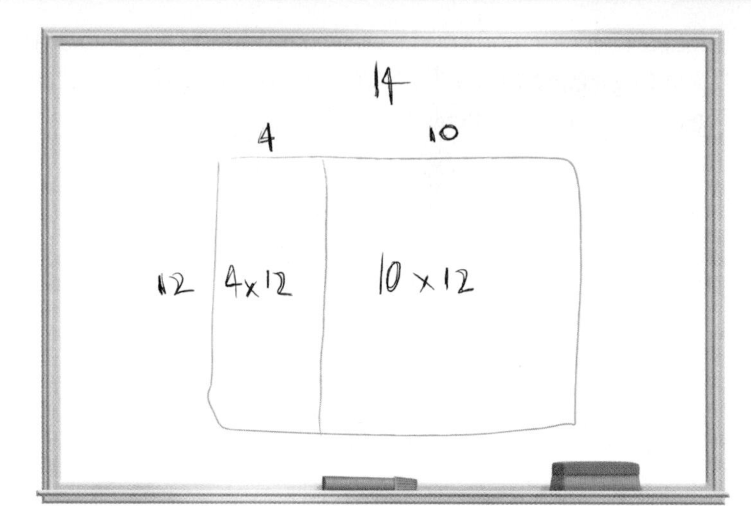

If you have additional time, ask for representations for Problem 4. This discussion, however, should be no more than 15 minutes. Students will have many more opportunities to discuss multiplication strategies and representations throughout the unit.

ACTIVITY

3 Multiplication Story Problems

25 MIN INDIVIDUALS PAIRS

On *Student Activity Book* page 2, students solve three story problems. In each problem, students use multiplication combinations (e.g., 8 × 9, 12 × 6, 10 × 9) to find the solution to a problem with larger numbers (e.g., 8 × 18, 15 × 6, 16 × 9).

Some students solve these problems by first solving each smaller problem and then combining the products (e.g., (8 × 9) + (8 × 9) = 72 + 72 = 144). Others first combine the two groups (9 + 9 = 18) and then use other number relationships they know to solve the larger problem (e.g., 8 × 18 = (8 × 10) + (8 × 8) = 80 + 64 = 144). While you observe students working, look for both of these strategies. As there will likely not be time to bring the class back together for a discussion about these problems, suggest that students who are using different strategies share them with one another for a few minutes before the end of class.

ONGOING ASSESSMENT: Observing Students at Work

Students solve 2-part multiplication problems.

- **Can students easily solve the multiplication combinations up to 12 × 12 (8 × 9, 12 × 6, 10 × 9)?** Can students easily multiply by 10?

- **Do students combine the results of both parts of the problem to get the final solution?**
- **Can students use multiplication notation to represent their thinking?**
- **Do some students represent the problem visually in order to solve it?** If so, can they combine groups by multiplying rather than by counting or adding?

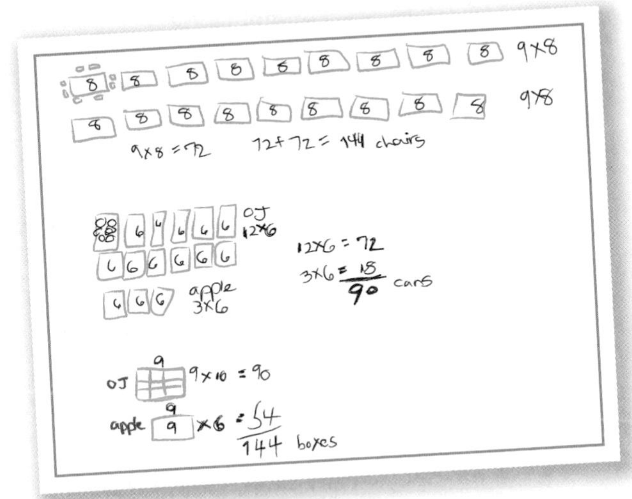

Sample Student Work

SESSION FOLLOW-UP

Daily Practice and Homework

Daily Practice: For reinforcement of this unit's content, have students complete *Student Activity Book* page 3.

Homework: As a homework assignment periodically throughout this unit, students use the Multiplication Cards to practice and continue learning the multiplication combinations to 12 × 12.❷ Each student needs a copy of Practicing with Multiplication Cards (M8) and an individual set of Multiplication Cards (M9–M14). Remind students of the procedure they followed when they used these cards earlier in the year. On *Student Activity Book* page 4, students record how they worked on the combinations.

Student Math Handbook: Students and families may use *Student Math Handbook* page 20 for reference and review. See pages 184–190 in the back of this unit.

Family Letter: Send home copies of the Family Letter (M15–M16).

Professional Development

❷ **Teacher Note:** Learning and Assessing Multiplication Combinations, p. 151

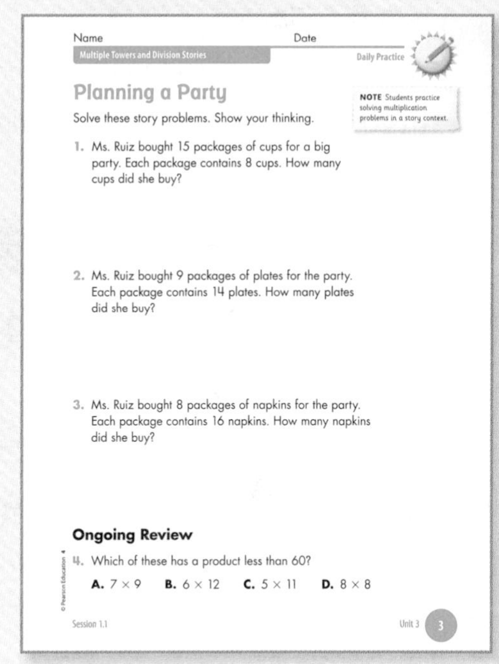

Name Date
Multiple Towers and Division Stories — Daily Practice

Planning a Party

NOTE Students practice solving multiplication problems in a story context.

Solve these story problems. Show your thinking.

1. Ms. Ruiz bought 15 packages of cups for a big party. Each package contains 8 cups. How many cups did she buy?
2. Ms. Ruiz bought 9 packages of plates for the party. Each package contains 14 plates. How many plates did she buy?
3. Ms. Ruiz bought 8 packages of napkins for the party. Each package contains 16 napkins. How many napkins did she buy?

Ongoing Review

4. Which of these has a product less than 60?
A. 7 × 9 **B.** 6 × 12 **C.** 5 × 11 **D.** 8 × 8

Session 1.1 Unit 3 3

▲ Student Activity Book, p. 3

Name Date
Multiple Towers and Division Stories — Homework

Practice with Multiplication Cards 1

NOTE Students are working on the multiplication combinations (facts) to 12 × 12. Help your child with this practice.
SMH 29–34

1. Which multiplication combinations are you practicing?
2. Write two multiplication combinations that are hard for you, and explain what helps you remember them.
Multiplication combination: ______
What helps me: ______
Multiplication combination: ______
What helps me: ______
3. How did you practice your multiplication combinations? Who helped you?

4 Unit 3 Session 1.1

▲ Student Activity Book, p. 4

Making Big Arrays

Math Focus Points

- Using arrays to model multiplication
- Developing strategies for multiplying that involve breaking apart numbers

Vocabulary

array
factor
product

Today's Plan			Materials
ACTIVITY **1** Two Arrays Make a Rectangle	45 MIN	PAIRS	• M17–M37* • M7* (from Session 1.1); T2 (optional) • Chart paper (4 × 9 array)*; blank transparency (optional)
DISCUSSION **2** How Many Ways Can You Make 8 × 9?	15 MIN	CLASS	• Chart paper (8 × 9 array)*
SESSION FOLLOW-UP **3** Daily Practice and Homework			• *Student Activity Book*, pp. 5–6 • *Student Math Handbook*, pp. 18–19

*See *Materials to Prepare*, p. 25.

Ten-Minute Math

Quick Images: Seeing Numbers Show *Quick Images: Seeing Numbers* (T34), Images 3 and 4, one at a time. For each pattern, ask students to write several different equations to find the total number of dots. For the first two viewings, give students 3 seconds to look at the pattern; the third time, leave the image displayed. Have two or three students explain how they saw the images (including any revisions they made) and their equations, showing how their numbers match the patterns. For example, Image 3 is an arrangement showing 3 groups of 9. Students might say $(3 \times 3) \times 3 = 27$ and $9 \times 3 = 27$.

ACTIVITY

1 Two Arrays Make a Rectangle

45 MIN PAIRS

Students continue to break problems into smaller parts. In this session, students work with their Array Cards (M17–M37) to find two or more small arrays that, when combined, match a larger array exactly. For example, students can combine the arrays for 4 × 4 and 4 × 5 to create an array for 4 × 9, illustrating (4 × 4) + (4 × 5) = 4 × 9. This work focuses on the idea that difficult multiplication expressions can always be broken down into smaller, more manageable components. Using arrays provides a visual image for this idea.

4 × 9

9 × 4

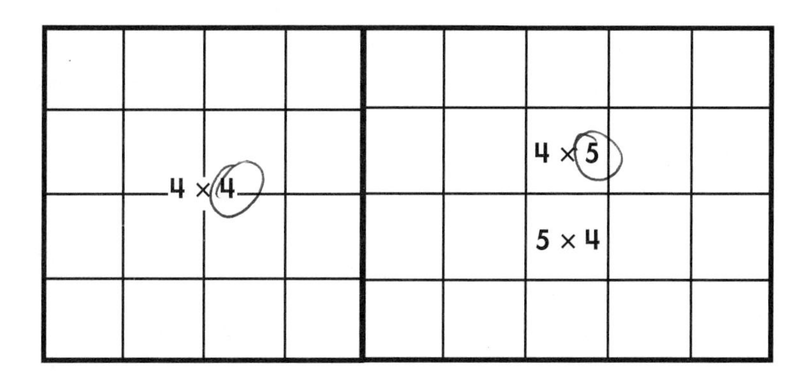

Today we are going to think about how we can use combinations of smaller arrays to make bigger arrays. This will help us think more about how to solve harder multiplication problems by breaking big problems into smaller problems that are easier to work with.

Call attention to the prepared poster with the unmarked array for 4 × 9. Ask students to find this array in their sets of Array Cards.➊ ➋

Teaching Note

➊ **Arrays** Rectangular arrays can be an important tool for students in visualizing and solving multiplication problems. When students first used arrays in Grade 3, they needed to see all the squares in the array. In order to continue using arrays as numbers get larger, students need to visualize how the outline of an array, showing just its dimensions, represents multiplication. Make sure that students can visualize how an unmarked array for 4 × 9 represents 4 rows of 9 squares (or 9 columns of 4 squares).

If students need support in visualizing, you can draw unmarked arrays on a blank transparency placed over a transparency of Centimeter Grid Paper (T2) so that students first see the array with all its squares. Then remove the grid so that they see only the outline.

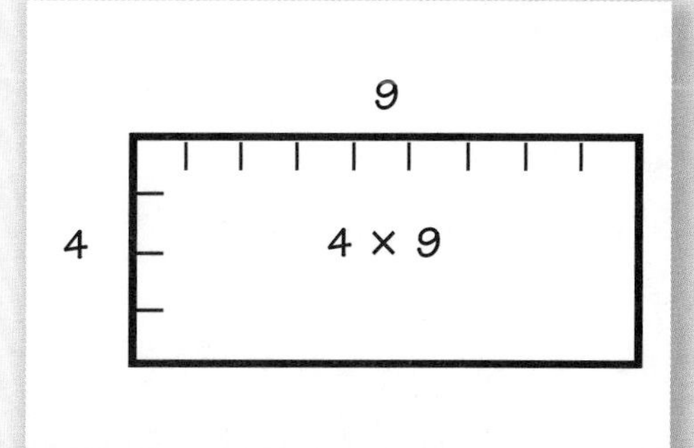

You can also, at first, make tick marks along the sides of the rectangle to show where the rows and columns are.

Professional Development

➋ **Teacher Note:** Visualizing Arrays, p. 154

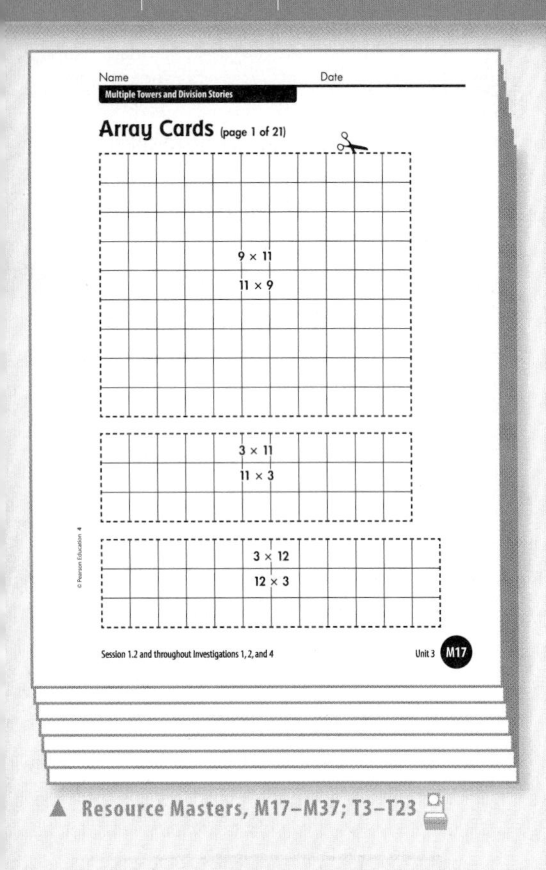

▲ Resource Masters, M17–M37; T3–T23

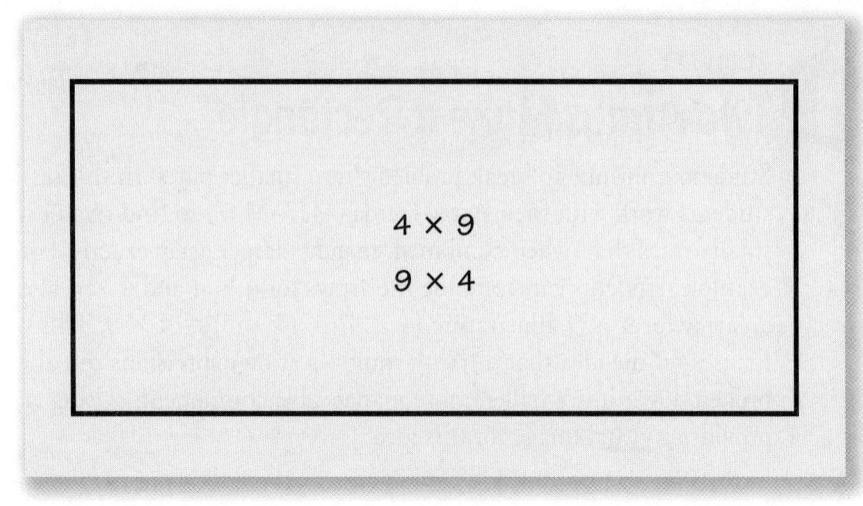

Find two arrays you can put together to make a rectangle that matches the 4 × 9 array exactly. Talk to your partner about this, and use your other Array Cards to try different combinations of two arrays.

Give students a few minutes to work in pairs. Students may suggest using more than two arrays, but for now, tell them that they should focus on finding all of the possible combinations with two arrays. Later, they will be breaking arrays into three or more smaller parts.

Write students' ideas on the chart paper. Draw each pair of arrays that they suggest as two unmarked arrays put together. Then write an equation that relates the two smaller arrays to the larger array. Explain to students that you are using parentheses to show each of the small arrays in the equation.

ACTIVITY

1 Two Arrays Make a Rectangle

45 MIN PAIRS

Students continue to break problems into smaller parts. In this session, students work with their Array Cards (M17–M37) to find two or more small arrays that, when combined, match a larger array exactly. For example, students can combine the arrays for 4 × 4 and 4 × 5 to create an array for 4 × 9, illustrating (4 × 4) + (4 × 5) = 4 × 9. This work focuses on the idea that difficult multiplication expressions can always be broken down into smaller, more manageable components. Using arrays provides a visual image for this idea.

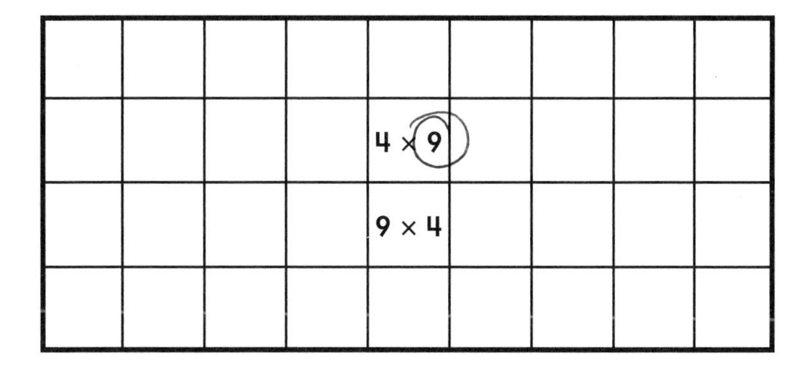

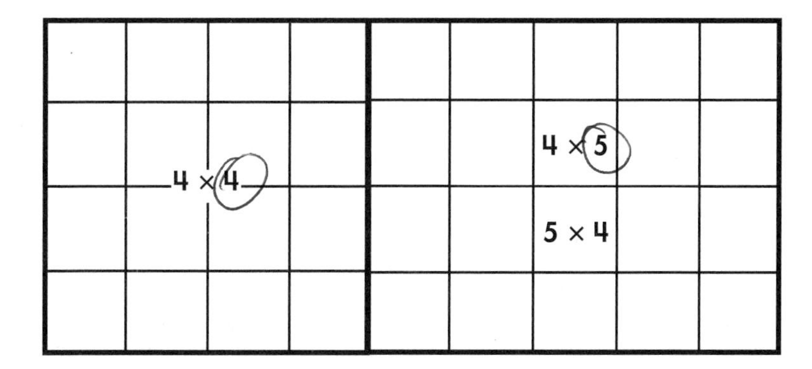

Today we are going to think about how we can use combinations of smaller arrays to make bigger arrays. This will help us think more about how to solve harder multiplication problems by breaking big problems into smaller problems that are easier to work with.

Call attention to the prepared poster with the unmarked array for 4 × 9. Ask students to find this array in their sets of Array Cards.❶ ❷

Teaching Note

❶ **Arrays** Rectangular arrays can be an important tool for students in visualizing and solving multiplication problems. When students first used arrays in Grade 3, they needed to see all the squares in the array. In order to continue using arrays as numbers get larger, students need to visualize how the outline of an array, showing just its dimensions, represents multiplication. Make sure that students can visualize how an unmarked array for 4 × 9 represents 4 rows of 9 squares (or 9 columns of 4 squares).

If students need support in visualizing, you can draw unmarked arrays on a blank transparency placed over a transparency of Centimeter Grid Paper (T2) so that students first see the array with all its squares. Then remove the grid so that they see only the outline.

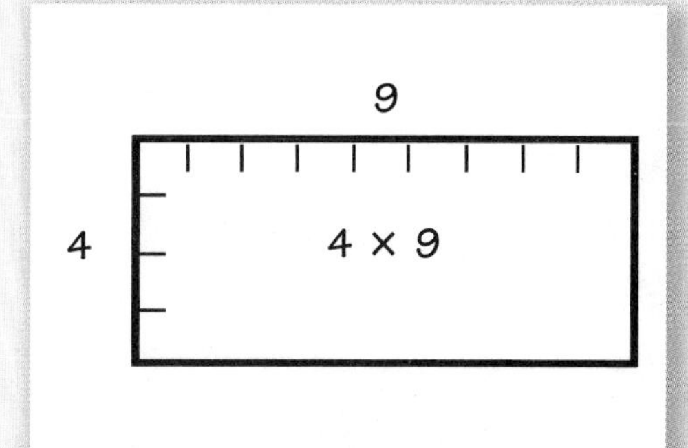

You can also, at first, make tick marks along the sides of the rectangle to show where the rows and columns are.

Professional Development

❷ **Teacher Note:** Visualizing Arrays, p. 154

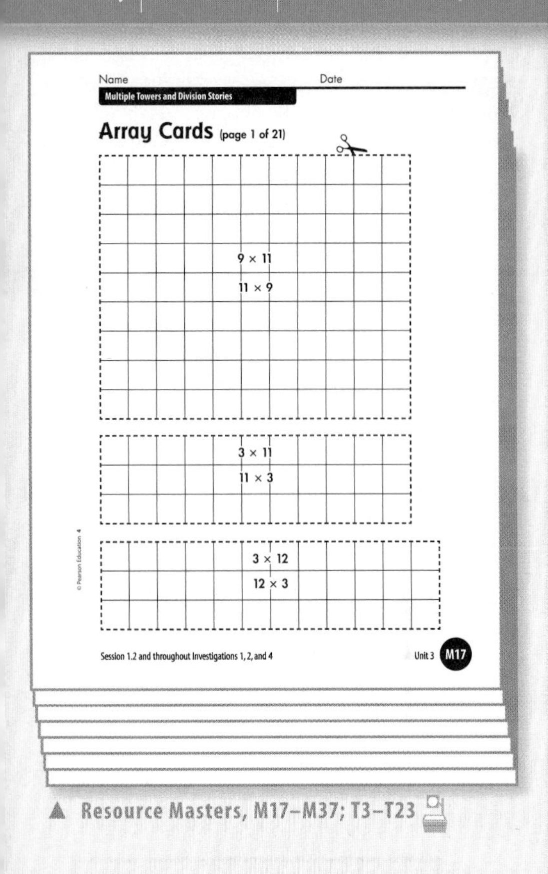

▲ Resource Masters, M17–M37; T3–T23

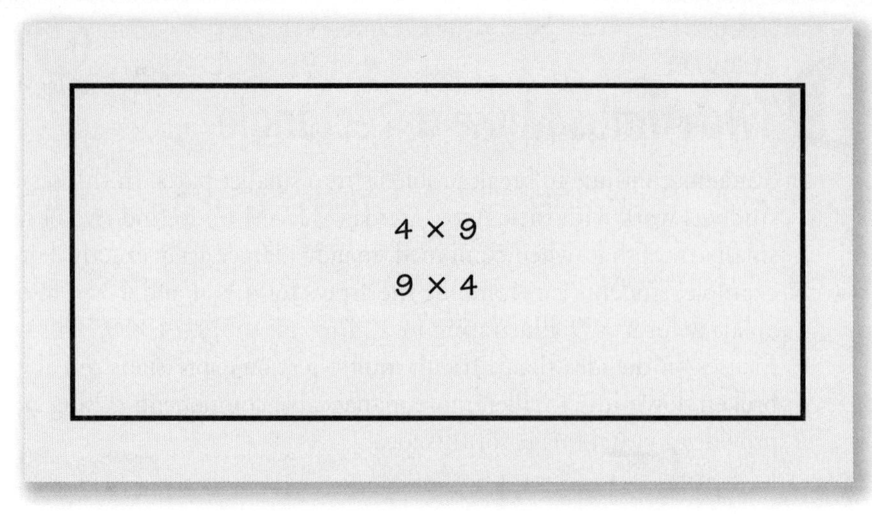

Find two arrays you can put together to make a rectangle that matches the 4 × 9 array exactly. Talk to your partner about this, and use your other Array Cards to try different combinations of two arrays.

Give students a few minutes to work in pairs. Students may suggest using more than two arrays, but for now, tell them that they should focus on finding all of the possible combinations with two arrays. Later, they will be breaking arrays into three or more smaller parts.

Write students' ideas on the chart paper. Draw each pair of arrays that they suggest as two unmarked arrays put together. Then write an equation that relates the two smaller arrays to the larger array. Explain to students that you are using parentheses to show each of the small arrays in the equation.

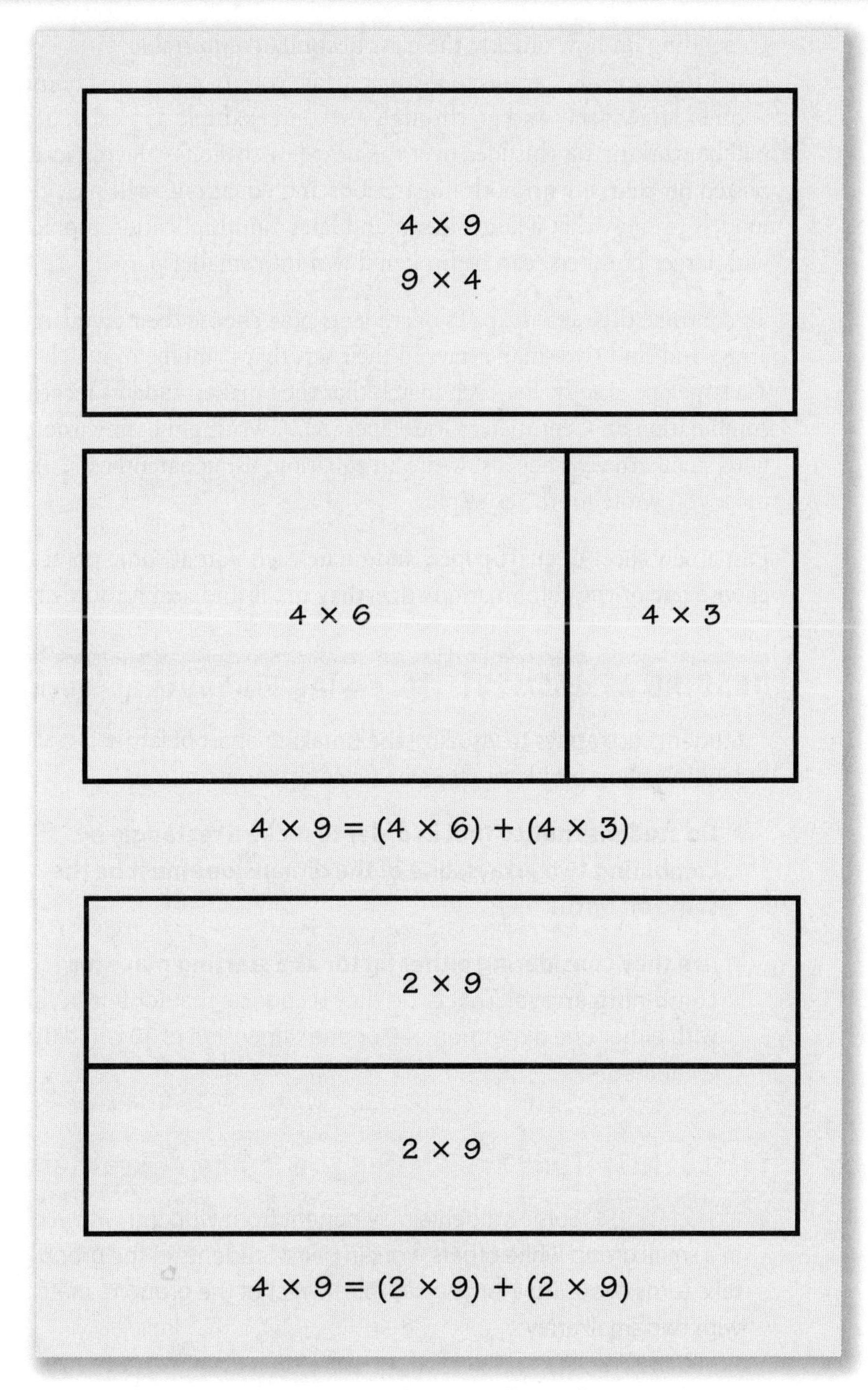

Be sure to collect examples that show a different factor broken apart, as in the two shown here. Keep in mind that, because the Array Card sets include only one of each array, students will have to either visualize a combination that involves doubling an array, as in $(2 \times 9) + (2 \times 9)$, or borrow a duplicate card from another set.

Depending on how quickly the class becomes comfortable with matching two small arrays to a larger array, you may want to choose another larger array and go through a second example as a class. Students will be working on this idea over the next few sessions. Having examples posted on charts, with both illustrations and equations, will provide models to show that a larger array, and later a multiplication problem with larger numbers, can be broken down into smaller parts.

To continue this activity, pairs of students now choose their own large arrays and find two small arrays in their sets that combine to match the large one exactly. For each match that they make, students record the combination on Centimeter Grid Paper (M7), writing the dimensions of both small arrays. They also write an equation, using parentheses, like those you wrote for the examples.

Post a new sheet of chart paper, and invite each pair at some point to choose one of the combinations that they made and add it to this chart.

ONGOING ASSESSMENT: Observing Students at Work

Students use arrays to visualize the breaking apart of larger multiplication problems into smaller components.

- **Do students notice that in order to make a rectangle by combining two arrays, one of the dimensions must be the same on both?**
- **Are they considering either factor as a starting place for combining arrays?** That is, do they recognize that for 9×10, arrays with either one dimension of 9 or one dimension of 10 could be combined?

DIFFERENTIATION: Supporting the Range of Learners

Intervention Some students may benefit from working with you in a small group while others work in pairs. Students in the group take turns choosing a large array for the rest of the group to match with two small arrays.

DISCUSSION

How Many Ways Can You Make 8 × 9?

Math Focus Points for Discussion

- Developing strategies for multiplying that involve breaking apart numbers

Display the prepared poster with the unmarked array for 8 × 9.

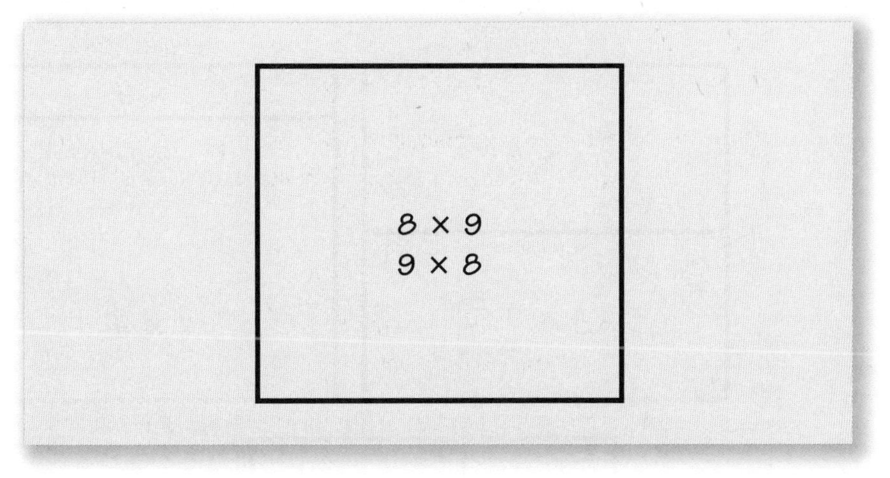

Take a look at this 8 × 9 array. Without looking at your Array Cards, how can we break this array into two smaller arrays? Which factor would you like to break apart?

Take suggestions from students, breaking apart either the 8 or the 9. Ask for more than one way to break that factor apart. For each suggestion, draw the two unmarked arrays on the chart. Then ask for at least two ways to break the second factor apart and record them.③

Teaching Note

③ **One Factor Must Stay the Same** It is important to explain that if a large array is to be made up of just two smaller arrays, one of the factors must stay the same. Students should also notice that either of the factors can be broken up. This constraint, which is part of the game *Small Array/Big Array* in the next session, maintains the connection between the distributive property and the visual representation that students are creating by dividing a larger array into smaller arrays.

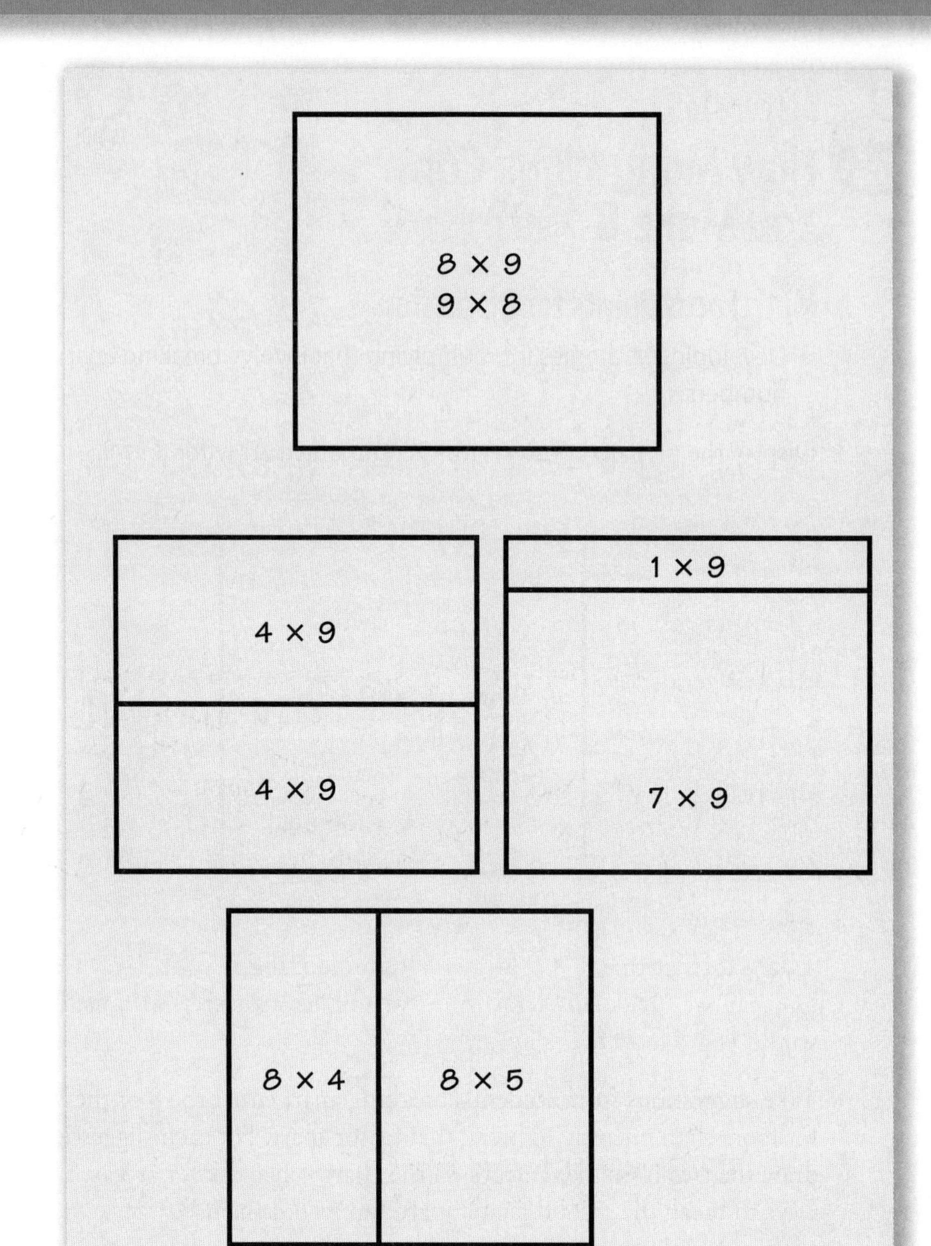

These arrays show a few different ways to break up the numbers in 8 × 9 into smaller multiplication problems, many of them easier to solve. Let's solve some of these. What do you think will happen if I find the answers to 8 × 5 and 8 × 4 and add them together?

Write the equation that represents this combination of arrays. Underneath, write the solutions as a second equation.

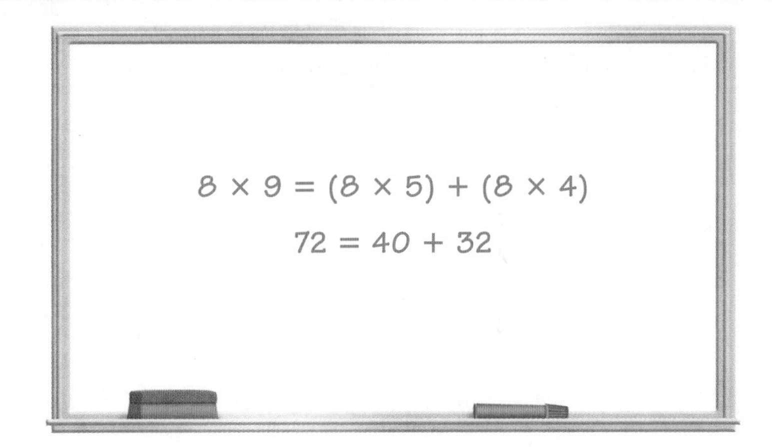

Do the same with the other equations, asking students to mentally solve the addition.

Why do you think the product is always 72?

Emphasize the idea that multiplication problems with larger numbers can always be broken down into smaller parts that make them easier to solve. Using the arrays in this way helps students see where those parts are and keep track of them. This becomes more important as they work with even larger numbers in multiplication problems. Tell students that they will continue to work on this idea when they learn a new Array Card game in the next session.

3 SESSION FOLLOW-UP
Daily Practice and Homework

Daily Practice: For ongoing review, have students complete *Student Activity Book* page 5.

Homework: For homework, students work on *Student Activity Book* page 6, which has problems about buying tickets for a play. In these problems, the larger factor is broken apart, and students must consider whether all of the tickets have been accounted for.

Student Math Handbook: Students and families may use *Student Math Handbook* pages 18–19 for reference and review. See pages 184–190 in the back of this unit.

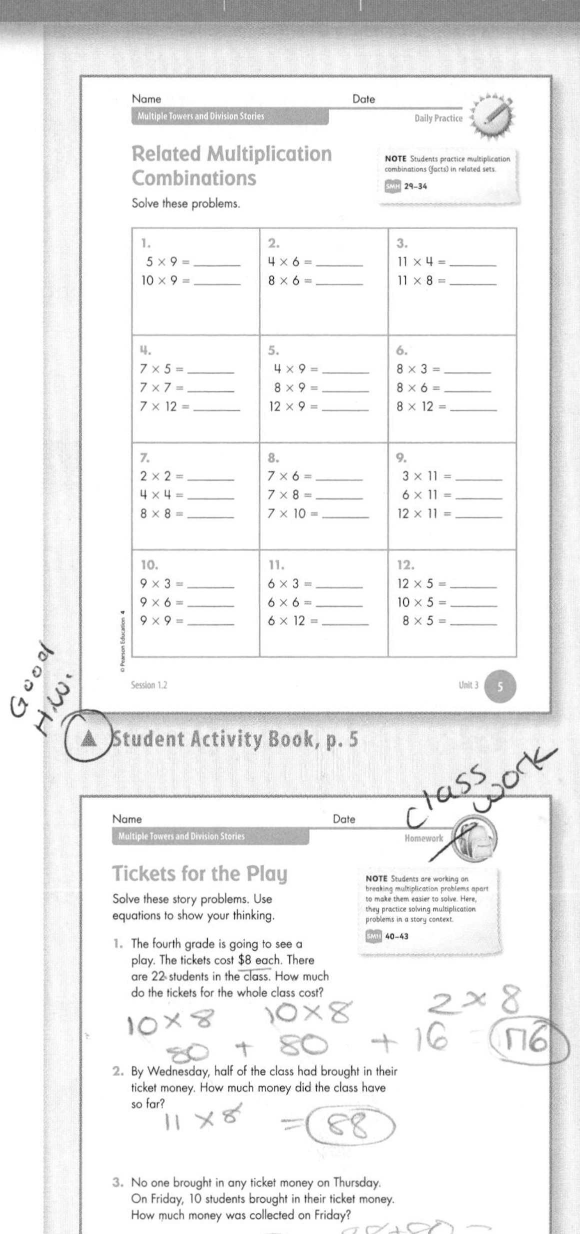

Name Date
Multiple Towers and Division Stories — Daily Practice

Related Multiplication Combinations

NOTE Students practice multiplication combinations (facts) in related sets.
SMH 29–34

Solve these problems.

1. $5 \times 9 =$ ___ $10 \times 9 =$ ___	2. $4 \times 6 =$ ___ $8 \times 6 =$ ___	3. $11 \times 4 =$ ___ $11 \times 8 =$ ___
4. $7 \times 5 =$ ___ $7 \times 7 =$ ___ $7 \times 12 =$ ___	5. $4 \times 9 =$ ___ $8 \times 9 =$ ___ $12 \times 9 =$ ___	6. $8 \times 3 =$ ___ $8 \times 6 =$ ___ $8 \times 12 =$ ___
7. $2 \times 2 =$ ___ $4 \times 4 =$ ___ $8 \times 8 =$ ___	8. $7 \times 6 =$ ___ $7 \times 8 =$ ___ $7 \times 10 =$ ___	9. $3 \times 11 =$ ___ $6 \times 11 =$ ___ $12 \times 11 =$ ___
10. $9 \times 3 =$ ___ $9 \times 6 =$ ___ $9 \times 9 =$ ___	11. $6 \times 3 =$ ___ $6 \times 6 =$ ___ $6 \times 12 =$ ___	12. $12 \times 5 =$ ___ $10 \times 5 =$ ___ $8 \times 5 =$ ___

Session 1.2 — Unit 3 — 5

Good H.W.

▲ Student Activity Book, p. 5

Class work

Name Date
Multiple Towers and Division Stories — Homework

Tickets for the Play

Solve these story problems. Use equations to show your thinking.

NOTE Students are working on breaking multiplication problems apart to make them easier to solve. Here, they practice solving multiplication problems in a story context.
SMH 40–43

1. The fourth grade is going to see a play. The tickets cost $8 each. There are 22 students in the class. How much do the tickets for the whole class cost?

10×8 10×8 2×8
80 + 80 + 16 (176)

2. By Wednesday, half of the class had brought in their ticket money. How much money did the class have so far?

11×8 = (88)

3. No one brought in any ticket money on Thursday. On Friday, 10 students brought in their ticket money. How much money was collected on Friday?

10×8 = 80 88+80 = (168)

4. Had the class collected all the money that they needed for the play by Friday? Explain how you know whether they have all the money.

No - missing 1 student

6 Unit 3 — Session 1.2

▲ Student Activity Book, p. 6

Small Array/Big Array

Math Focus Points

- Developing strategies for multiplying that involve breaking apart numbers
- Using arrays to model multiplication

Vocabulary

equation

Today's Plan		Materials
ACTIVITY **1** Introducing *Small Array/Big Array*	20 MIN CLASS	• *Student Activity Book*, p. 7 • M17–M37* (from Session 1.2); M38–M39; T3–T23 (optional); T40 • Construction paper
ACTIVITY **2** *Small Array/Big Array*	40 MIN PAIRS	• *Student Activity Book*, p. 7 • M17–M37 (from Session 1.2) • Construction paper
SESSION FOLLOW-UP **3** Daily Practice and Homework		• *Student Activity Book*, pp. 8–9 • *Student Math Handbook*, pp. 18–19; G10–G11 • M41–M42, Family Letter*

*See *Materials to Prepare*, p. 25.

Ten-Minute Math

Quick Images: Seeing Numbers Show *Quick Images: Seeing Numbers* (T35), Images 5 and 6, one at a time. For each pattern, ask students to write several different equations to find the total number of dots. For the first two viewings, give students 3 seconds to look at the pattern; the third time, leave the image displayed. Have two or three students explain how they saw the images (including any revisions they made) and their equations, showing how their numbers match the patterns.

ACTIVITY 1

Introducing *Small Array/Big Array*

Begin this session by introducing *Small Array/Big Array* with a demonstration game.

Today we are going to play a game that is about the same idea we worked on yesterday: How can you combine two or three small arrays to make a big array? If you have a big array, what smaller arrays can it be broken into?

The game is called *Small Array/Big Array,* and it uses the Array Cards. You will be trying to cover a big array with two or three smaller arrays. One important rule for making this match is that your small array must have one of the dimensions, or factors, of the big array. One side has to match exactly.❶

Make available copies of *Small Array/Big Array* (M38–M39). Reassure students that although the rules seem complex, they will become familiar through practice.

Spread the cards out in such a way that everyone can see them.❷ Place the 6 center cards on a sheet of construction paper. Ask for a volunteer to be your partner, and give each player 10 Array Cards. Play a few rounds of the game, carefully reviewing the directions with students as you go along. For each round, ask students to suggest which cards you or your partner should play.

Placing the 6 center cards on a mat of construction paper helps distinguish these cards from each player's 10 cards.

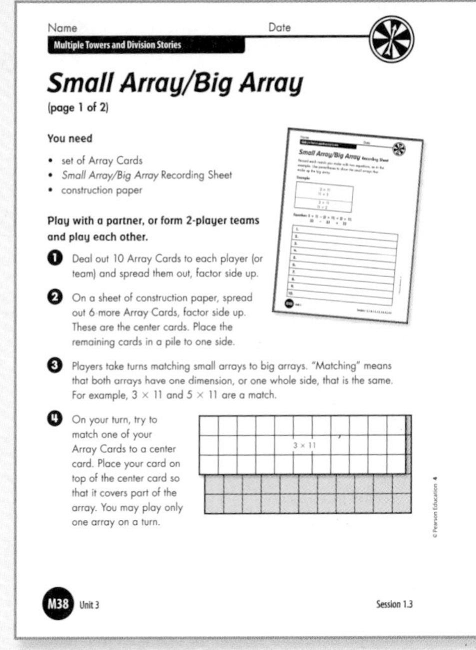

Name Date

Multiple Towers and Division Stories

Small Array/Big Array

(page 1 of 2)

You need

- set of Array Cards
- *Small Array/Big Array* Recording Sheet
- construction paper

Play with a partner, or form 2-player teams and play each other.

1. Deal out 10 Array Cards to each player (or team) and spread them out, factor side up.
2. On a sheet of construction paper, spread out 6 more Array Cards, factor side up. These are the center cards. Place the remaining cards in a pile to one side.
3. Players take turns matching small arrays to big arrays. "Matching" means that both arrays have one dimension, or one whole side, that is the same. For example, 3×11 and 5×11 are a match.
4. On your turn, try to match one of your Array Cards to a center card. Place your card on top of the center card so that it covers part of the array. You may play only one array on a turn.

M38 Unit 3 Session 1.3

▲ Resource Masters, M38

Professional Development

❶ **Teacher Note:** Playing *Small Array/Big Array,* p. 156

Teaching Note

❷ **Demonstration Game** Because the game is played with Array Cards spread out in front of the players, you may want to gather the students around a group of desks to demonstrate. If you demonstrate at the overhead with transparent Array Cards (T3–T23), you'll need to make some adjustments to fit the game on the projector. Use only 3 center cards and limit the players' cards to 3 or 4 at a time. If you make these adjustments, make sure that students understand that they should still play with the number of cards specified in the directions (6 center cards, plus 10 cards per player).

Name Date

Multiple Towers and Division Stories

Small Array/Big Array

(page 2 of 2)

5. If none of your Array Cards matches a center card, you may do one of these two things:
   (a) Draw a card from the pile. Play it if you can, or add it to your Array Cards if you cannot.
   (b) Choose one center array that matches another center array, and play that card. This is particularly useful when there are small arrays in the center.
6. If you use a center array to cover another center array, you must either
   (a) replace it with a card from the pile; or
   (b) put one of your own Array Cards in the center. There must always be 6 cards in the center.
7. The goal is to make a complete match by covering a big array with a combination of 2 or 3 smaller arrays. When you play a card that makes a complete match, you collect both the big array and the smaller arrays covering it. Then you replace the center card with one from the pile. On the *Small Array/Big Array* Recording Sheet, use equations to record the complete match, using parentheses to show the smaller arrays. For example:
   $5 \times 11 = (3 \times 11) + (2 \times 11)$
   $55 = 33 + 22$
8. Keep in mind that there is only one card for each array. Sometimes, to complete a match, you need an array that has already been used. When this happens, you may use your turn to say what the needed card is and complete the match.
9. The game is over when there are no more cards or no more matches can be made.

Session 1.3 Unit 3 M39

▲ Resource Masters, M39

Algebra Note

3 Conventional Order for Carrying Out Operations In an equation such as $8 \times 9 = (8 \times 7) + (8 \times 2)$, parentheses are not required mathematically because, according to the conventional order for carrying out operations, multiplication is carried out before addition. However, for fourth graders, using parentheses clarifies the way 8×9 is being broken up and helps students see how the distributive property is being applied in their equations.

Use the overhead to introduce the *Small Array/Big Array* Recording Sheet (T40), and demonstrate how to record a complete match.

You will write equations to record each complete match you make, just as we did yesterday, showing the big array and using parentheses for the small arrays that cover it.3

Spend no more than 20 minutes demonstrating the game to the whole class. Allow pairs of students to get started on their own. Stay with those students who still have questions, and play a few more rounds of the demonstration game.

ACTIVITY 2

Small Array/Big Array

For the rest of the session, students play the game *Small Array/Big Array* in pairs. Check that each pair has a construction paper mat for the center cards and *Student Activity Book* page 7 for recording.

ONGOING ASSESSMENT: Observing Students at Work

Students use arrays to visualize breaking larger multiplication problems apart into smaller components.

- **When part of an array is covered, can students visualize what other arrays will complete a match?**
- **Can students record their matches correctly with an equation?**

DIFFERENTIATION: Supporting the Range of Learners

ELL Preview the game rules as well as game-related vocabulary: match, matching, center, parentheses.

SESSION FOLLOW-UP

3 Daily Practice and Homework

Daily Practice: For reinforcement of this unit's content, have students complete *Student Activity Book* page 8.

Homework: On *Student Activity Book* page 9, students find either the missing factor or the missing product in equations.

Student Math Handbook: Students and families may use *Student Math Handbook* pages 18–19 and G10–G11 for reference and review. See pages 184–190 in the back of this unit.

Family Letter: Send home copies of the Family Letter (M41–M42).

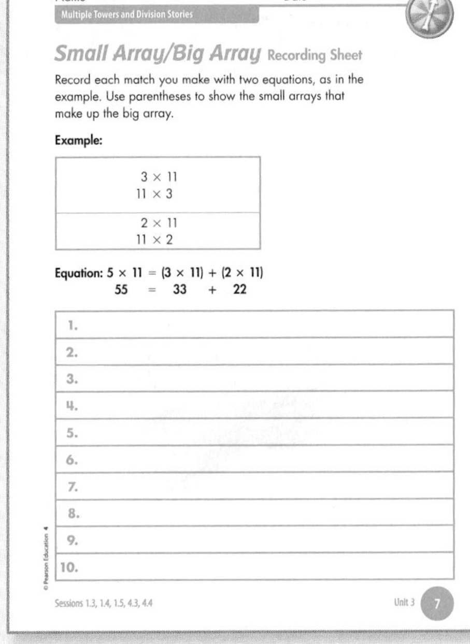

Name Date

Multiple Towers and Division Stories

Small Array/Big Array Recording Sheet

Record each match you make with two equations, as in the example. Use parentheses to show the small arrays that make up the big array.

Example:

3 × 11 11 × 3
2 × 11 11 × 2

Equation: $5 \times 11 = (3 \times 11) + (2 \times 11)$
$55 = 33 + 22$

1.
2.
3.
4.
5.
6.
7.
8.
9.
10.

© Pearson Education 4

Sessions 1.3, 1.4, 1.5, 4.3, 4.4 Unit 3 7

▲ Student Activity Book, p. 7; Resource Masters, M40; T40

Name Date

Multiple Towers and Division Stories Homework

Factors and Products 1

Fill in the chart with the missing factors or products.

NOTE Students continue to practice multiplication combinations (facts) for fluency. They find a factor or product in some of the more difficult combinations.

SMH 40

Factor	×	Factor	=	Product
12	×	9	=	
	×	7	=	63
11	×	8	=	
9	×		=	54
8	×	8	=	
	×	6	=	48
5	×	9	=	
6	×		=	60
4	×		=	28

© Pearson Education 4

Session 1.3 Unit 3 9

▲ Student Activity Book, p. 9

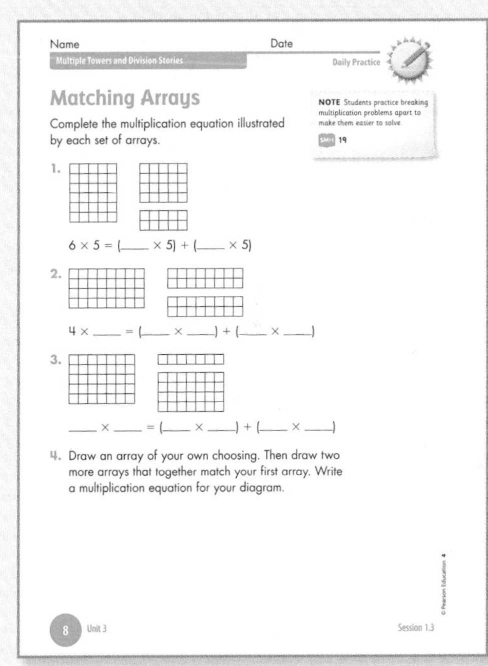

Name Date

Multiple Towers and Division Stories Daily Practice

Matching Arrays

Complete the multiplication equation illustrated by each set of arrays.

NOTE Students practice breaking multiplication problems apart to make them easier to solve.

SMH 19

1. $6 \times 5 = (\_\_ \times 5) + (\_\_ \times 5)$

2. $4 \times \_\_ = (\_\_ \times \_\_) + (\_\_ \times \_\_)$

3. $\_\_ \times \_\_ = (\_\_ \times \_\_) + (\_\_ \times \_\_)$

4. Draw an array of your own choosing. Then draw two more arrays that together match your first array. Write a multiplication equation for your diagram.

© Pearson Education 4

8 Unit 3 Session 1.3

▲ Student Activity Book, p. 8

Small Array/Big Array, *continued*

Math Focus Points

- Developing strategies for multiplying that involve breaking apart numbers
- Using arrays to model multiplication

Today's Plan		Materials
MATH WORKSHOP **1 Using Arrays to Model Multiplication** 1A *Small Array/Big Array* 1B Breaking Up Arrays 1C Solving Multiplication Problems	40 MIN	1A • *Student Activity Book,* p. 7 (from Session 1.3) • M40*; M17–M38 (from Session 1.2) • Construction paper 1B • *Student Activity Book,* p. 11 • M17–M37 (from Session 1.2) 1C • *Student Activity Book,* pp. 12–13 • M7* • Connecting cubes; color tiles
DISCUSSION **2 Using Arrays to Solve Multiplication Problems**	20 MIN CLASS	• M17–M37 (from Session 1.2)
SESSION FOLLOW-UP **3 Daily Practice**		• *Student Activity Book,* p. 14 • *Student Math Handbook,* pp. 18, 19; G10

*See *Materials to Prepare,* p. 27.

Ten-Minute Math

Counting Around the Class **Students count around the class by 8s. Each student says another multiple of 8 until all students have counted once. Highlight the multiples of 8 by writing them on the board as students say them.**

How many students have counted at 48? 96? 160?

What is a multiplication equation that would represent 9 people counting by 8s? ($9 \times 8 = 72$)

40 MIN

MATH WORKSHOP

Using Arrays to Model Multiplication

During this session's Math Workshop, students continue to play *Small Array/Big Array*. They also work on breaking apart specific arrays, and they solve more multiplication problems.

Activity 1B provides support for finding ways to break a larger array into smaller arrays. All students should complete this activity, but some students may benefit from doing it *before* they play *Big Array/Small Array* during this Math Workshop. Direct those students to do this activity first.

It's important that students spend a substantial amount of time on *Small Array/Big Array* because this game provides a basis for visualizing what happens when multiplication problems are broken apart to make them easier to solve. Students will continue with these Math Workshop activities in Session 1.5.

PAIRS

1A Small Array/Big Array

For complete details about this activity, see Session 1.3, pages 43–44. When students complete *Student Activity Book* page 7 for 10 arrays, provide copies of *Small Array/Big Array* Recording Sheet (M40).

Playing Small Array/Big Array *helps students develop strategies for breaking apart numbers to make multiplying easier.*

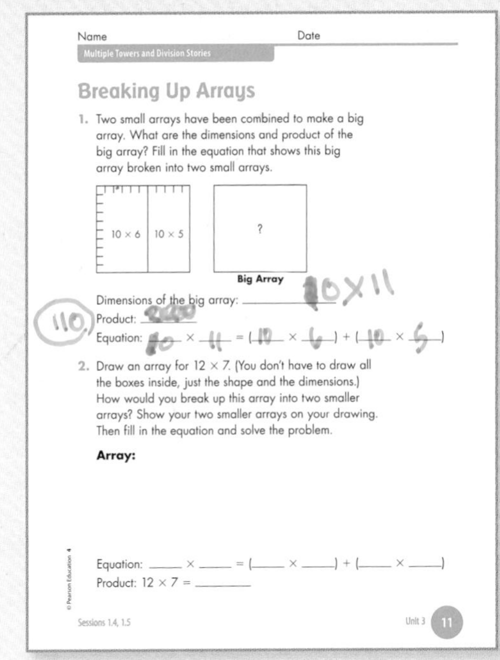

Name Date

Multiple Towers and Division Stories

Breaking Up Arrays

1. Two small arrays have been combined to make a big array. What are the dimensions and product of the big array? Fill in the equation that shows this big array broken into two small arrays.

Dimensions of the big array: 10 × 11

Product: 110

Equation: 10 × 11 = (10 × 6) + (10 × 5)

2. Draw an array for 12 × 7. (You don't have to draw all the boxes inside, just the shape and the dimensions.) How would you break up this array into two smaller arrays? Show your two smaller arrays on your drawing. Then fill in the equation and solve the problem.

Array:

Equation: ___ × ___ = (___ × ___) + (___ × ___)

Product: 12 × 7 = ______

© Pearson Education 4

Sessions 1.4, 1.5 Unit 3 11

▲ Student Activity Book, p. 11

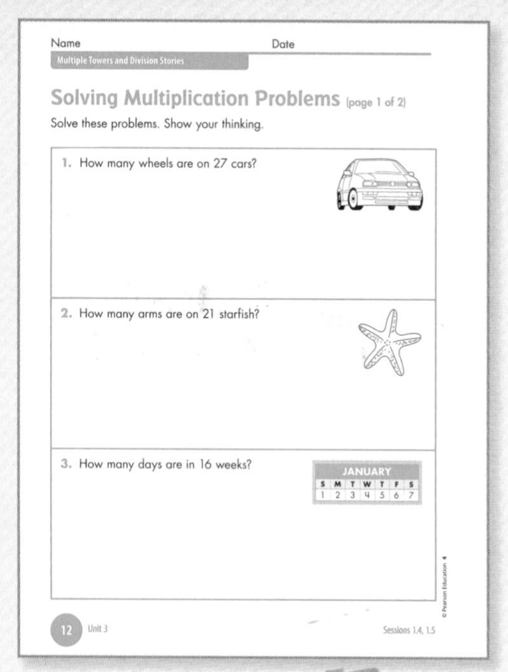
Name Date

Multiple Towers and Division Stories

Solving Multiplication Problems (page 1 of 2)

Solve these problems. Show your thinking.

1. How many wheels are on 27 cars?
2. How many arms are on 21 starfish?
3. How many days are in 16 weeks?

12 Unit 3 Sessions 1.4, 1.5

▲ Student Activity Book, p. 12 PORTFOLIO

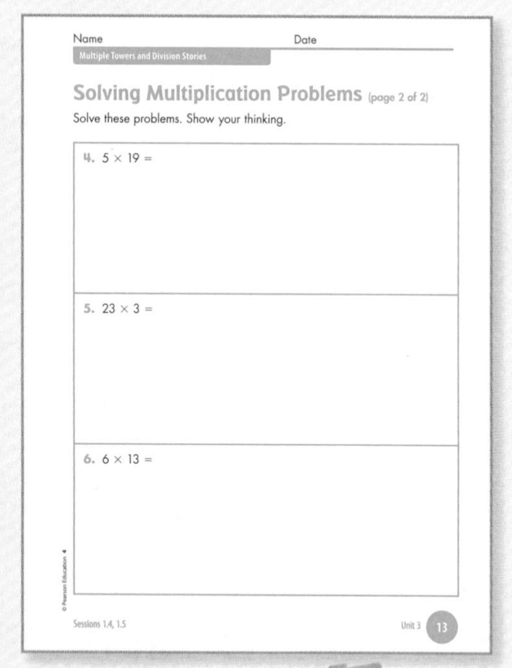
Name Date

Multiple Towers and Division Stories

Solving Multiplication Problems (page 2 of 2)

Solve these problems. Show your thinking.

4. $5 \times 19 =$
5. $23 \times 3 =$
6. $6 \times 13 =$

Sessions 1.4, 1.5 Unit 3 13

▲ Student Activity Book, p. 13 PORTFOLIO

1B Breaking Up Arrays

INDIVIDUALS

On *Student Activity Book* page 11, students look at two small arrays that are combined and determine the dimensions and total of the larger array that is created. Students also draw two smaller arrays to show the solution to one of the harder multiplication combinations, 12×7.

ONGOING ASSESSMENT: Observing Students at Work

Students combine two smaller arrays to make a larger array and break a larger array into smaller arrays.

- **Can students identify the larger array that is created when the two smaller ones are combined?**
- **Can students break a larger array into two smaller arrays, maintaining one of the dimensions?**
- **Can students write an equation that describes how a larger array is broken apart?**

Although this activity is not a formal assessment, observing students as they work will help you get a picture of how well they are understanding the ideas of *Small Array/Big Array*—that multiplication problems can be broken apart into smaller, more manageable parts.

DIFFERENTIATION: Supporting the Range of Learners

Intervention For students who may be having difficulty with the game *Small Array/Big Array*, this activity may help them see the relationship between two small arrays and a larger array. It also provides a model for writing equations with parentheses.

1C Solving Multiplication Problems

INDIVIDUALS

On *Student Activity Book* pages 12–13, students solve six multiplication problems, some in a story context and some not. Remind students that they can use math tools—connecting cubes, color tiles, or grid paper—to represent these problems as they solve them.

ONGOING ASSESSMENT: Observing Students at Work

Students solve 2-digit by 1-digit multiplication problems.

- **Do students solve these problems by breaking them apart into smaller products?** What familiar multiplication relationships, including multiplication combinations, do they use? Can they multiply easily by 10?
- **Can students show their thinking with multiplication notation?**
- **Do students use math tools to represent and help them visualize the groups in the problems?**

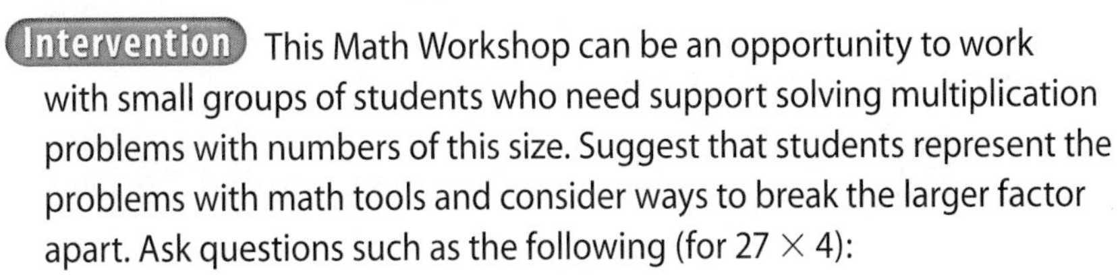

DIFFERENTIATION: Supporting the Range of Learners

Intervention This Math Workshop can be an opportunity to work with small groups of students who need support solving multiplication problems with numbers of this size. Suggest that students represent the problems with math tools and consider ways to break the larger factor apart. Ask questions such as the following (for 27×4):

- What combinations do you know with 4 as a factor that can help you here?
- Can you see a way to break apart the 27 to make problems that are easier to work with?
- How many groups of 4 wheels can you put together easily?
- How many more groups would you need to get 27 cars?

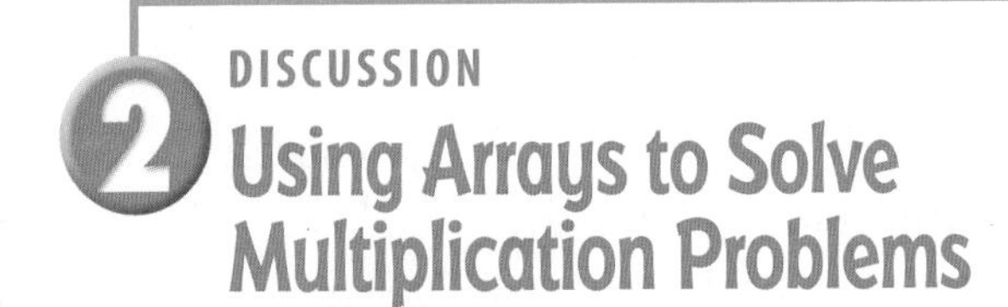

DISCUSSION

2 Using Arrays to Solve Multiplication Problems

20 MIN CLASS

Math Focus Points for Discussion

- Using arrays to model multiplication
- Developing strategies for multiplying that involve breaking apart numbers

Bring the class together to think about how to use smaller problems to solve multiplication problems with factors larger than those in their Array Cards. Write 17×6 on the board or overhead.

Professional Development

① **Dialogue Box:** Solving 17 × 6, p. 178

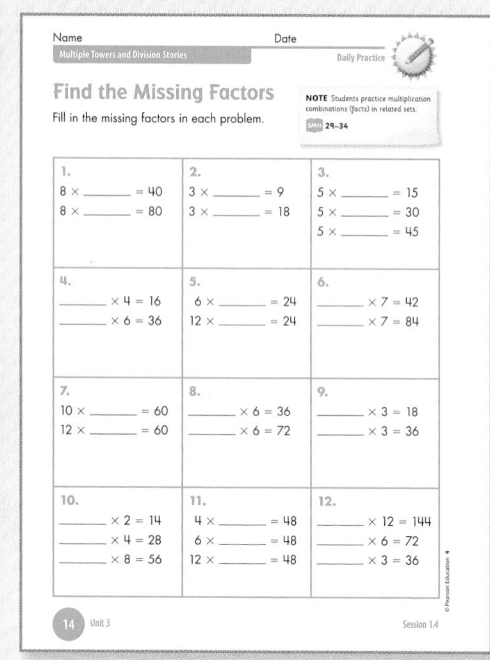
Name Date
Multiple Towers and Division Stories
Daily Practice

Find the Missing Factors

Fill in the missing factors in each problem.

NOTE Students practice multiplication combinations (facts) in related sets.
SMH 29–34

1. 8 × ____ = 40 8 × ____ = 80	2. 3 × ____ = 9 3 × ____ = 18	3. 5 × ____ = 15 5 × ____ = 30 5 × ____ = 45
4. ____ × 4 = 16 ____ × 6 = 36	5. 6 × ____ = 24 12 × ____ = 24	6. ____ × 7 = 42 ____ × 7 = 84
7. 10 × ____ = 60 12 × ____ = 60	8. ____ × 6 = 36 ____ × 6 = 72	9. ____ × 3 = 18 ____ × 3 = 36
10. ____ × 2 = 14 ____ × 4 = 28 ____ × 8 = 56	11. 4 × ____ = 48 6 × ____ = 48 12 × ____ = 48	12. ____ × 12 = 144 ____ × 6 = 72 ____ × 3 = 36

© Pearson Education 4

14 Unit 3 Session 1.4

▲ Student Activity Book, p. 14

Here's a problem that's not in your Array Card sets. Work with your partner to solve this problem. Think about the arrays you know that may help you.

Give students a few minutes to work on this. They may use their Array Cards if they choose. Then collect a variety of solutions.

Because breaking apart numbers by place value is a familiar strategy for many students, you should expect to see the solution $(10 \times 6) + (7 \times 6)$. Other students may break apart the 6 or break the 17 in other ways. Collect a variety of solutions, recording them as equations and as unmarked arrays. Then ask the class to examine the list.

All of these solutions equal 17 × 6. Some of you broke the problem into two pieces and others broke it into several pieces. How did you use what you already know to help you?①

Students might say:

"I know 17 × 2 = 34. Then I added 34 three times because 2 × 3 = 6."

"I know 17 × 1 = 17. Then I used that to build up to 17 × 6."

3

SESSION FOLLOW-UP

Daily Practice

Daily Practice: For ongoing review, have students complete *Student Activity Book* page 14.

Student Math Handbook: Students and families may use *Student Math Handbook* pages 18, 19 and G10 for reference and review. See pages 184–190 in the back of this unit.

Assessment: Solving 18 × 7

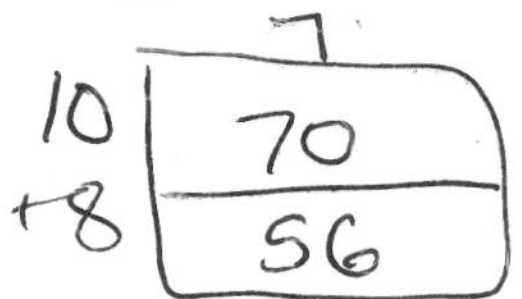

Math Focus Points

- Developing strategies for multiplying that involve breaking apart numbers
- Using arrays to model multiplication

Today's Plan		Materials
1 ASSESSMENT ACTIVITY **Solving 18 × 7**	20 MIN INDIVIDUALS	• M43*
2 MATH WORKSHOP **Using Arrays to Model Multiplication** 2A *Small Array/Big Array* 2B Breaking Up Arrays 2C Solving Multiplication Problems	40 MIN	2A • *Student Activity Book*, p. 7 (from Session 1.3) • M40* (from Session 1.3) • Array Cards (from Session 1.2) • Construction paper 2B • *Student Activity Book*, p. 11 (from Session 1.4) • Array Cards 2C • *Student Activity Book*, pp. 12–13 (from Session 1.4) • M7* • Connecting cubes; color tiles
3 SESSION FOLLOW-UP **Daily Practice**		• *Student Activity Book*, p. 15 • *Student Math Handbook*, pp. 20; G10

*See *Materials to Prepare*, p. 27.

Ten-Minute Math

Counting Around the Class **Ask questions about a class that is counting by 6s.**

When the class finished counting, the last number was 132. How many students are in that group?

Encourage students to consider what they know about how many 6s there are in 120.

What number did the 5th person say? What number did the 10th person say?

Collect answers as well as explanations about how students found their answers.

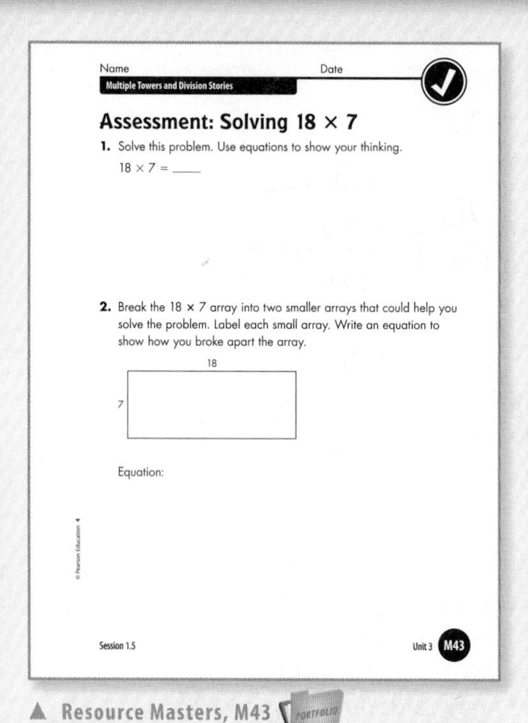

Name Date

Multiple Towers and Division Stories

Assessment: Solving 18 × 7

1. Solve this problem. Use equations to show your thinking.

   18 × 7 = ____

2. Break the 18 × 7 array into two smaller arrays that could help you solve the problem. Label each small array. Write an equation to show how you broke apart the array.

   18

   7

   Equation:

© Pearson Education 4

Session 1.5 Unit 3 M43

▲ Resource Masters, M43 PORTFOLIO

Professional Development

➊ **Teacher Note:** Assessment: Solving 18 × 7, p. 158

ASSESSMENT ACTIVITY

➊ Solving 18 × 7

20 MIN INDIVIDUALS

With this activity you have an opportunity to assess Benchmark 1: Multiply 2-digit numbers by 1-digit and small 2-digit numbers (e.g., 12, 15, 20), using strategies that involve breaking the numbers apart. You will be able to determine how well students are solving multiplication problems by breaking apart the numbers to create problems that are easier to solve and then combining the results.

Hand out copies of Assessment: Solving 18 × 7 (M43). Students solve one problem, 18 × 7, and show their solution with equations. They also break apart an 18 × 7 array to show two smaller arrays. Students may choose to break apart the array either to represent the way they solved the problem or to show a different solution.➊

DIFFERENTIATION: Supporting the Range of Learners

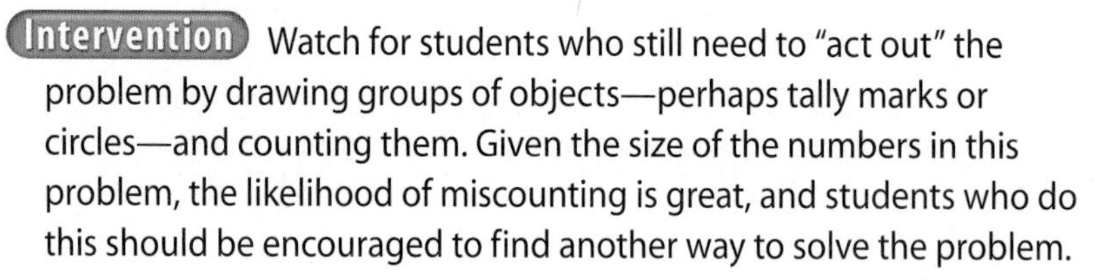

Intervention Watch for students who still need to "act out" the problem by drawing groups of objects—perhaps tally marks or circles—and counting them. Given the size of the numbers in this problem, the likelihood of miscounting is great, and students who do this should be encouraged to find another way to solve the problem.

Ask students whether they see any way they can break apart the problem. If the idea of breaking apart 18 by place value does not come up, you may need to do further work with these students to help them recognize that 2-digit numbers are composed of tens and ones.

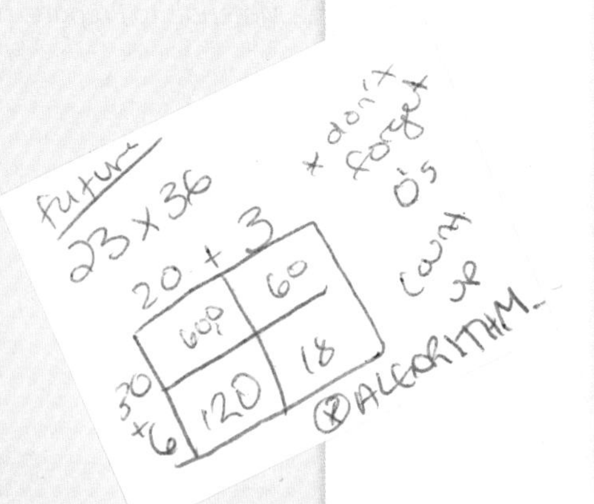

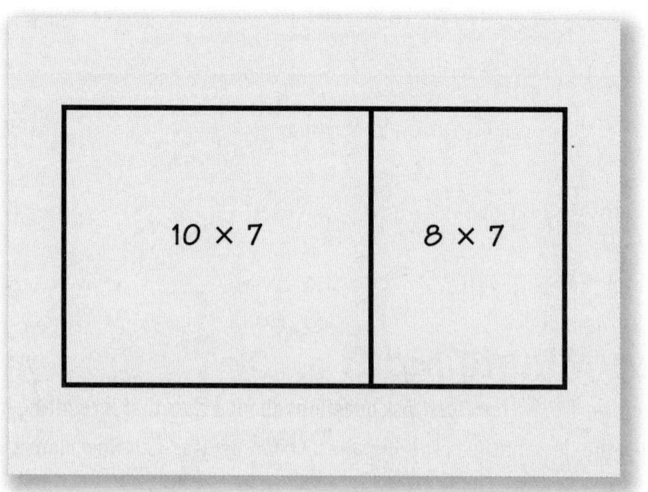

Breaking apart 18 by place value

2-digit by 1-digit

10x 7 =

8x7= +

If a student can break apart the numbers in some way but is unsure about how to put the problem back together, introduce a story context with something in groups of 7.

What if this were 18 bags of apples with 7 apples in each bag? You said you knew that 10 × 7 is 70, so we know that there are 70 apples in 10 bags. How many more bags do you have to figure out?

This student will need more work with breaking apart numbers and recombining them, being sure to keep track of all the parts of the problem.

40 MIN

MATH WORKSHOP

Using Arrays to Model Multiplication

When students have completed the assessment, they return to the Math Workshop activities from the previous session. Students should complete the activity Solving Multiplication Problems (*Student Activity Book* pages 12–13) if they have not already. Decide which students need to spend more time with *Small Array/Big Array* at this point and which should work only on Breaking Up Arrays and Solving Multiplication Problems. Students will have more opportunities to play *Small Array/ Big Array* in the next investigation.

PAIRS

2A *Small Array/Big Array*

For complete details about this activity, see Session 1.3, pages 43–44.

INDIVIDUALS

2B Breaking Up Arrays

For complete details about this activity, see Session 1.4, page 48.

INDIVIDUALS

2C Solving Multiplication Problems

For complete details about this activity, see Session 1.4, page 48.

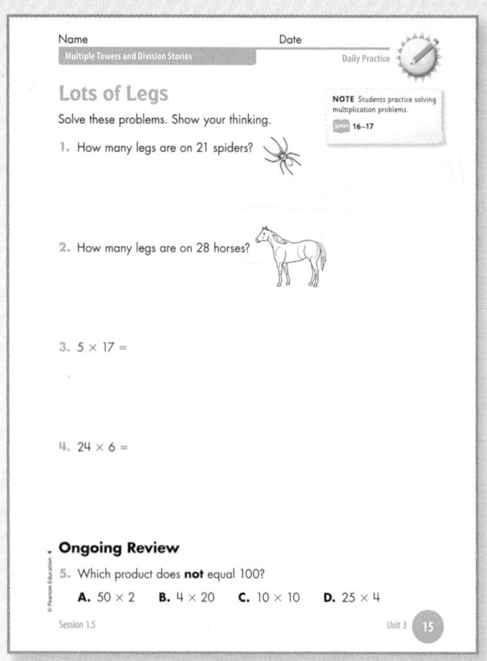

Name Date

Multiple Towers and Division Stories Daily Practice

Lots of Legs

Solve these problems. Show your thinking.

NOTE Students practice solving multiplication problems.

SMH 16–17

1. How many legs are on 21 spiders?

2. How many legs are on 28 horses?

3. $5 \times 17 =$

4. $24 \times 6 =$

Ongoing Review

5. Which product does **not** equal 100?

A. 50×2 **B.** 4×20 **C.** 10×10 **D.** 25×4

© Pearson Education 3

Session 1.5 Unit 3 15

▲ **Student Activity Book, p. 15**

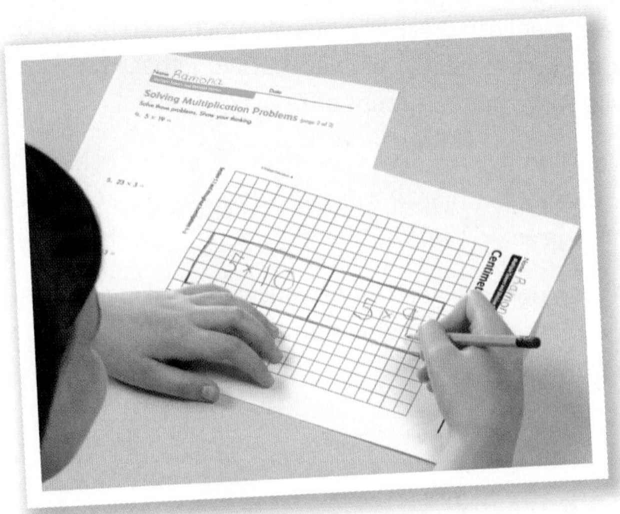

Students often use what they have learned about breaking up arrays to solve the given multiplication problems: $5 \times 19 = (5 \times 10) + (5 \times 9)$.

SESSION FOLLOW-UP

3 Daily Practice

Daily Practice: For ongoing review, have students complete *Student Activity Book* page 15.

Student Math Handbook: Students and families may use *Student Math Handbook* pages 20 and G10 for reference and review. See pages 184–190 in the back of this unit.

INVESTIGATION 2

Mathematical Emphases

Computational Fluency Solving multiplication problems with 2-digit numbers

Math Focus Points

- Developing strategies for multiplying that involve breaking apart numbers

Whole Number Operations Understanding and using the relationship between multiplication and division to solve division problems

Math Focus Points

- Solving division story problems
- Using and interpreting division notation
- Solving division problems by making groups of the divisor
- Using known multiplication combinations to solve division problems

Whole Number Operations Representing the meaning of multiplication and division

Math Focus Points

- Making sense of remainders in terms of the problem context
- Representing a division problem with pictures, diagrams, or models
- Creating a story problem to represent a division expression

Division

	Student Activity Book	Student Math Handbook	Professional Development: Read Ahead of Time
SESSION 2.1 p. 60 **Looking at Division** Students solve a division problem and discuss strategies with a focus on their first steps. They use these strategies as they work on a set of division story problems.	16–19	44, 46	• **Teacher Note:** Two Kinds of Division: Sharing and Grouping, p. 160
SESSION 2.2 p. 65 **Division with Remainders** Students discuss strategies for solving division problems that involve making groups of the divisor. They solve division problems with remainders.	16–17, 21–24	47	
SESSION 2.3 p. 72 **Division Stories** Students discuss division problems with remainders, focusing on how the remainder affects the solution in each problem situation. They solve division story problems and continue playing *Small Array/Big Array.*	21–22, 25–28	48–49; G10	• **Teacher Note:** What Do You Do with the Remainders?, p. 162 • **Dialogue Box:** What Do You Do with the Extras?, p. 180
SESSION 2.4 p. 77 **Strategies for Division** Students develop strategies for division by solving division problems and finding the missing dimension on an array when given the number of squares in the array and one dimension.	25–26, 29–31	50–52; G8, G10	

Ten-Minute Math See page 20 for an overview.

Quick Images: Seeing Numbers

- T35–T37, *Quick Images: Seeing Numbers*

Counting Around the Class

- No materials needed

Materials to Gather	Materials to Prepare
• **M8, Practicing with Multiplication Cards** (from Session 1.1) • **M17–M37, Array Cards** (1 set per pair; from Session 1.2) • **M9–M14, Multiplication Cards** (1 set per student; from Session 1.1) • **Connecting cubes** (as needed) • **Color tiles** (as needed)	• **M7, Centimeter Grid Paper** Make copies. (as needed) • **Chart paper** On a sheet of chart paper, write the following story problem for discussion: Ms. Santos owns a neighborhood grocery store. She has 56 apples to arrange in rows for her window display. She has room for 4 rows in her window. How many apples will there be in each row if she puts the same number in each row?
• **M17–M37, Array Cards** (1 set per pair; from Session 1.2) • **Connecting cubes** (as needed) • **Color tiles** (as needed)	• **M7, Centimeter Grid Paper** Make copies. (as needed)
• **M17–M37, Array Cards** (1 set per pair; from Session 1.2) • **Construction paper** (1 sheet per pair) • **Connecting cubes** (as needed) • **Color tiles** (as needed)	• **M7, Centimeter Grid Paper** Make copies. (as needed) • **M40, *Small Array/Big Array* Recording Sheet** Make copies. (as needed)
• **T41, *Missing Factors* Recording Sheet** • **M17–M37, Array Cards** (1 set per pair; from Session 1.2) • **Posted story problem** (from Session 2.1) • **Construction paper** (1 sheet per pair) • **Connecting cubes** (as needed) • **Color tiles** (as needed)	• **M7, Centimeter Grid Paper** Make copies. (as needed) • **M40, *Small Array/Big Array* Recording Sheet** Make copies. (as needed) • **M44, *Missing Factors*** Make copies. (as needed) Read the rules ahead of time to familiarize yourself with the game. • **M45, *Missing Factors* Recording Sheet** Make copies. (as needed) • **Chart paper** To make a poster for introducing *Missing Factors,* draw a 4×14 unmarked array on a sheet of chart paper. Write a large 56 in the center of the rectangle, and a small 4 at the left side (as on the back of an Array Card).

Overhead Transparency

Division, *continued*

Session	Student Activity Book	Student Math Handbook	Professional Development: Read Ahead of Time
SESSION 2.5 p. 84 **Related Multiplication and Division Problems** Students solve and represent pairs of related multiplication and division problems.	29, 33–35	35; G8	• **Teacher Note:** The Relationship Between Multiplication and Division, p. 163; **Teacher Note:** Learning and Assessing Multiplication Combinations, p. 151
SESSION 2.6 p. 88 **Assessment: Writing and Solving a Division Problem** After discussing related multiplication and division problems, students complete an assessment focused on writing and solving a division story problem.	33, 36	46	• **Teacher Note:** Assessment: Writing and Solving a Division Problem, p. 164

Materials to Gather	Materials to Prepare
• **T2, Centimeter Grid Paper** • **Connecting cubes** (90; optional) • **M17–M37, Array Cards** (1 set per pair; from Session 1.2)	• **M45, *Missing Factors* Recording Sheet** Make copies. (as needed)
• **Connecting cubes** (as needed) • **Color tiles** (as needed)	• **M7, Centimeter Grid Paper** Make copies. (as needed) • **M46, Assessment: Writing and Solving a Division Problem** Make copies. (1 per student)

Overhead Transparency

Looking at Division

Math Focus Points

- Solving division story problems
- Using and interpreting division notation

Vocabulary

division

Today's Plan		Materials
1 DISCUSSION **Rows of Apples: 56 ÷ 4**	20 MIN CLASS PAIRS	• M7*; M17–M37 (from Session 1.2) • Chart paper (story problem)* • Connecting cubes; color tiles
2 ACTIVITY **Division Stories**	40 MIN INDIVIDUALS PAIRS	• *Student Activity Book,* pp. 16–17 • M7*; M17–M37 (from Session 1.2) • Connecting cubes; color tiles
3 SESSION FOLLOW-UP **Daily Practice and Homework**		• *Student Activity Book,* pp. 18–19 • M8* (from Session 1.2); M9–M14 • *Student Math Handbook,* pp. 44, 46

*See *Materials to Prepare,* p. 57.

Ten-Minute Math

Counting Around the Class **Students count around the class by 9s. Each student says another multiple of 9 until all students have counted once. Highlight the multiples of 9 by writing them on the board as students say them.**

How many students have counted at 45? 99? 171? What is a multiplication equation that would represent 11 people counting by 9s? ($11 \times 9 = 99$)

DISCUSSION

Rows of Apples: 56 ÷ 4

Math Focus Points for Discussion

- Solving division story problems

Read aloud the problem you have written on chart paper while students read along.

> Ms. Santos owns a neighborhood grocery store. She has 56 apples to arrange in rows for her window display. She has room for 4 rows in her window.
>
> How many apples will there be in each row if she puts the same number in each row?

Students work with partners to solve this division problem. Make available color tiles, cubes, Array Cards, and grid paper for use as needed. When students have finished, bring them together to share their strategies for solving the problem.

Notice that in this problem we are dividing up the 56 apples into 4 rows. Therefore, this is a division problem. Let's hear how some of you solved it.

Expect to hear a range of strategies. Some students, for example, may directly model the problem by starting with 56 cubes or tiles and doling them out into 4 rows, either one at a time or in groups. Others may reason from known multiplication combinations such as 4×5 or 4×10.

Listen for examples of strategies that use known multiplication combinations. Focus the class's attention on the first steps of these strategies. Throughout this unit, as students share strategies, help them think about how to use clear notation to keep track of their work.

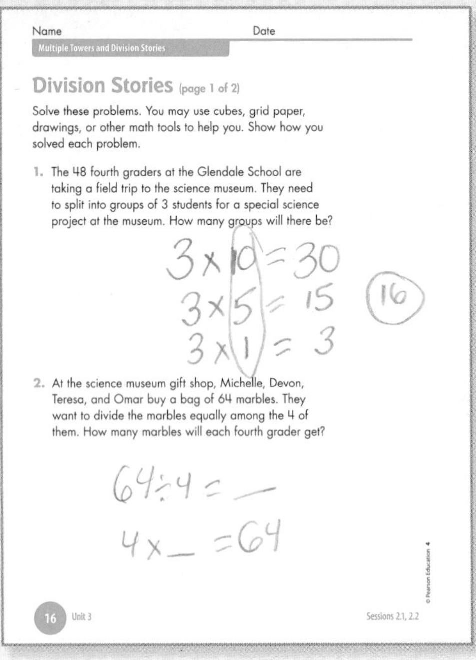

Name Date

Multiple Towers and Division Stories

Division Stories (page 1 of 2)

Solve these problems. You may use cubes, grid paper, drawings, or other math tools to help you. Show how you solved each problem.

1. The 48 fourth graders at the Glendale School are taking a field trip to the science museum. They need to split into groups of 3 students for a special science project at the museum. How many groups will there be?

3 x 10 = 30
3 x 5 = 15
3 x 1 = 3
(16)

2. At the science museum gift shop, Michelle, Devon, Teresa, and Omar buy a bag of 64 marbles. They want to divide the marbles equally among the 4 of them. How many marbles will each fourth grader get?

64 ÷ 4 = __
4 x __ = 64

16 Unit 3 Sessions 2.1, 2.2

▲ Student Activity Book, p. 16

Algebra Note

❶ **Using Multiplication for Division** Because division and multiplication have an inverse relationship, the relationship among the numbers 4, 14, and 56 can be expressed in all of these ways:

$56 \div 4 = 14 \qquad 4 \times 14 = 56$

$56 \div 14 = 4 \qquad 14 \times 4 = 56$

As students use their knowledge of multiplication to solve division problems, they are also building their understanding of the operation of division and its inverse relationship with multiplication. See Algebra Connections in This Unit, p. 16.

Multiplication Towers

4 x 10 = 40
4 x 11 = 44
4 x 12 = 48
4 x 13 = 52
4 x 14 = 56

4)56

Richard used tiles to solve the problem. The first thing he did was to put 5 tiles in each of the 4 rows. Can anyone explain why you think Richard did this and what he had to do next?

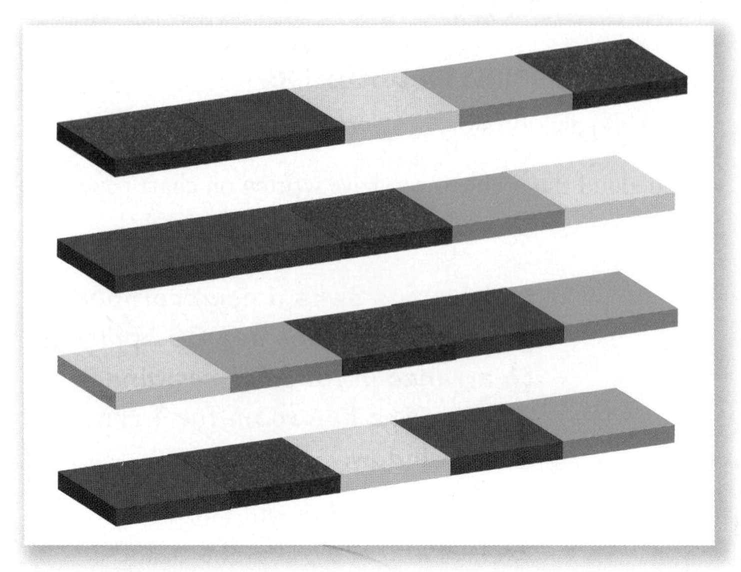

Record 4 × 5 on the board.

Then Richard said that he added 5 more tiles to each row, using 40 tiles in all. What multiplication equation could you use to show your second step? How can you show that you used up 40 tiles?

Record several ways to show the same information.

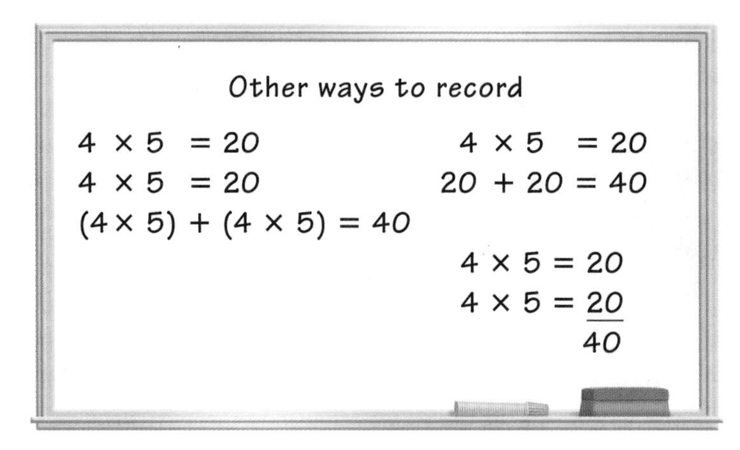

Then, ask for other possible strategies.

Noemi said that her first step in solving this problem was 4 × 10 = 40. Why do you think she decided to multiply 4 times 10? What did she have to do next to find out how many apples will be in each row?❶

Keep this division story problem posted for reference during Session 2.4.

2 ACTIVITY
Division Stories

Students solve the four division story problems on *Student Activity Book* pages 16–17. Have math tools available for use as needed. As students are working, look for examples of solution strategies for the first problem that involve considering more than one group of 3 at a time.

Let students know that the next session will begin with a discussion about their work on this page.❷ ❸

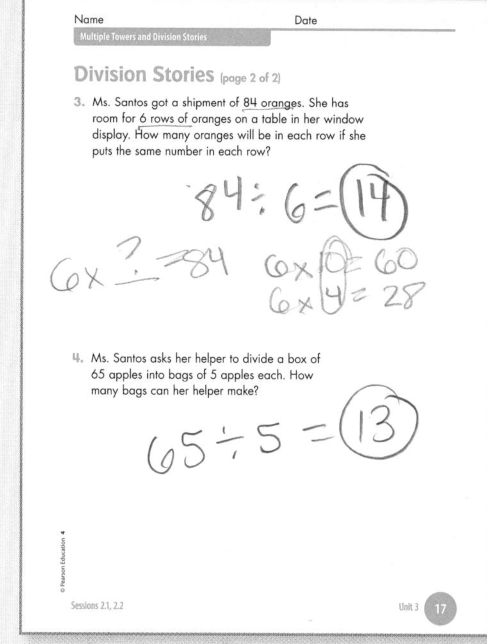

Name Date

Multiple Towers and Division Stories

Division Stories (page 2 of 2)

3. Ms. Santos got a shipment of 84 oranges. She has room for 6 rows of oranges on a table in her window display. How many oranges will be in each row if she puts the same number in each row?

$84 \div 6 = 14$

$6 \times ? = 84$ $6 \times 10 = 60$ $6 \times 4 = 28$

4. Ms. Santos asks her helper to divide a box of 65 apples into bags of 5 apples each. How many bags can her helper make?

$65 \div 5 = 13$

© Pearson Education 4

Sessions 2.1, 2.2 Unit 3 17

▲ Student Activity Book, p. 17

ONGOING ASSESSMENT: Observing Students at Work

Students solve and represent division story problems.

- **Do students solve these problems by acting out the situation, showing either the grouping or the number being divided?**
- **What known multiplication or division relationships do students use to solve these division problems?** To solve $48 \div 3$, do they use multiplication combinations such as $5 \times 3 = 15$, $8 \times 3 = 24$, or $10 \times 3 = 30$?

As you circulate and observe, ask students questions about their strategies. Use this activity to assess what they know about solving division problems.

DIFFERENTIATION: Supporting the Range of Learners

Intervention Students who are not yet using known multiplication or division relationships to solve these problems will benefit from modeling the action of the problems by using cubes or drawings. Help students connect multiplication and division notation to what they do with the cubes.

If some students are solving a grouping problem by successively removing groups of cubes, encourage them to think about the multiplication combinations they know that will allow them to remove the largest possible number of groups at a time. For example, in Problem 1, ask students to think about removing 2 groups of 3, 5 groups of 3, or 10 groups of 3, instead of one group at a time.

Professional Development

❷ **Teacher Note:** Two Kinds of Division: Sharing and Grouping, p. 160

❸ **Sharing and Grouping** The problems on *Student Activity Book* pages 16–17 represent two types of division situations, sharing and grouping. Problem 1, for example, is a grouping problem in which 48 students are organized in groups of 3 students each. Problem 2, on the other hand, represents a sharing situation in which 64 marbles are shared equally among 4 friends. Students do not need to know and use the names of these two types of division, but they should recognize both sharing and grouping as division situations and should be able to visualize each situation.

In a sharing problem, ask students to think about the largest amount that they can put in each group at one time. For Problem 3, ask questions such as the following:

You know that there are 6 rows of oranges. Instead of putting one orange at a time in each row, can you start by putting (4, or 5, or 10) oranges at a time in each row? How many of the 84 oranges have you used up? How many do you still need to put in rows?

Because individual cubes are easily linked, using connecting cubes to model division situations can help students begin to think in larger groups.

SESSION FOLLOW-UP

3 Daily Practice and Homework

Daily Practice: For ongoing review, have students complete *Student Activity Book* page 18.

Homework: Students use their Multiplication Cards (from Session 1.1) to practice or to continue learning the multiplication combinations to 12 × 12. Provide copies of Practicing with Multiplication Cards (M8) as needed to remind students of the procedures. Students record details of their practice on *Student Activity Book* page 19.

Student Math Handbook: Students and families may use *Student Math Handbook* pages 44, 46 for reference and review. See pages 184–190 in the back of this unit.

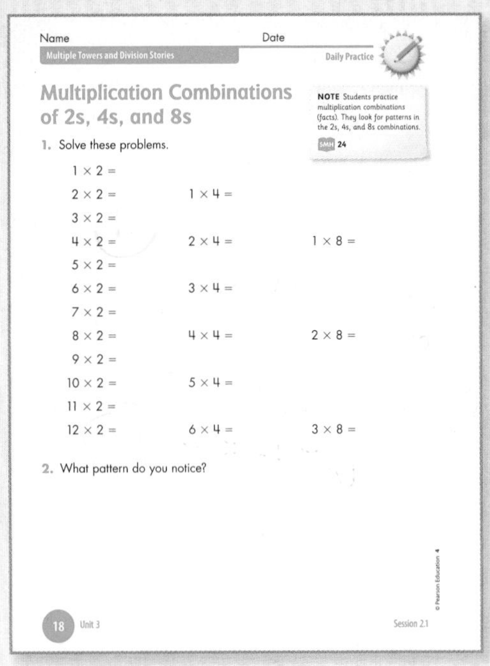

Name Date

Multiple Towers and Division Stories — Daily Practice

Multiplication Combinations of 2s, 4s, and 8s

NOTE Students practice multiplication combinations (facts). They look for patterns in the 2s, 4s, and 8s combinations.

SMH 24

1. Solve these problems.

1 × 2 =		
2 × 2 =	1 × 4 =	
3 × 2 =		
4 × 2 =	2 × 4 =	1 × 8 =
5 × 2 =		
6 × 2 =	3 × 4 =	
7 × 2 =		
8 × 2 =	4 × 4 =	2 × 8 =
9 × 2 =		
10 × 2 =	5 × 4 =	
11 × 2 =		
12 × 2 =	6 × 4 =	3 × 8 =

2. What pattern do you notice?

© Pearson Education 4

18 Unit 3 Session 2.1

▲ Student Activity Book, p. 18

Name Date

Multiple Towers and Division Stories — Homework

Practice with Multiplication Cards 2

NOTE Students are working on the multiplication combinations (facts) to 12 × 12. Help your child with this practice.

SMH 33–34

1. Which multiplication combinations are you practicing?

2. Write two multiplication combinations that are hard for you, and explain what helps you remember them.

Multiplication combination: ____

What helps me: ____

Multiplication combination: ____

What helps me: ____

3. How did you practice your multiplication combinations? Who helped you?

© Pearson Education 4

Session 2.1 Unit 3 19

▲ Student Activity Book, p. 19

Division with Remainders

Math Focus Points

- Using and interpreting division notation
- Solving division problems by making groups of the divisor
- Making sense of remainders in terms of the problem context

Vocabulary

remainder

Today's Plan		Materials
1 DISCUSSION How Many Groups?	20 MIN CLASS	• *Student Activity Book*, pp. 16–17 (from Session 2.1) • M17–M37 (from Session 1.2)
2 ACTIVITY Problems with Remainders	40 MIN CLASS INDIVIDUALS PAIRS	• *Student Activity Book*, pp. 21–22 • M7* • Connecting cubes; color tiles
3 SESSION FOLLOW-UP Daily Practice and Homework		• *Student Activity Book*, pp. 23–24 • *Student Math Handbook*, p. 47

*See *Materials to Prepare*, p. 57.

Ten-Minute Math

Counting Around the Class **Students count around the class by 7s. Ask for predictions for what the last number will be. Each student says another multiple of 7 until all students have counted once. Highlight the multiples of 7 by writing them on the board as students say them.**

How many students have counted at 56? 91? 126? What is a multiplication equation that would represent 9 people counting by 7s? ($9 \times 7 = 63$)

Math Note

➊ **Standard Division Notation** It is important that your students learn to recognize standard notations for multiplication and division. This unit uses the division notation 64 ÷ 4 and introduces the notation $\overline{)}$. Your challenge is to help students interpret both notations meaningfully so that they can use their understanding of the number relationships in the problem to find the quotient. When they see either notation, students should be able to interpret it as division (e.g., "How many 4s are in 64?" or "64 divided into 4 equal parts"). Learning how to read these two notations can be difficult because the order of the numbers is not the same. Students may read $4\overline{)64}$ incorrectly as "4 divided by 64." Students will work with both division notations in *How Many Packages? How Many Groups?*

DISCUSSION

1 How Many Groups?

20 MIN CLASS

Math Focus Points for Discussion

- Solving division problems by making groups of the divisor

Students need their completed copies of *Student Activity Book* pages 16–17 from Session 2.1 for this discussion. Start by writing the notation 64 ÷ 4 on the board.

How would you read this division expression? Which problem on these pages does it describe? What does the 64 mean? What does the 4 mean?

When students have related this expression to the story context in Problem 2 (64 marbles shared by 4 people), write another form of division notation next to the first and ask students to read it.

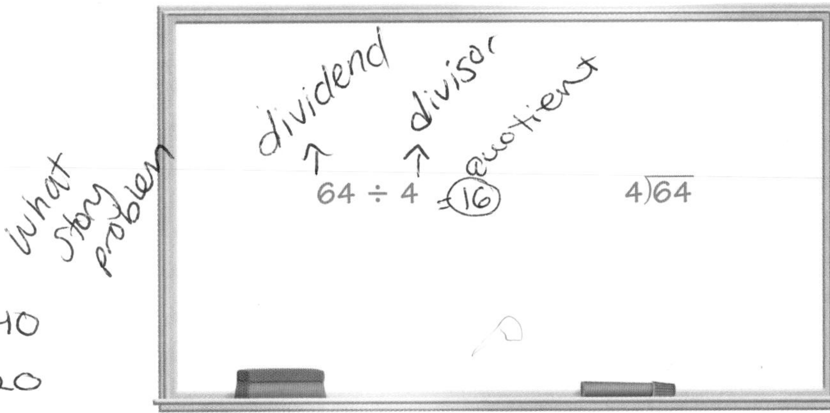

Although students should be able to read the first expression as "64 divided by 4," they may be unsure of how to read the second. Explain the way that each problem is read. Point out that when using the ÷ notation, the number being divided appears first. In the other notation, the number being divided appears second, inside the division symbol.➊

It helps some students to think of the $\overline{)}$ symbol as indicating an array, with 64 representing the area of the array (the product of its dimensions) and 4 representing one dimension. Have students imagine the product side of an Array Card for 4 × 16. Some will easily relate the second division notation to this array, with the amount to be divided (the dividend) inside the division symbol and the known factor (divisor) on the left edge.

Turn the discussion to Problem 1 on page 16 (organizing 48 students into groups of 3). Ask students what division equation they wrote to represent this problem. Write $48 \div 3 =$ ____ on the board. Then ask those students whose strategies you identified in the last session to share their first steps in solving this problem.

Possible first steps include the following:

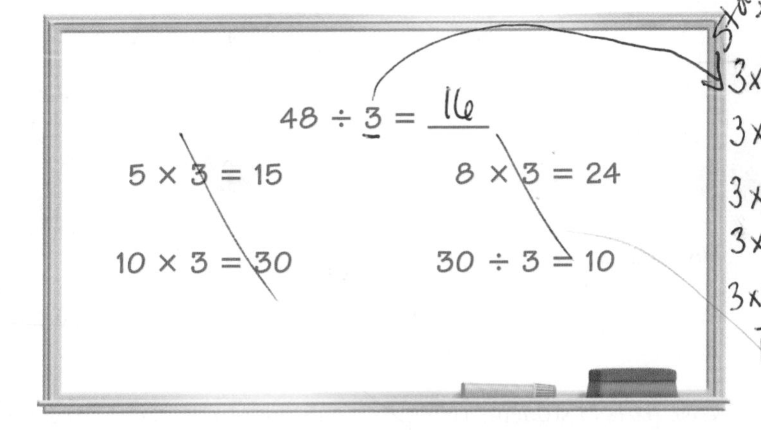

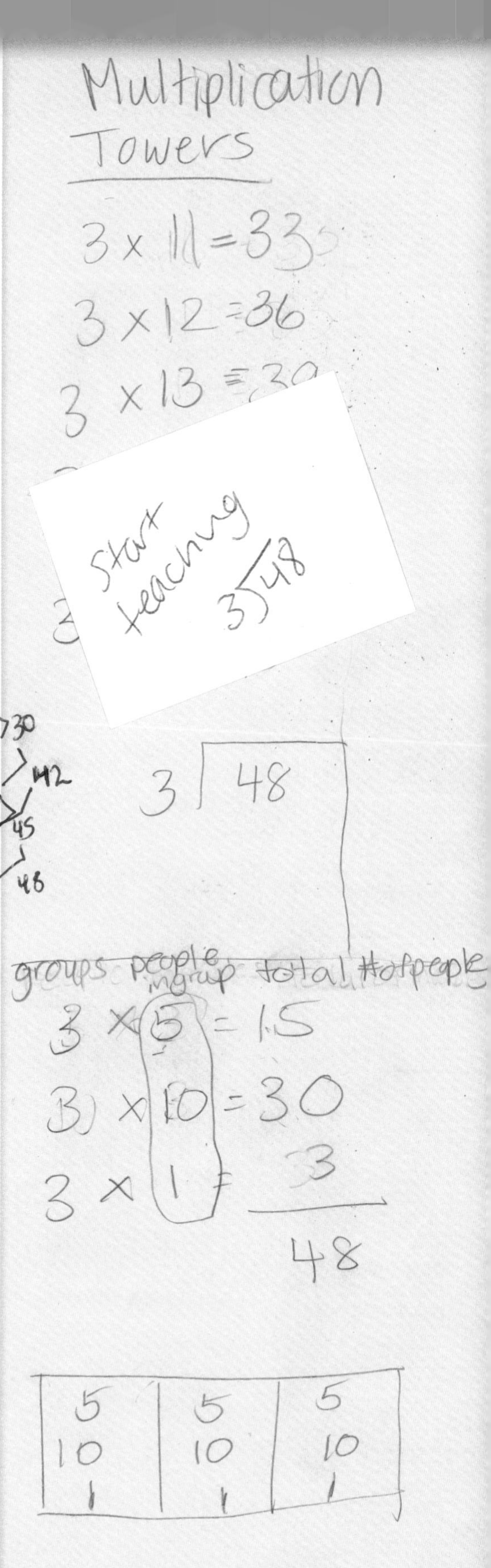

You can see that different people started with different numbers. Damian, you and Anna started solving this problem by thinking about 5 groups of 3. You wrote 5 × 3 = 15 on your paper. Can you tell us why you started this way and what you did next?

Students might say:

"We knew that 5 groups of 3 would get us to 15 people. 5 more groups of 3 would be 15 more, so that would get us to 30. There are 48 people in all, so that left us with 18 people to divide into groups of 3. We know that 6 × 3 = 18, so that's 6 more groups of 3. That's 5 groups plus 5 groups plus 6 groups, or 16 groups of 3. We knew that we were done because we had used up all the people—15 plus 15 plus 18 is 48 people."

To help students articulate and record their strategies clearly, ask questions such as the following:

- How many students have you organized into groups of 3 so far?
- How many students are left to organize?
- How many groups of 3 did you make in all?
- How do you know when you're done and that you have found an answer to the problem?

Discuss additional first steps, depending on what students in your classroom have done. If no one started by multiplying 10×3, bring up this first step.

What if we started solving this problem by writing $10 \times 3 = 30$? How would that equation help solve this problem? How many students would be left to organize into groups of 3? What would your next step be?

ACTIVITY 2

Problems with Remainders

40 MIN CLASS   INDIVIDUALS  PAIRS

Write $36 \div 5$ on the board.

What is a situation in which you would divide 36 by 5? What story problem can you write for 36 divided by 5?

Give pairs of students two or three minutes to generate story problems that can be represented by $36 \div 5$. Bring the class back together and list two or three of the students' ideas on the board. Using these situations to illustrate this problem, discuss how you would find the solution to $36 \div 5$.

Students will notice that when they divide 36 by 5, they are left with a remainder, or leftover, of 1. Because students may be unfamiliar with how to notate the remainder, show them that one way to write this is 7 R1.

In some division situations that we encounter in real life, the numbers don't divide evenly. What you do with the extra that's left over, called the remainder, depends on the situation.

Pick one or two of the students' stories and discuss the answer to the story problem.

Students might say:

"I have 36 candies that I need to put into bags of 5 each. I fill up 7 bags, but that's only 35 candies. So I eat the last one myself!"

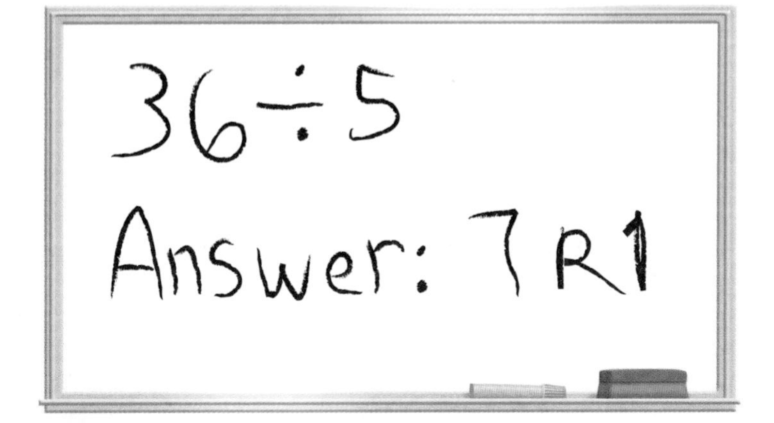

"I have 36 feet of rope to make jump ropes for presents for my 5 friends. I can make each jump rope 7 feet long, but then I'll have one foot of rope left over, and I want to use it all. So I'll make each jump rope 7 and $\frac{1}{5}$ feet long."

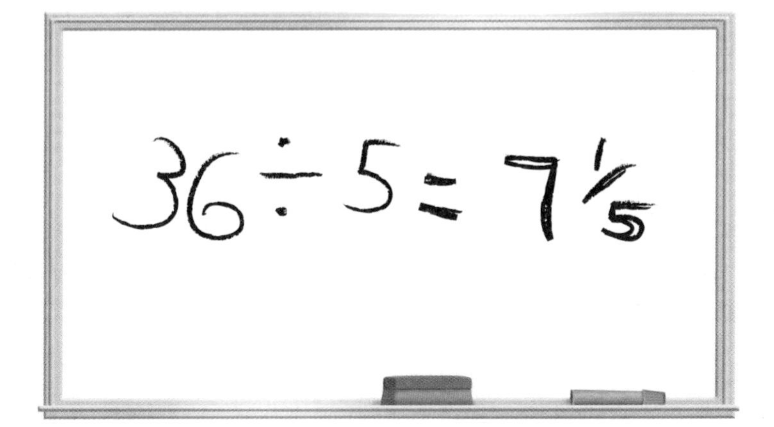

Some students may understand that this extra can be expressed as a fraction, a decimal, or a remainder or leftover amount, but this idea may be new for others. Emphasize that the expression must be an accurate representation of the solution for that particular problem. Encourage students not to disregard the remainder but to think of real situations in which they would encounter leftovers and to think about what they might do with them.❷

Math Note

❷ **Standard Notation for Remainders** In these materials, the convention used for recording division that results in a remainder is R1. This notation means that there are 7 groups of 5 in 36 plus 1 extra, or $36 \div 5 = (7 \times 5) + 1$. Some students might be interested in learning fraction notation for division, $36 \div 5 = 7\frac{1}{5}$, which can be interpreted as 7 groups of 5 plus 1 out of the next group of 5. For example, if 36 students are forming teams of 5, they can form 7 teams, with 1 out of the 5 needed for an 8th team—they have 7 and $\frac{1}{5}$ teams. At this stage in their work on division, the first notation, 7 R1 will be easiest for most students. Nonetheless, students should always think through the difference between the specific answer to the computation (7 R1) and the answer to the problem that best fits the story context.

Students may at first write equations such as $36 \div 5 = 7$ R1 to indicate their answer to a division problem. However, the notation $36 \div 5 = 7$ R1 is not correct mathematically because "7 R1" does not indicate a number (i.e., it can not be placed on a number line). For example, 7 R1 can also be an answer for $15 \div 2$. However, the quotient for $36 \div 5$, expressed as a number is $7\frac{1}{5}$, whereas the quotient for $15 \div 2 = 7\frac{1}{2}$. Even though both answers can be expressed as 7 R1, $36 \div 5$ and $15 \div 2$ are not equivalent. The meaning of R1 depends on the specific numbers in the problem. Steer students away from using the "R" notation as part of an equation. They can use it to write the result of division (e.g., the example on this page). When they use the "box" division symbol (given at the top of *Student Math Handbook,* page 52) to show their answer, they can use the R notation to write their answer on top of the "box."

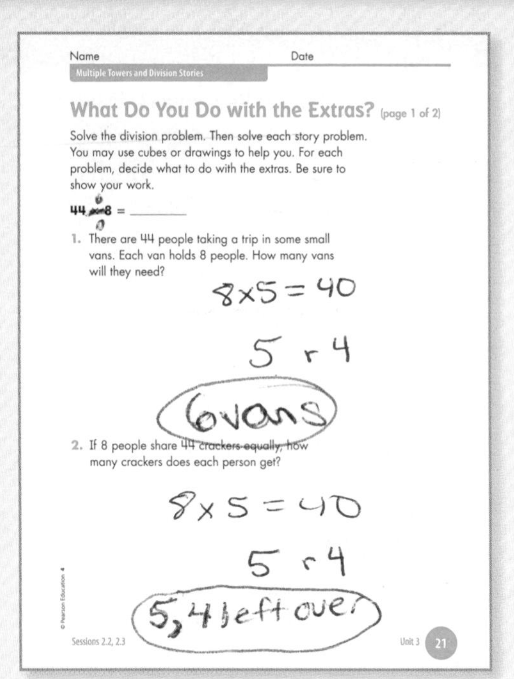
Name Date

Multiple Towers and Division Stories

What Do You Do with the Extras? (page 1 of 2)

Solve the division problem. Then solve each story problem. You may use cubes or drawings to help you. For each problem, decide what to do with the extras. Be sure to show your work.

44 ÷ 8 = ________

1. There are 44 people taking a trip in some small vans. Each van holds 8 people. How many vans will they need?

   8×5 = 40

   5 r 4

   6 vans

2. If 8 people share 44 crackers equally, how many crackers does each person get?

   8 × 5 = 40

   5 r 4

   5, 4 left over

Sessions 2.2, 2.3 Unit 3 21

▲ Student Activity Book, p. 21

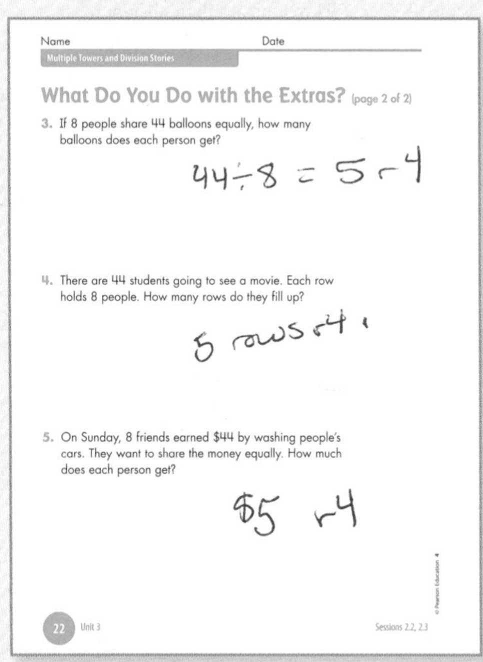
Name Date

Multiple Towers and Division Stories

What Do You Do with the Extras? (page 2 of 2)

3. If 8 people share 44 balloons equally, how many balloons does each person get?

   44 ÷ 8 = 5 r 4

4. There are 44 students going to see a movie. Each row holds 8 people. How many rows do they fill up?

   5 rows r 4

5. On Sunday, 8 friends earned $44 by washing people's cars. They want to share the money equally. How much does each person get?

   $5 r 4

22 Unit 3 Sessions 2.2, 2.3

▲ Student Activity Book, p. 22

For the rest of this session, students work individually or in pairs on *Student Activity Book* pages 21–22. Tell students that these are all division problems in which they cannot divide the dividend evenly. Although all five problems involve the same numbers ($44 \div 8$), each situation is different and may require a different solution.

Students first solve the division problem $44 \div 8$ without a story problem context. Help students record their answer as 5 R4. You may want to keep the class together for this first problem to help students with the notation. Have math tools available for students to use as needed.

The main task for students is to decide what to do with the extras in each case. Ask them to write their reasoning as well as the answer to the question posed in each problem. Let students know that the next session will begin with a discussion of this work.

Because cubes cannot be cut in half, students may find it more useful to draw pictures when they are working with remainders.

ONGOING ASSESSMENT: Observing Students at Work

Students work on division problems that result in remainders and consider what to do with the remainders, according to the particular situation in each problem.

- **Are students able to solve $44 \div 8$ by using number relationships that they know, such as 8×5 and 8×6?** Do they act out the problem by either sharing or grouping 44 things?
- **Are students able to determine what to do with remainders in the context of the problem situation?**

DIFFERENTIATION: Supporting the Range of Learners

Intervention Encourage students to visualize the stories and think about the remainders.

What would you do with the 4 extra crackers? What would you do about the 4 extra people?

Extension Individual students or student pairs who finish early should meet with other students or pairs to share their solutions and discuss what they decided to do with the remainder in each situation.

ELL Use pictures or actual objects to help English Language Learners envision each situation. Once they understand the relevant vocabulary, ask questions to help them explain what they will do with the extras.

Will you need another van for these extra people? Will they fill the van? Can you cut a balloon in half? After five rows are filled, where will the extra people sit?

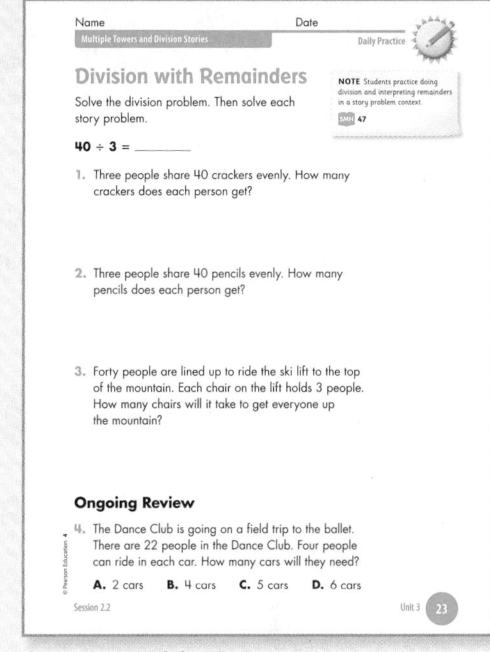

Name Date

Multiple Towers and Division Stories — Daily Practice

Division with Remainders

Solve the division problem. Then solve each story problem.

NOTE Students practice doing division and interpreting remainders in a story problem context. SMH 47

$40 \div 3 =$ ______

1. Three people share 40 crackers evenly. How many crackers does each person get?

2. Three people share 40 pencils evenly. How many pencils does each person get?

3. Forty people are lined up to ride the ski lift to the top of the mountain. Each chair on the lift holds 3 people. How many chairs will it take to get everyone up the mountain?

Ongoing Review

4. The Dance Club is going on a field trip to the ballet. There are 22 people in the Dance Club. Four people can ride in each car. How many cars will they need?

A. 2 cars **B.** 4 cars **C.** 5 cars **D.** 6 cars

© Pearson Education 4

Session 2.2 Unit 3 23

▲ Student Activity Book, p. 23

3 SESSION FOLLOW-UP
Daily Practice and Homework

Daily Practice: For reinforcement of this unit's content, have students complete *Student Activity Book* page 23.

Homework: Students solve a set of division story problems on *Student Activity Book* page 24.

Student Math Handbook: Students and families may use *Student Math Handbook* page 47 for reference and review. See pages 184–190 in the back of this unit.

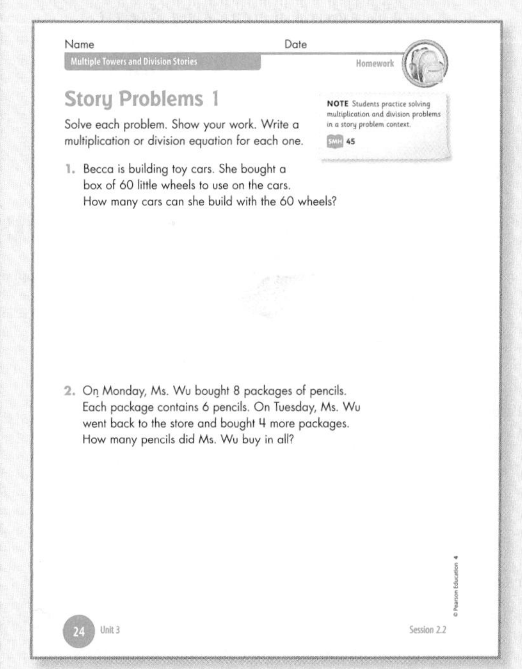

Name Date

Multiple Towers and Division Stories — Homework

Story Problems 1

Solve each problem. Show your work. Write a multiplication or division equation for each one.

NOTE Students practice solving multiplication and division problems in a story problem context. SMH 45

1. Becca is building toy cars. She bought a box of 60 little wheels to use on the cars. How many cars can she build with the 60 wheels?

2. On Monday, Ms. Wu bought 8 packages of pencils. Each package contains 6 pencils. On Tuesday, Ms. Wu went back to the store and bought 4 more packages. How many pencils did Ms. Wu buy in all?

© Pearson Education 4

24 Unit 3 Session 2.2

▲ Student Activity Book, p. 24

Division Stories

Math Focus Points

- Making sense of remainders in terms of the problem context
- Representing a division problem with pictures, diagrams, or models
- Solving division story problems

Today's Plan		Materials
DISCUSSION 1 What Do You Do with the Extras?	20 MIN CLASS	• *Student Activity Book*, pp. 21–22 (from Session 2.2)
MATH WORKSHOP 2 Division Stories 2A *Small Array/Big Array* 2B More Division Stories	40 MIN	2A • M40* • Array cards (from Session 1.2) • Construction paper 2B • *Student Activity Book*, pp. 25–26 • M7* • Connecting cubes; color tiles
SESSION FOLLOW-UP 3 Daily Practice and Homework		• *Student Activity Book*, pp. 27–28 • *Student Math Handbook*, pp. 48–49; G10

*See *Materials to Prepare*, p. 57.

Ten-Minute Math

Counting Around the Class Ask questions about a class that is counting by 25s. When the class finished counting, the last number was 475. How many students are in that class? What number did the 8th person say? What number did the 13th person say? For each question, collect answers as well as explanations about how students found their answer.

DISCUSSION

What Do You Do with the Extras?

Math Focus Points for Discussion

- Making sense of remainders in terms of the problem context

Ask students to look at their work on *Student Activity Book* pages 21–22. Begin the discussion by asking two students to share the strategies they used to solve the problem $44 \div 8$. Establish that dividing 44 by 8 results in an answer of 5 with a remainder of 4.

Then discuss Problems 1, 2, and 4. For each problem, ask for volunteers to share their solutions. Invite two or three students to write their solutions on the board, including any representations they made for the problem.❶ ❷

Students should recognize that the remainder affects the answer to the problem in different ways, depending on the problem context. In Problem 1, the answer is 6 vans—an entire additional van is needed for the 4 extra people, even though it won't be full. In Problem 2, the crackers can be split in half, so a possible answer is $5\frac{1}{2}$ crackers. (Some students may say that each person gets 5 crackers, and the other 4 are just left over—an acceptable answer.) In Problem 4, the answer is either 5 full rows with 4 students in the sixth row or $5\frac{1}{2}$ rows. Students' diagrams for Problems 2 and 4 can offer a visual image of the remainder represented as a fraction or decimal.❸

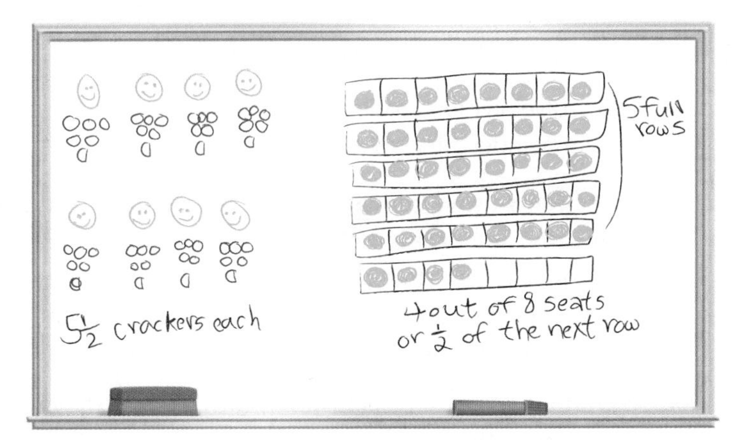

Professional Development

❶ **Teacher Note:** What Do You Do with the Remainders?, p. 162

❷ **Dialogue Box:** What Do You Do with the Extras?, p. 180

Algebra Note

❸ **Equal Sign** In recording answers to these problems, help students distinguish between the answer that completes the equation $44 \div 8 =$ _____ and the answer to a question posed in a problem context. For example, although the answer to problem 1 is "6 vans," it is not correct to write $44 \div 8 = 6$. If students record the answer to Problem 1 as $44 \div 8 = 6$, discuss with them whether this equation is correct. You may need to review with them the meaning of the equal sign—that a number or expression on one side of the equal sign in an equation must be equivalent to the number or expression on the other side. Students can also consider whether the related multiplication equation, $8 \times 6 = 44$, is true.

Name Date

Multiple Towers and Division Stories

More Division Stories (page 1 of 2)

Solve these problems. You may use cubes, grid paper, or other math tools. Keep track of all the steps you take. Write equations to show the steps of your solution.

1. Cheyenne and her father baked 72 cookies for the school bake sale. They plan to put them in bags of 4 cookies each. How many bags of cookies can they fill?

   Division equation: 72 ÷ 4 = 18

   Answer: ______

   4 × 10 = 40 4 × 3 = 12
   4 × 5 = 20

2. Aliya, Ethan, Brianna, and Will saved up a total of $74 from returning bottles and cans. They want to share it equally among the 4 of them. How much money will each of the friends receive?

   Division equation: 74 ÷ 4 = 18 r 2

   Answer: ______

   4 × 18 = 72 ... 73 .. 74

   $18.50

© Pearson Education 4

Sessions 2.3, 2.4 Unit 3 25

▲ **Student Activity Book, p. 25** PORTFOLIO

Name Date

Multiple Towers and Division Stories

More Division Stories (page 2 of 2)

3. Juice boxes come in packages of 3. The fourth graders at Glendale School need 125 juice boxes for their field trip. How many packages of juice boxes will they have to buy?

   Division equation: 125 ÷ 3 = 41 r 2

   Answer: 42

   3 × 20 = 60
   3 × 20 = 60
   3 × 1 = 3

4. The art teacher at Center School bought a box of 80 pencils for the 6 students in her drawing class. How many pencils will each student get if they share the pencils equally?

   Division equation: 80 ÷ 6 = 13 r 2

   Answer: 13 + give 2 away

5. Ms. Washington's class counted around the class by 5s. Each student said one number. The number they ended on was 115. How many students counted?

   Division equation: ______ ÷ ______ = ______

   Answer: ______

© Pearson Education 4

26 Unit 3 Sessions 2.3, 2.4

▲ **Student Activity Book, p. 26** PORTFOLIO

2 MATH WORKSHOP

Division Stories

40 MIN

Explain that for the rest of this session and the next, students will be doing Math Workshop activities. Alert them that everyone needs to complete *Student Activity Book* pages 25–26 for discussion at the end of the next session.

Use Math Workshop time to work with small groups of students who need support.

2A *Small Array/Big Array*

PAIRS

For complete details about this activity, see Session 1.3, pages 43–44.

2B More Division Stories

INDIVIDUALS PAIRS

Students work on the division story problems on *Student Activity Book* pages 25–26. Some of these problems result in answers with remainders and some divide evenly. Students may work alone or in pairs. Ask students working alone to share their work with another student before the end of the work time.

As students work, look for solution strategies for Problem 1 that involve considering more than one group of 4 at a time. You will highlight these strategies in the discussion at the end of the next session.

ONGOING ASSESSMENT: Observing Students at Work

Students solve division problems and, where appropriate, determine how the remainder affects the solution in a particular division context.

- **Are students using known multiplication relationships in solving division problems?** Do they multiply the known factor or divisor by 10 as a strategy? That is, in Problem 1, do they use $\underline{10} \times 4 = 40$ plus $\underline{8} \times 4 = 32$ to determine that Cheyenne and her father can fill 18 bags?
- **Do students consider the problem situation as they decide what to do with remainders?** Do they use appropriate notation to represent remainders in their solutions?

- **Do students recognize that the answer to the question posed in the problem may be different from the answer as expressed in a division equation?** That is, do they know that the equation for Problem 3 can be written as $125 \div 3 = 41\frac{2}{3}$, or one answer can be 41 R2, whereas the *answer* to the question posed is 42 packages?

DIFFERENTIATION: Supporting the Range of Learners

Intervention Some students benefit from modeling the action of the problems with cubes or drawings. When possible, work with small groups of these students and help them connect multiplication and division notation to the work they are doing with the cubes or drawings.

For example, if students have solved Problem 1 by drawing bags of 4 cookies each or by making groups of 4 cubes each and counting until all 72 cookies have been accounted for, ask these students questions about their representations.

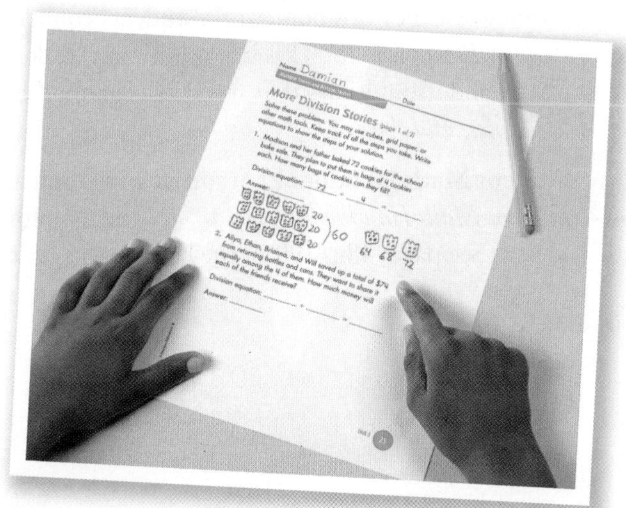

Help students link their drawings to multiplication and division notation.

What equations could we write under the groups of 4 you made? *($5 \times 4 = 20$, $5 \times 4 = 20$, $5 \times 4 = 20$, and $3 \times 4 = 12$)* What multiplication and division equations would show how many groups of 4 there are in 72? *(____ $\times 4 = 72$ and $72 \div 4 =$ ____)*

Name Date

Multiple Towers and Division Stories — Daily Practice

Factor Pairs

For each of these numbers, list as many pairs of factors as you can.

NOTE Students practice multiplication combinations (facts) by finding pairs of factors for a given product.

1. 36 Example: 3 × 12	2. 30
3. 40	4. 48
5. 60	6. 72

Ongoing Review

7. Which of these has the greatest product?

A. 8 × 7 B. 9 × 6 C. 10 × 5 D. 11 × 4

© Pearson Education 4

Session 2.3 Unit 3 27

▲ Student Activity Book, p. 27

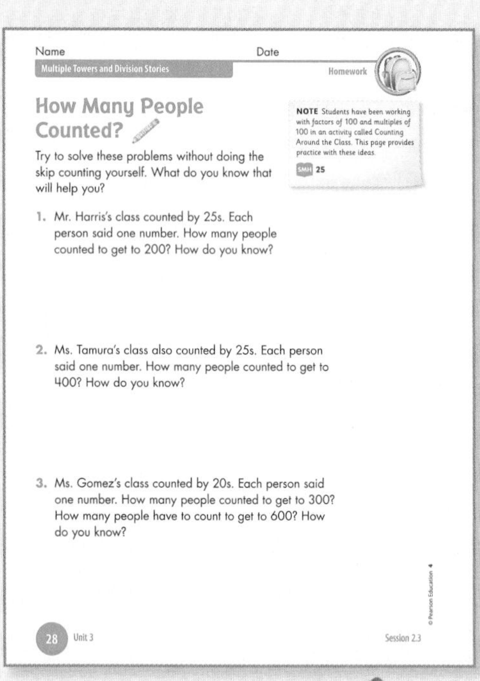
Name Date

Multiple Towers and Division Stories — Homework

How Many People Counted?

Try to solve these problems without doing the skip counting yourself. What do you know that will help you?

NOTE Students have been working with factors of 100 and multiples of 100 in an activity called Counting Around the Class. This page provides practice with these ideas.

SMH 25

1. Mr. Harris's class counted by 25s. Each person said one number. How many people counted to get to 200? How do you know?

2. Ms. Tamura's class also counted by 25s. Each person said one number. How many people counted to get to 400? How do you know?

3. Ms. Gomez's class counted by 20s. Each person said one number. How many people counted to get to 300? How many people have to count to get to 600? How do you know?

© Pearson Education 4

28 Unit 3 Session 2.3

▲ Student Activity Book, p. 28 WRITING

If students are solving a grouping problem by successively removing groups of cubes, encourage them to think about the multiplication combinations they know that will allow them to remove the largest possible number of cubes at one time. In a sharing problem, ask students to think about the biggest amount that they can dole out to each person at one time. For Problem 2, you might say this:

What if you started by giving $10 to each of the 4 people? How much money would that be? How much would you have left to give out?

3 SESSION FOLLOW-UP
Daily Practice and Homework

Daily Practice: For ongoing review, have students complete *Student Activity Book* page 27.

Homework: For this homework, students complete *Student Activity Book* page 28. This page continues work with factors of 100 and its multiples that students began in Unit 1: *Factors, Multiples, and Arrays*.

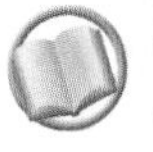
Student Math Handbook: Students and families may use *Student Math Handbook* pages 48–49 and G10 for reference and review. See pages 184–190 in the back of this unit.

Strategies for Division

Math Focus Points

- Using known multiplication combinations to solve division problems
- Solving division problems by making groups of the divisor
- Making sense of remainders in terms of the problem context

Vocabulary

factor

Today's Plan		Materials
1 ACTIVITY **Introducing *Missing Factors***	10 MIN CLASS	• M44*; M45; T41, ; M17–M37 (from Session 1.2) • Chart paper (array with missing factor)*; posted story problem (from Session 2.1)
2 MATH WORKSHOP **Strategies for Division** 2A *Missing Factors* 2B *Small Array/Big Array* 2C More Division Stories	30 MIN	2A • *Student Activity Book*, p. 29 • M45* • Array Cards (from Session 1.2) 2B • M40* (from Session 1.3) • Array Cards (from Session 1.2); Construction paper 2C • *Student Activity Book*, pp. 25–26 (from Session 2.3) • M7* • Connecting cubes; color tiles
3 DISCUSSION **Developing Strategies for Division**	20 MIN CLASS	• *Student Activity Book*, pp. 25–26 (completed work from Activity 2C)
4 SESSION FOLLOW-UP **Daily Practice and Homework**		• *Student Activity Book*, pp. 30–31 • *Student Math Handbook*, pp. 50–52; G8, G10

*See *Materials to Prepare*, p. 57.

Ten-Minute Math

Quick Images: Seeing Numbers Show *Quick Images: Seeing Numbers* (T35–T36), Images 7 and 8, one at a time. For each pattern, ask students to write several different equations to find the total number of dots. For the first two viewings, give students 3 seconds to look at the pattern; the third time, leave the image displayed. Have two or three students explain how they saw the images (including any revisions they made) and their equations, showing how their numbers match the patterns.

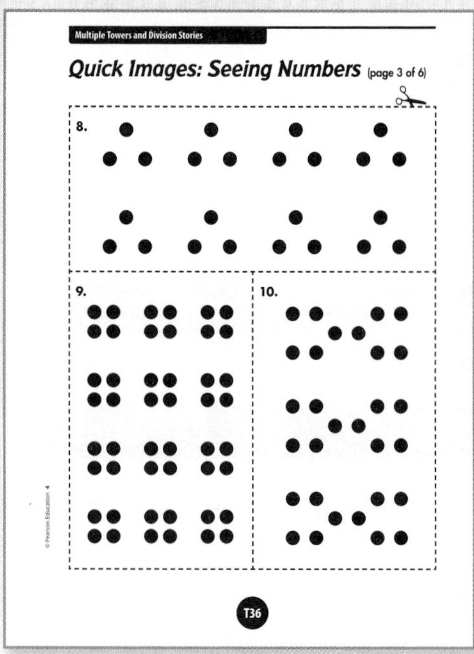
Multiple Towers and Division Stories

Quick Images: Seeing Numbers (page 3 of 6)

8.

9.

10.

© Pearson Education 4

T36

▲ Transparences, T36

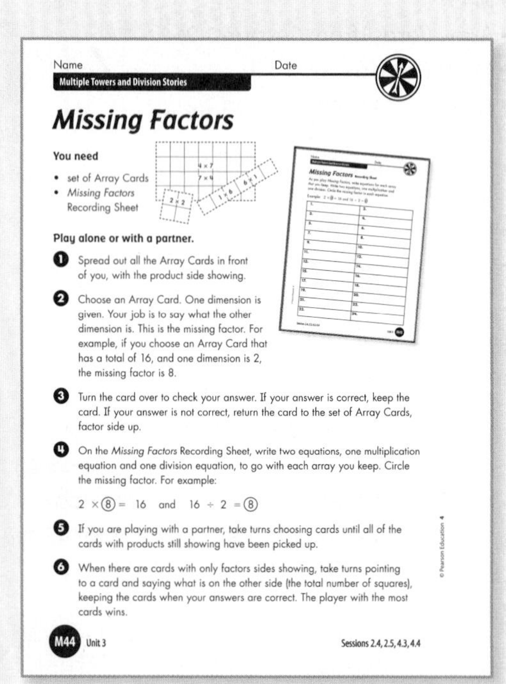
Name Date

Multiple Towers and Division Stories

Missing Factors

You need

- set of Array Cards
- *Missing Factors* Recording Sheet

Play alone or with a partner.

1. Spread out all the Array Cards in front of you, with the product side showing.
2. Choose an Array Card. One dimension is given. Your job is to say what the other dimension is. This is the missing factor. For example, if you choose an Array Card that has a total of 16, and one dimension is 2, the missing factor is 8.
3. Turn the card over to check your answer. If your answer is correct, keep the card. If your answer is not correct, return the card to the set of Array Cards, factor side up.
4. On the *Missing Factors* Recording Sheet, write two equations, one multiplication equation and one division equation, to go with each array you keep. Circle the missing factor. For example:

   $2 \times (8) = 16$ and $16 \div 2 = (8)$

5. If you are playing with a partner, take turns choosing cards until all of the cards with products still showing have been picked up.
6. When there are cards with only factors sides showing, take turns pointing to a card and saying what is on the other side (the total number of squares), keeping the cards when your answers are correct. The player with the most cards wins.

© Pearson Education 4

M44 Unit 3 Sessions 2.4, 2.5, 4.3, 4.4

▲ Resource Masters, M44

ACTIVITY

1 Introducing *Missing Factors*

Draw students' attention to the array you have posted with one missing factor, and relate it to the division story problem you worked through in Session 2.1.

4	56

Mrs. Santos owns a neighborhood grocery store. She has 56 apples to arrange in rows for her window display. She has room for 4 rows in her window.

How many apples will there be in each row if she puts the same number in each row?

Today we are going to play another game that uses your Array Cards. This game is called *Missing Factors.*

The back sides of the Array Cards are very much like the problem we did about Ms. Santos's window display, when she had 56 apples to divide into 4 rows. The cards tell us the total number of squares in the array, just as we knew the total number of apples that Ms. Santos had. The cards also show us one factor, the same way we knew the number of rows in the apple problem. The other factor is missing, and that is like the information we need to find in the apple problem—the number of apples in each row.

Spread out several Array Cards, with the product sides facing up. Alternatively, simply draw the backs of several Array Cards on the board, writing the product and one dimension.

Play one or two demonstration rounds with the class.

- Choose one array from the cards that you have displayed.

- Display the transparency of the *Missing Factors* Recording Sheet (T41). Point out that players need to write two equations for each array they choose: one multiplication and one division. Take students' suggestions to fill in the first numbered space for the array that you have chosen. Write both a multiplication equation and a division equation for the array, inserting a blank for the missing factor (e.g., $7 \times \_\_\_\_ = 63$ and $63 \div 7 = \_\_\_\_$).
- Working together as a class, find the missing factor, and write it in the blank space in each equation.
- Circle the missing factor in each equation.

Explain that when students play the game during the Math Workshop, they will record both a multiplication equation and a division equation for each array on the *Missing Factors* Recording Sheet on *Student Activity Book* page 29.❶

MATH WORKSHOP

30 MIN

2 Strategies for Division

Students continue with the Math Workshop activities from the previous session, adding the new game *Missing Factors* (M44). Remind them to be sure to complete *Student Activity Book* pages 25–26 for discussion at the end of the session.

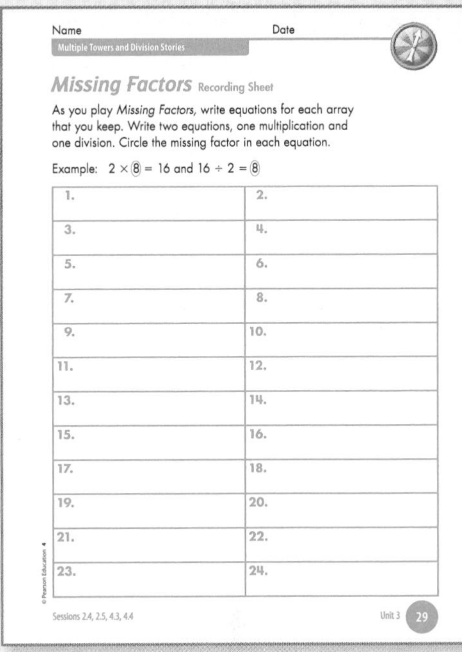

Name Date

Multiple Towers and Division Stories

Missing Factors Recording Sheet

As you play *Missing Factors*, write equations for each array that you keep. Write two equations, one multiplication and one division. Circle the missing factor in each equation.

Example: $2 \times 8 = 16$ and $16 \div 2 = 8$

1.	2.
3.	4.
5.	6.
7.	8.
9.	10.
11.	12.
13.	14.
15.	16.
17.	18.
19.	20.
21.	22.
23.	24.

© Pearson Education 4

Sessions 2.4, 2.5, 4.3, 4.4 Unit 3 29

▲ Student Activity Book, p. 29; Resource Masters, M45; T41

Algebra Note

❶ **Inverse Relationship** As students record their answers in the *Missing Factors* game, they are working with the inverse relationship between multiplication and division. They are also associating the factors in the multiplication expression with the dimensions of a rectangle and the product of the multiplication with the area of the rectangle. A rectangular array can also represent division. The quantity to be divided (the dividend) is represented by the area of the rectangle. The divisor is represented by one of the dimensions of the rectangle and the quotient is represented by the other. Using the area model to represent both multiplication and division helps students form mental models for these operations and for the relationships between them. See Algebra Connections in This Unit, p. 16, for more information.

2A *Missing Factors*

Students may work alone or with partners as they play the Array Card game *Missing Factors.* As students complete equations for 12 arrays on the *Missing Factors* Recording Sheet on *Student Activity Book* page 29, make additional copies available of *Missing Factors* Recording Sheet (M45).

The game Missing Factors *highlights the relationship between multiplication and division.*

ONGOING ASSESSMENT: Observing Students at Work

Students determine the missing dimension of an array (one factor of the factor pair) when the product and one dimension (the other factor) are given.

- **How do students find the missing factor?** Do they use known multiplication combinations? Do they find the missing factor through skip counting or repeated addition?
- **Are students able to write multiplication equations that represent the problem accurately?** Are they able to write division equations to represent dividing the total number of squares in the array by one of its dimensions (the number of rows or the number in each row)?

As students work, encourage them to develop more efficient strategies based on multiplication relationships that they know. If you see a student who is skip counting to find missing factors, suggest thinking about known multiplication relationships that might help. Ask questions such as the following:

- How can you figure out how many rows of 4 are in an array of 28?
- Can you skip count to find the missing factor? What number can you skip count by?
- Is there a 4s combination that you know, such as 5 × 4, that will get you partly there without counting all the way by 4s?

4	28

PAIRS

2B Small Array/Big Array

For complete details about this activity, see Session 1.3, pages 43–44.

INDIVIDUALS PAIRS

2C More Division Stories

For complete details about this activity, see Session 2.3, page 74.

20 MIN CLASS

DISCUSSION

3 Developing Strategies for Division

Math Focus Points for Discussion

- Solving division problems by making groups of the divisor

Refer students to their work on *Student Activity Book* pages 25–26, More Division Stories. Focus most of this discussion on strategies for division that involve using multiplication to create groups of the known factor (divisor) that are successively removed from the number being divided (dividend).

Problem 1 says, "Cheyenne and her father baked 72 cookies for the school bake sale. They plan to put them in bags of 4 cookies each. How many bags of cookies can they fill?" What is the division expression for this problem?

Write 72 ÷ 4 on the board. Ask students whose work you identified in the previous session to share their first steps in solving this problem.

Name Date

Multiple Towers and Division Stories

Daily Practice

Division and Remainders

Solve these problems. Write a division equation for each one.

NOTE Students practice doing division and interpreting remainders in story problem contexts.

SMH 47–49

1. There are 70 people in line for the roller coaster. Each car holds 8 people. How many cars will it take for everyone to ride at the same time?
   Division equation: ______ ÷ ______ = ______
   Answer: ______

2. Eighty people bought tickets for a boat ride. Twelve people can ride in one boat. How many boats can be completely filled?
   Division equation: ______ ÷ ______ = ______
   Answer: ______

3. How many prizes could you get with 100 tickets?
   Division equation:
   ______ ÷ ______ = ______
   Answer: ______

   ARCADE PRIZES
   6 tickets per prize

4. Mr. Brown's class counted around the class by 5s. The number they ended with was 135. How many students counted?
   Division equation: ______ ÷ ______ = ______
   Answer: ______

Ongoing Review

5. Ms. Gold's class counted around the class by 4s. There are 29 students in her class. Which of these numbers would NOT be said?
   A. 54 **B.** 100 **C.** 76 **D.** 64

30 Unit 3 Session 2.4

▲ **Student Activity Book, p. 30**

Possible first steps include the following:

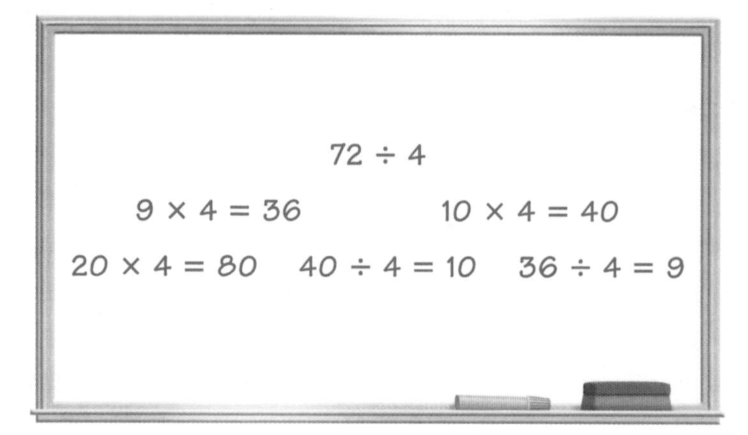

Choose one of the first steps offered and ask students to explain their reasoning for this step in terms of the problem context.

Students might say:

"We know that 9 × 4 = 36, so if we made 9 bags of 4 cookies, that would be 36 cookies so far."

Then ask the class to consider how they would go on to solve the problem after each first step. Ask questions such as the following as students discuss their subsequent steps in each case:

- How many cookies have you divided into groups of 4 so far?
- How many cookies are left to divide?
- How many groups of 4 did you make in all?
- How do you know when you're done?
- What is the answer to the question in the problem?

Using multiples of 10 is an important starting place for solving division problems. Encourage students to think, "Can I use 10 (or 20 or 30) groups of the known factor (in this case, 4) to get close to the number being divided? How close will I be?" Raise this approach yourself if it has not already come up in the class discussion.

What would happen if we started with 10 groups of 4? Did anyone do that? Can you share what you did?

As needed, give students time to finish the problem using 10×4 as a first step.

Students might say:

"We started with 10 bags of cookies. $10 \times 4 = 40$ cookies. 5 more bags is 20 more cookies, and that would get us to 60 cookies. $15 \times 4 = 60$. There are 12 more cookies, and that's another 3 bags, so $18 \times 4 = 72$. They can fill 18 bags."

After the class has discussed two or three different first steps, repeat the process with Problem 3. Make sure that students are able to differentiate between the notation of the division equation ($125 \div 3 = 41\frac{2}{3}$, or the answer of 41 R2) and the answer to the question posed in the problem (42 packages of juice boxes).

SESSION FOLLOW-UP

Daily Practice and Homework

Daily Practice: For reinforcement of this unit's content, have students complete *Student Activity Book* page 30.

Homework: Students complete *Student Activity Book* page 31. This homework asks them to write story problems for two division expressions, $45 \div 9$ and $84 \div 7$. They then solve each problem.❷

Student Math Handbook: Students and families may use *Student Math Handbook* pages 50–52 and G8, G10 for reference and review. See pages 184–190 in the back of this unit.

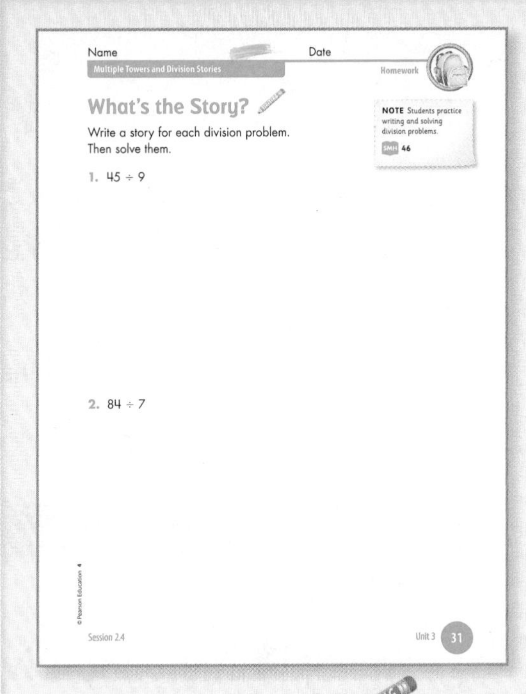

Name Date

Multiple Towers and Division Stories

Homework

What's the Story?

Write a story for each division problem. Then solve them.

NOTE Students practice writing and solving division problems.

SMH 46

1. $45 \div 9$

2. $84 \div 7$

© Pearson Education 4

Session 2.4

Unit 3 31

▲ Student Activity Book, p. 31

Differentiation

❷ **English Language Learners** Meet with English Language Learners to preview this homework assignment. Explain that they will be writing story problems like the ones they have been solving in class. Encourage them to use the division stories they have previously completed in the *Student Activity Book* to find words to use in their own stories. Write the sign for division, and together find expressions for *divide,* such as *split into groups.* For beginning English Language Learners, you might reduce the number of stories to be written or allow them to draw rather than write the story contexts. Later, you or another student can help them put their stories into words.

Related Multiplication and Division Problems

Math Focus Points

- Using known multiplication combinations to solve division problems
- Solving division story problems

Today's Plan		Materials
1 ACTIVITY **Introducing Related Multiplication and Division Problems**	15 MIN CLASS	• M7; T2 • Connecting cubes
2 MATH WORKSHOP **Multiplication and Division Problems** 2A *Missing Factors* 2B Related Multiplication and Division Problems	45 MIN	2A • *Student Activity Book*, p. 29 (from Session 2.4) • M45* (from Session 2.4) • Array Cards (from Session 1.3) 2B • *Student Activity Book*, pp. 33–34
3 SESSION FOLLOW-UP **Daily Practice**		• *Student Activity Book*, p. 35 • *Student Math Handbook*, p. 35; G8

*See *Materials to Prepare*, p. 59.

Ten-Minute Math

Quick Images: Seeing Numbers Show *Quick Images: Seeing Numbers* (T36), Images 9 and 10, one at a time. For each pattern, ask students to write several different equations to find the total number of dots. For the first two viewings, give students 3 seconds to look at the pattern; the third time, leave the image displayed. Have two or three students explain how they saw the images (including any revisions they made) and their equations, showing how their numbers match the patterns.

ACTIVITY

1 Introducing Related Multiplication and Division Problems

Write these two related problems on the board.

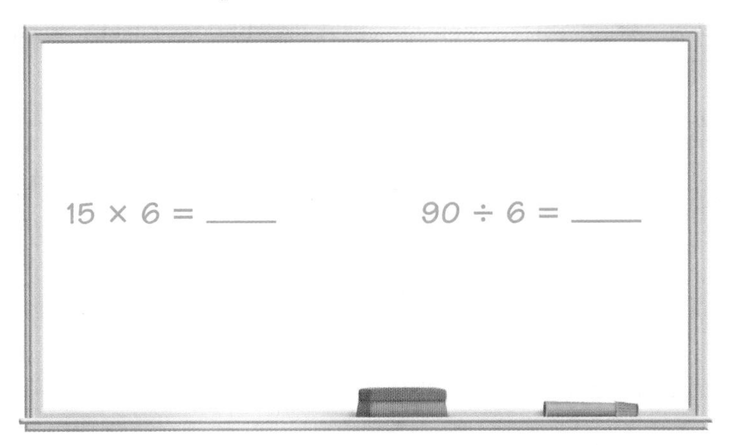

Give students a few minutes to solve these problems. Then ask them to share strategies for solving each one. Some students may notice that the two problems are related and use the work they did in the first problem to help answer the second. Others may not notice this relationship or may notice it only after both problems have been solved.[1]

What do you notice about the numbers in these two problems? How could you represent these problems with cubes or grid paper? Let's start with the first one.

Have students talk together about this question. Then take suggestions from the class. Using connecting cubes or the transparency of Centimeter Grid Paper (T2), work as a class to construct a representation for 15×6.

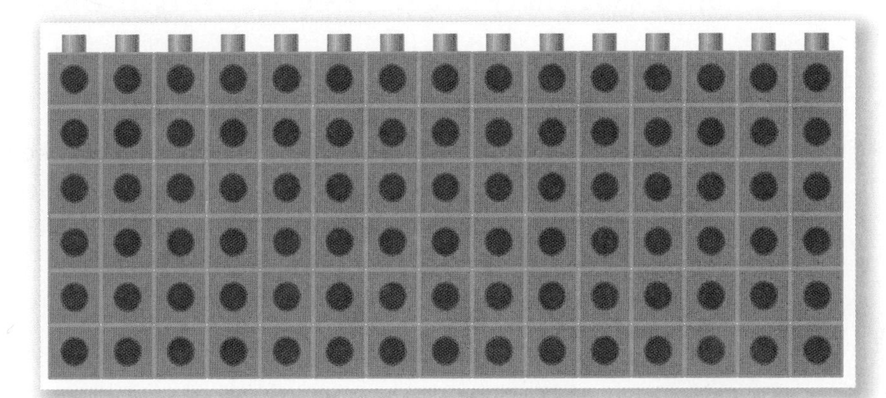

Algebra Note

[1] **Inverse Relationship** Much of the work in this unit focuses on helping students understand the relationship between multiplication and division. Recognizing and understanding this relationship helps students learn their multiplication combinations and the related division facts, as well as develop efficient strategies for solving division problems. See Algebra Connections in This Unit, p. 16.

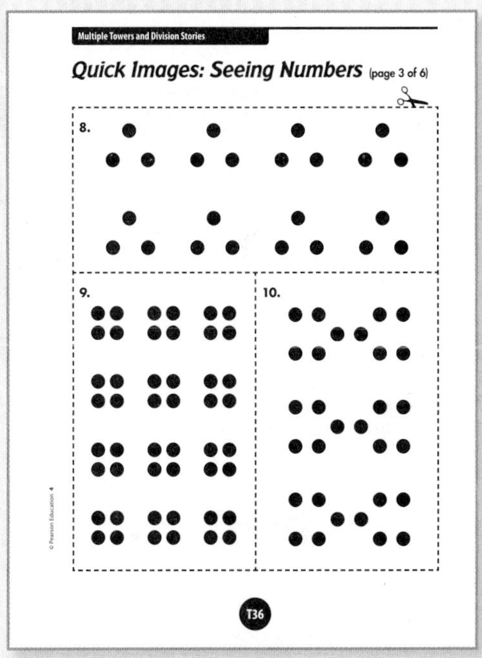

▲ Transparencies, T36

Professional Development

❷ **Teacher Note:** The Relationship Between Multiplication and Division, p. 163.

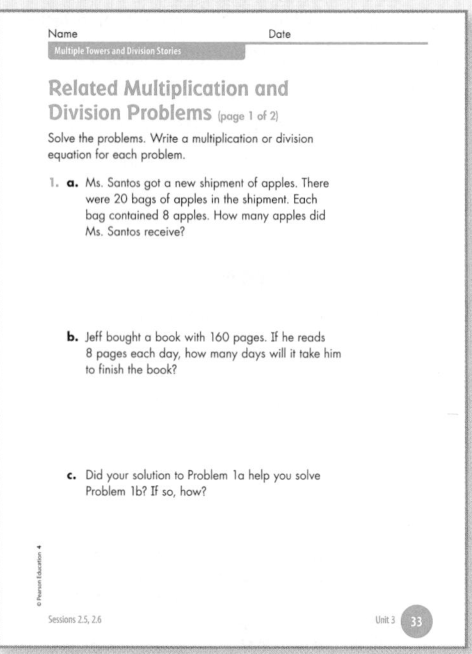
Name Date

Multiple Towers and Division Stories

Related Multiplication and Division Problems (page 1 of 2)

Solve the problems. Write a multiplication or division equation for each problem.

1. a. Ms. Santos got a new shipment of apples. There were 20 bags of apples in the shipment. Each bag contained 8 apples. How many apples did Ms. Santos receive?

   b. Jeff bought a book with 160 pages. If he reads 8 pages each day, how many days will it take him to finish the book?

   c. Did your solution to Problem 1a help you solve Problem 1b? If so, how?

© Pearson Education 4

Sessions 2.5, 2.6 Unit 3 33

▲ Student Activity Book, p. 33

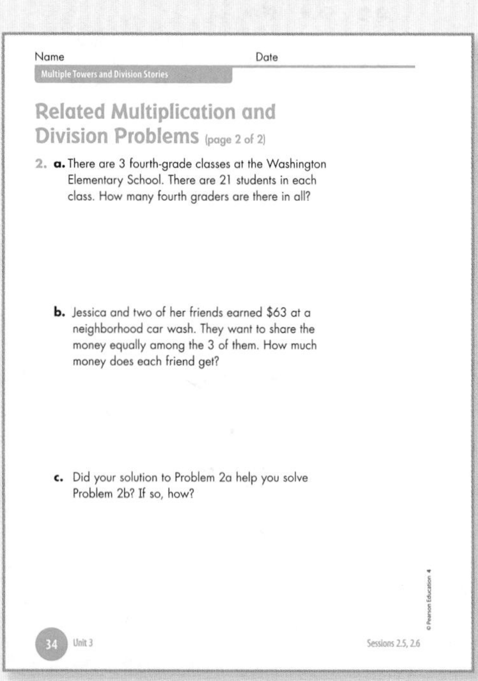
Name Date

Multiple Towers and Division Stories

Related Multiplication and Division Problems (page 2 of 2)

2. a. There are 3 fourth-grade classes at the Washington Elementary School. There are 21 students in each class. How many fourth graders are there in all?

   b. Jessica and two of her friends earned $63 at a neighborhood car wash. They want to share the money equally among the 3 of them. How much money does each friend get?

   c. Did your solution to Problem 2a help you solve Problem 2b? If so, how?

© Pearson Education 4

34 Unit 3 Sessions 2.5, 2.6

▲ Student Activity Book, p. 34

Where is the 15 in this representation? What does 15 mean? Where is the 6? What does 6 mean? Where do you see the product of 15 × 6? We made this [cube representation] to show 15 × 6. Can it also show 90 ÷ 6? How?

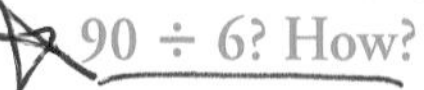

Students will continue to explore the inverse relationship between multiplication and division in the Math Workshop that follows and will discuss this relationship at the beginning of the next session.❷

MATH WORKSHOP

2 Multiplication and Division Problems

45 MIN

In this Math Workshop, students continue to play *Missing Factors.* They also solve pairs of related multiplication and division story problems. Use this time to observe and work with small groups of students as needed.

2A *Missing Factors*

INDIVIDUALS

PAIRS

For complete details about this activity, see Session 2.4, page 80.

2B Related Multiplication and Division Problems

INDIVIDUALS

Students work on *Student Activity Book* pages 33–34, which have two pairs of related multiplication and division problems. Point out that after solving each pair of problems in Parts *a* and *b,* they are to explain in Part *c* what is the same and what is different about those related problems.

ONGOING ASSESSMENT: Observing Students at Work

Students solve related multiplication and division problems and describe the relationship between them.

- **Are students recognizing and using the relationship between the numbers in each pair of problems?** If a student determines that 20 bags of 8 apples contain 160 apples (20 × 8 = 160) in Problem 1a, does the student demonstrate understanding that 160 pages divided by 8 pages per day must equal 20 days in Problem 1b?

DIFFERENTIATION: Supporting the Range of Learners

Intervention Continue to work with those students who are directly modeling each problem. Encourage them to use the multiplication or division relationships that they know. Help them multiply or divide several groups at a time. For example, if a student adds up twenty 8s for Problem 1a, ask the following:

Do you know the product of 2 × 8? What about 5 × 8? 10 × 8? How might those combinations help you solve the problem?

Make sure that these students continue to work on their multiplication combinations.③

3 SESSION FOLLOW-UP
Daily Practice

Daily Practice: For ongoing review, have students complete *Student Activity Book* page 35.

Student Math Handbook: Students and families may use *Student Math Handbook* pages 35 and G8 for reference and review. See pages 184–190 in the back of this unit.

Professional Development

③ **Teacher Note:** Learning and Assessing Multiplication Combinations, p. 151

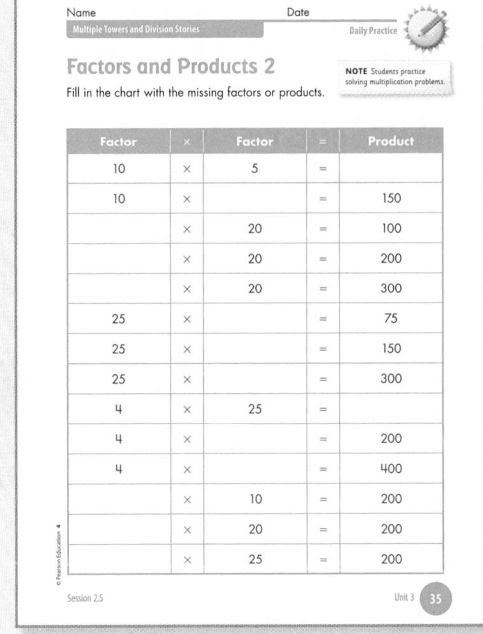

Name Date

Multiple Towers and Division Stories — Daily Practice

Factors and Products 2

NOTE Students practice solving multiplication problems.

Fill in the chart with the missing factors or products.

Factor	×	Factor	=	Product
10	×	5	=	
10	×		=	150
	×	20	=	100
	×	20	=	200
	×	20	=	300
25	×		=	75
25	×		=	150
25	×		=	300
4	×	25	=	
4	×		=	200
4	×		=	400
	×	10	=	200
	×	20	=	200
	×	25	=	200

Session 2.5 Unit 3 35

▲ Student Activity Book, p. 35

Assessment: Writing and Solving a Division Problem

Math Focus Points

- Solving division story problems
- Creating a story problem to represent a division expression
- Using known multiplication combinations to solve division problems

Today's Plan		Materials
1 DISCUSSION **Related Multiplication and Division Problems**	30 MIN CLASS PAIRS	• *Student Activity Book,* pp. 33 (from Session 2.5) • M7* • Connecting cubes; color tiles
2 ASSESSMENT ACTIVITY **Writing and Solving a Division Problem**	30 MIN INDIVIDUALS	• M46*
3 SESSION FOLLOW-UP **Daily Practice**		• *Student Activity Book,* p. 36 • *Student Math Handbook,* p. 46

*See *Materials to Prepare,* p. 59.

Ten-Minute Math

Quick Images: Seeing Numbers Show *Quick Images: Seeing Numbers* (T37), Images 11 and 12, one at a time. For each pattern, ask students to write several different equations to find the total number of dots. For the first two viewings, give students 3 seconds to look at the pattern; the third time, leave the image displayed. Have two or three students explain how they saw the images (including any revisions they made) and their equations, showing how their numbers match the patterns.

DISCUSSION

30 MIN CLASS PAIRS

Related Multiplication and Division Problems

Math Focus Points for Discussion

- Using known multiplication combinations to solve division problems

Refer students to their work on *Student Activity Book* page 33.

Before we talk about these problems, I want you to work with a partner and use cubes, tiles, grid paper, or a drawing to show us what is happening in Problems 1a and 1b. As you work, think about where each number appears in the representation you are making. I want to be able to look at your representation and see all parts of the problems.

Give students 5 to 10 minutes to make their representations. Then call them back together to share.

What representation did you make for these two problems? How does it show all the numbers in Problem 1a?

Students might say:

"We used cubes. We made 20 groups of 8 cubes for the 20 bags of 8 apples. 10 groups of 8 is 80, and 10 more 8s make 160, so we had 160 cubes in all. That shows that Ms. Santos had 160 apples."

"We made a 20×8 array. The 20 columns show the 20 bags of apples and the 8 in each column show the 8 apples in each bag. There are 160 squares in the whole array—that's 160 apples in all."

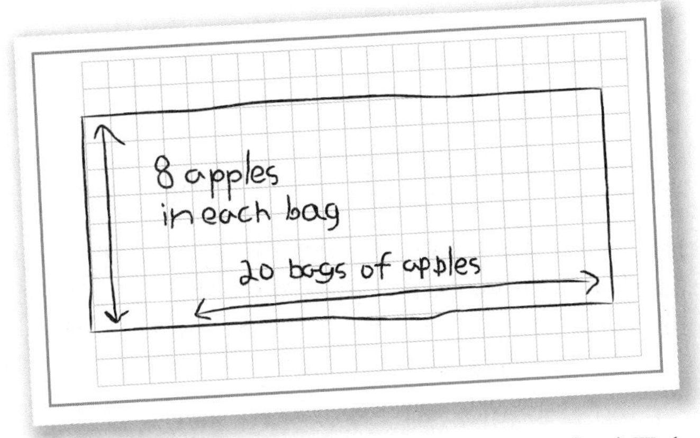

Lucy's Work

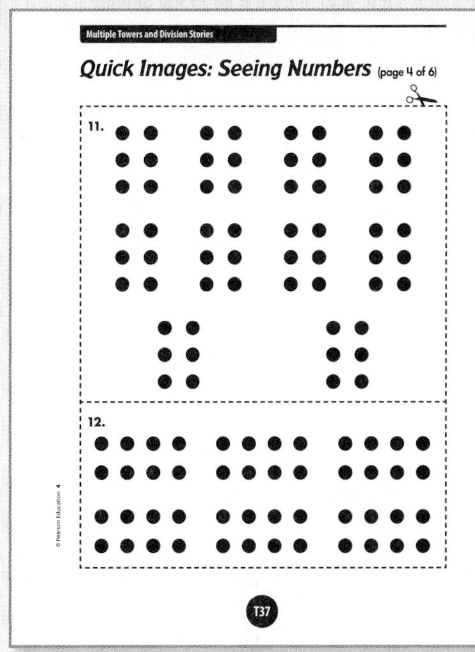

▲ Transparencies, T37

When students have explained how their representation describes the multiplication problem, ask these questions:

Where in these same representations can you see the numbers in Problem 1b?

Where do you see the number of pages in Jeff's book?

Where do you see the number of pages he reads each day?

Where is the number of days it will take him to finish the book?

As students respond to this question, make sure they demonstrate the understanding that each representation shows the total number of pages in Jeff's book (160) and the number of pages he reads each day (8), as well as the number of days it will take him to finish (20).

Students might say:

"There are 160 cubes in our representation. That's like the number of pages in Jeff's book. The groups of 8 equal the number of pages he reads each day. There are 20 groups of 8, so it will take him 20 days to read the whole book."

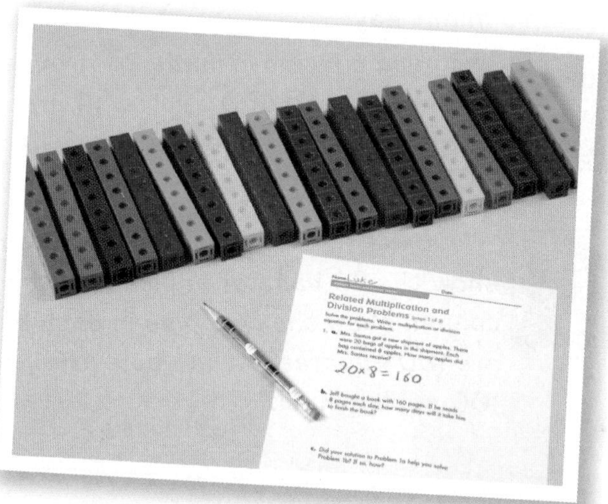

A single representation can support both $8 \times 20 = 160$ and $160 \div 8 = 20$.

End the discussion by referring back to the questions in Part 1c.

How do these representations help us think about what is the same and what is different about these two problems? What are the pieces of information that we know and don't know in each one?

Students should recognize that both of these problems are about equal groups and that both problems involve the same numbers. Listen for students' understanding that in the multiplication problem, the number of groups (20) and the number in each group (8) are known and the total number, or product (160), is unknown. Conversely, in the division problem, the total number and the number in each group are known, but the number of groups (the number of groups of 8, which is the number of days needed) is unknown.

2 ASSESSMENT ACTIVITY

Writing and Solving a Division Problem

30 MIN INDIVIDUALS

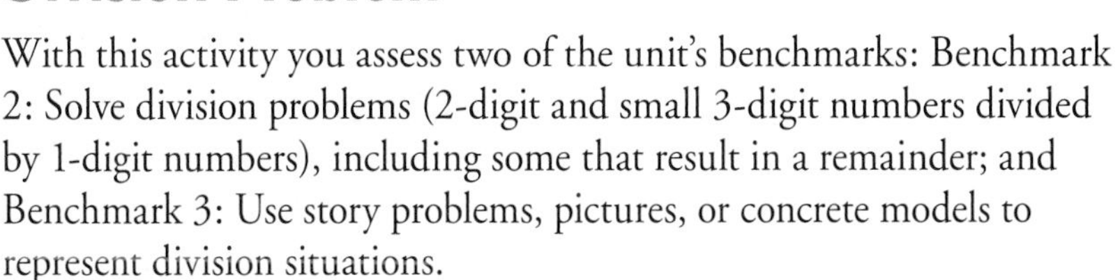

With this activity you assess two of the unit's benchmarks: Benchmark 2: Solve division problems (2-digit and small 3-digit numbers divided by 1-digit numbers), including some that result in a remainder; and Benchmark 3: Use story problems, pictures, or concrete models to represent division situations.

Hand out Assessment: Writing and Solving a Division Problem (M46), and give students 30 minutes to complete the assessment. They write a story problem based on the division expression $104 \div 8$ and then solve the problem.[1]

3 SESSION FOLLOW-UP

Daily Practice

Daily Practice: For reinforcement of this unit's content, have students complete *Student Activity Book* page 36.

Student Math Handbook: Students and families may use *Student Math Handbook* page 46 for reference and review. See pages 184–90 in the back of this unit.

Professional Development

[1] **Teacher Note:** Assessment: Writing and Solving a Division Problem, p. 164

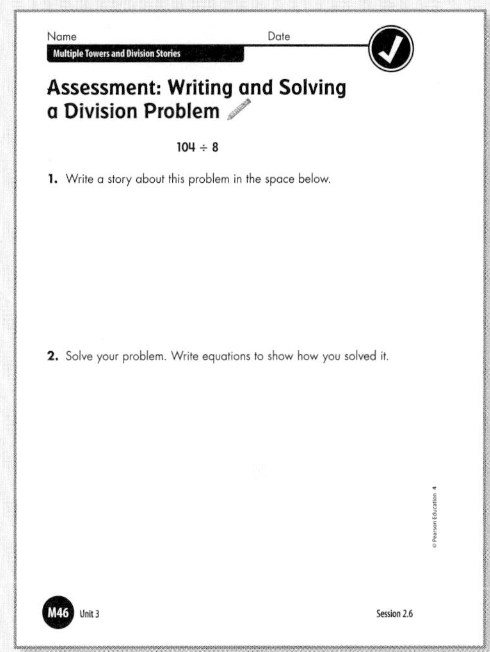

Name Date

Multiple Towers and Division Stories

Assessment: Writing and Solving a Division Problem

$104 \div 8$

1. Write a story about this problem in the space below.

2. Solve your problem. Write equations to show how you solved it.

M46 Unit 3 Session 2.6

▲ Resource Masters, M46

Name Date

Multiple Towers and Division Stories — Daily Practice

Simpler Parts

Solve each problem by following the clues.

NOTE Students practice breaking division problems apart into smaller problems.

SMH 50–52

1. $136 \div 4 =$ ______
   How many 4s are in 100? ______
   How many 4s are in 36? ______
   How many 4s are in 136? ______
2. $104 \div 8 =$ ______
   How many 8s are in 80? ______
   How many 8s are in 24? ______
   How many 8s are in 104? ______
3. $162 \div 6 =$ ______
   How many 6s are in 120? ______
   How many 6s are in 42? ______
   How many 6s are in 162? ______

Ongoing Review

4. Which of these expressions is equal to 6?
   A. $100 \div 20$ **B.** $48 \div 8$ **C.** $63 \div 9$ **D.** $30 \div 3$

36 Unit 3 Session 2.6

▲ Student Activity Book, p. 36

INVESTIGATION 3

Mathematical Emphases

Computational Fluency Solving multiplication problems with 2-digit numbers

Math Focus Points

- Reviewing multiplication combinations to 12 × 12
- Multiplying multiples of 10

Whole Number Operations Reasoning about numbers and their factors

Math Focus Points

- Understanding the effect of multiplying by a multiple of 10 (e.g., describing the relationship between 3 × 4 and 3 × 40)
- Finding multiples of 2-digit numbers
- Describing a sequence of multiples in order to predict other multiples

Whole Number Operations Representing the meaning of multiplication and division

Math Focus Points

- Representing a multiplication problem with pictures, diagrams, or models
- Comparing visual representations of multiplication situations

Multiplying 10s

Session	Student Activity Book	Student Math Handbook	Professional Development: Read Ahead of Time
SESSION 3.1 p. 96 **Building Multiple Towers** Students generate an ordered series of multiples of 2-digit numbers and examine patterns and relationships in their lists of multiples. They identify *landmark* multiples, such as the 10th and 20th multiple of a number.	37–40	36	• **Dialogue Box:** Building a Multiple Tower, p. 182
SESSION 3.2 p. 105 **Multiplying Groups of 10** Students solve and represent related problems that involve multiples of 10 (e.g., 6×4 and 6×40) and describe the relationship between the products.	41–46	37–38	• **Teacher Note:** Multiplying by Multiples of 10, p. 167
SESSION 3.3 p. 111 **Multiplying 2-Digit Numbers** Students solve 2-digit multiplication problems and examine the mathematical relationship that underlies the pattern that they see when a number is multiplied by a multiple of 10.	42–43, 47–50	37–38	
SESSION 3.4 p. 116 **Assessment: Multiplication Combinations** Students are assessed on their knowledge of the multiplication combinations to 12×12. They continue to solve 2-digit multiplication problems.	42–43, 47–48, 51	29–34	• **Teacher Note:** Learning and Assessing Multiplication Combinations, p. 151 • **Dialogue Box:** What Does It Mean to "Add a Zero"?, p. 183

Ten-Minute Math See page 20 for an overview.

Counting Around the Class

- **No materials needed**

	Materials to Gather	Materials to Prepare
	• **M8, Practicing with Multiplication Cards** • **M9–M14, Multiplication Cards** (1 set per student; from Session 1.1) • **3 x 5 index cards or 3 x 3 self-stick notes** (about 40) • **Transparent tape** • **Inch/centimeter rulers** (1 per pair) • **Calculators** (as needed)	• **M47, 300 Chart** Make copies. (1 per pair) • **Chart paper** Prepare and post a list of "Starting Numbers for Multiple Towers" that includes these numbers: 14 15 16 18 20 24 25 27 32 35 36 40 44 45 48 50 60 70 • **Adding machine tape** Cut adding machine tape (or strips of paper about 2″ wide) into 5-foot strips for making multiple towers. (1 per student, plus extras)
	• **M47, 300 Chart** (as needed; from Session 3.1) • **Connecting cubes** (as needed) • **Chart: "Starting Numbers for Multiple Towers"** (from Session 3.1) • **Multiple tower strips** (1 per student; from Session 3.1) • **Inch/centimeter rulers** (as needed) • **Calculators** (as needed)	• **M7, Centimeter Grid Paper** Make copies. (as needed) • **M48–M49, About Our Multiple Tower** Make copies. (1 per student, plus extras)
	• **M47, 300 Chart** (as needed; from Session 3.1) • **Connecting cubes** (as needed)	• **M7, Centimeter Grid Paper** Make copies. (as needed)
	• **Connecting cubes** (as needed)	• **M7, Centimeter Grid Paper** Make copies. (as needed) • **M50, Assessment: Multiplication Combinations** Make copies. (1 per student)

Building Multiple Towers

Math Focus Points

- Understanding the effect of multiplying by a multiple of 10 (e.g., describing the relationship between 3×4 and 3×40)
- Finding multiples of 2-digit numbers
- Describing a sequence of multiples in order to predict other multiples

Vocabulary

multiple
factor

Today's Plan			Materials
1 DISCUSSION **Multiples of 3 and 30**	15 MIN	CLASS	
2 ACTIVITY **Introducing Multiple Towers**	20 MIN	CLASS	• 3 x 5 index cards or 3 x 3 self-stick notes; transparent tape
3 ACTIVITY **Building Multiple Towers**	25 MIN	PAIRS	• *Student Activity Book,* pp. 37–38 • M47* • Chart: "Starting Numbers for Multiple Towers"*; adding machine tape*; inch/centimeter rulers; calculators
4 SESSION FOLLOW-UP **Daily Practice and Homework**			• *Student Activity Book,* pp. 39–40 • M8; M9–M14 (from Session 1.1) • *Student Math Handbook,* p. 36

*See *Materials to Prepare,* p. 95.

Ten-Minute Math

Counting Around the Class **Ask questions about a class that is counting by 40s.**

When the class finished counting, the last number was 840. How many students are in that class?

Encourage students to consider what they know about how many 40s there are in 400.

What number did the 9th person say? What number did the 17th person say?

For each question, collect answers as well as explanations about how students found their answer.

DISCUSSION

Multiples of 3 and 30

Math Focus Points for Discussion

- Understanding the effect of multiplying by a multiple of 10 (e.g., describing the relationship between 3×4 and 3×40)

Begin this session by asking the class to review the meanings of the terms multiple and factor.

Who remembers the difference between a factor and a multiple?

Students might say:

"When you are skip counting, factors are the numbers you are skip counting by. Like, if you count by 2s, then 2 is a factor of each number."

"The numbers you land on when you are skip counting are multiples."

What are some numbers that are multiples of 5? Of 10? . . . Let's count around the class by 3. I'll list the multiples of 3 on the board as you count.

3	21	39	57
6	24	42	60
9	27	45	63
12	30	48	66
15	33	51	69
18	36	54	72

These numbers are all multiples of 3, and 3 is a factor of all the numbers in this list. Now suppose that I ask, "What are the multiples of 30?" What are some ways that you would go about finding multiples of 30?

Take a few suggestions, and then have the class count around by 30 (the first person says 30, the next 60, and so on). As they count, list the multiples on the board next to the multiples of 3.

Multiples of 3				Multiples of 30			
3	21	39	57	30	210	390	570
6	24	42	60	60	240	420	600
9	27	45	63	90	270	450	630
12	30	48	66	120	300	480	660
15	33	51	69	150	330	510	690
18	36	54	72	180	360	540	720

As students count, pause occasionally and ask students how they are figuring out what the next multiple is.

In our class, when we count by 30s, we get to [720]. What do you notice about the list of multiples of 30? Do you see anything that can help you predict what number comes next? Do you see any relationship between the multiples of 3 and the multiples of 30?

Students are likely to notice that both lists have the same series of nonzero digits and that the multiples of 30 have a zero in the ones place.

Why do you think both lists have the numbers we say when we count by 3s, except that the numbers on our 30s list all end in 0?

Collect students' ideas, but keep this discussion brief because students will continue to think about this pattern throughout this investigation. Leave the lists posted for the next activity.

ACTIVITY

Introducing Multiple Towers

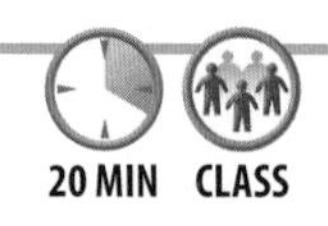

20 MIN CLASS

Ask for two volunteers to help you build a multiple tower of 30, explaining that they will make a tower of cards (or self-stick notes) as tall as a volunteer is. As students in the class call out the multiples of 30 from the board, one volunteer writes each multiple in large print on either an index card or a self-stick note. The other student builds the tower by taping the card or note to the wall, starting at floor level. You can help students visualize the accumulation of 30s by suggesting a story context.

Imagine that we have boxes of oranges, each of which holds 30 oranges. We're going to pile these boxes up, one on top of the other, until they're as tall as [Derek] is! But we want to keep track of how many oranges we have altogether each time we put a new box onto the tower.

When the tower has 13 cards, with 390 on the top card, stop and ask the class how many 30s they have so far.

Is there anything in our list that can help us know how many boxes we have without counting each one?

Students may refer to their knowledge of multiplication combinations, and any patterns they've noticed about multiplying by 10s. For example, they may recognize 300 as the 10th multiple (10×30) and know that 3 more 30s take them to 390. They may notice that because $12 \times 3 = 36$, $12 \times 30 = 360$, and 390 is one more 30.

So, we have 13 multiples so far, and the tower is nearly up to [Derek's shoulder]. What number do you predict we'll land on when the tower is as high as his head?❶

Using skip-counting patterns to make reasonable predictions about multiples of 30 involves strategies that apply to division as well.

When the tower is as tall as the student, ask further questions about it.

How many multiples are there in our finished tower? Try to figure out the number of multiples without counting them one by one.

Professional Development

❶ **Dialogue Box:** Building a Multiple Tower, p. 182

Take ideas from students. Then, on the top card, write the multiplication expression that corresponds to the multiple.

Sample Student Work

Now, again without counting, which number in our tower is the 10th multiple of 30? Which is the 20th multiple?

Write students' responses as multiplication expressions on the appropriate cards. Then ask students to predict a multiple beyond the highest multiple in your tower.

What would the [25th] multiple be?

If possible, leave your multiple tower on display for the next few sessions. Then you can refer and add to it while students are working on their own multiple towers.

DIFFERENTIATION: Supporting the Range of Learners

ELL For this activity, English Language Learners need to recognize ordinal numbers. Work with a small group before this activity to preview the words. List the numerals 1–5, then 10, 15, 20, 25, and 30, pairing each number with its corresponding ordinal. Then display a tower of different colored cubes. "We use different number words to describe the *order* of objects. The *first* cube in this tower (point) is blue, the *second* cube (point) is green, and the *third* cube (point) is red." Call attention to the relevant line of the list as you say each ordinal. Check students' understanding by asking questions. "What color is the 10th cube? Show me the 20th book on this shelf." Finally, list multiples of 2 and ask questions such as, "What is the 15th multiple of 2?"

3 ACTIVITY Building Multiple Towers

25 MIN PAIRS

For the remainder of the session, students work in pairs to build multiple towers of other 2-digit numbers. Rather than taping cards or notes to the walls, students use the long strips of adding machine tape that you prepared.

The first step is to mark off boxes on the strips of paper tape, using rulers that are about an inch wide. Demonstrate how to lay the ruler down and draw lines on both sides of the ruler's edges, making evenly sized boxes up the length of the paper strip.

Students mark off boxes on long paper strips to prepare their multiple towers.

Draw attention to the list of "Starting Numbers for Multiple Towers" that you prepared.

Starting Numbers for Multiple Towers

14	15	16	18	20
24	25	27	32	35
36	40	44	45	48
	50	60	70	

With your partner, choose a number from this list and build a multiple tower that is as tall as you or your partner—it doesn't matter who because you will have a chance to make more than one tower over the next couple of days. When you finish, you will have some questions to answer about your tower.

Name Date

Multiple Towers and Division Stories

300 Chart

1	2	3	4	5	6	7	8	9	10
11	12	13	14	15	16	17	18	19	20
21	22	23	24	25	26	27	28	29	30
31	32	33	34	35	36	37	38	39	40
41	42	43	44	45	46	47	48	49	50
51	52	53	54	55	56	57	58	59	60
61	62	63	64	65	66	67	68	69	70
71	72	73	74	75	76	77	78	79	80
81	82	83	84	85	86	87	88	89	90
91	92	93	94	95	96	97	98	99	100
101	102	103	104	105	106	107	108	109	110
111	112	113	114	115	116	117	118	119	120
121	122	123	124	125	126	127	128	129	130
131	132	133	134	135	136	137	138	139	140
141	142	143	144	145	146	147	148	149	150
151	152	153	154	155	156	157	158	159	160
161	162	163	164	165	166	167	168	169	170
171	172	173	174	175	176	177	178	179	180
181	182	183	184	185	186	187	188	189	190
191	192	193	194	195	196	197	198	199	200
201	202	203	204	205	206	207	208	209	210
211	212	213	214	215	216	217	218	219	220
221	222	223	224	225	226	227	228	229	230
231	232	233	234	235	236	237	238	239	240
241	242	243	244	245	246	247	248	249	250
251	252	253	254	255	256	257	258	259	260
261	262	263	264	265	266	267	268	269	270
271	272	273	274	275	276	277	278	279	280
281	282	283	284	285	286	287	288	289	290
291	292	293	294	295	296	297	298	299	300

Sessions 3.1, 3.2, 3.3, 3.4 Unit 3 M47

▲ Resource Masters, M47

Students build their towers from the bottom up, as they did for yours, by starting with their chosen number and then writing successive multiples of that number in each box. Students can display these strips around the room or fold them and keep them in their math folders.

Suggest that students make lists of at least 10 or 12 multiples of their number before beginning to write numbers on their tower. Urge them to check their lists for accuracy. Have calculators and copies of the 300 Chart (M47) available for those students who would benefit from using a skip-counting tool to generate or to check their multiples.❷

After students complete a multiple tower, they answer the questions on *Student Activity Book* pages 37–38, referring to the numbers in their tower.

When you get to the questions in your *Student Activity Book,* you'll be thinking about certain multiples, such as the 10th multiple or the 20th multiple. It is often easy to find the 10th, 20th, or 30th multiples, because these are multiples of 10.

If you know these, they can help you find other multiples. For example, if you know the 20th multiple, you can easily find the 21st. We will call these useful multiples *landmark multiples* because they help us find our way among all the multiples. As you work, think about other multiples that we could consider to be landmarks.

By answering the questions about their multiple towers, students reason about important number relationships. For example, they discover that they can use the product of 10 times their number to determine the 5th multiple in the sequence (half of the 10th multiple), the 20th multiple (double the 10th multiple), or the 15th multiple (the 5th multiple added to the 10th).

Students mark these landmark multiples on their towers by labeling them with multiplication expressions, just as you did on your demonstration tower.❸

Teaching Notes

❷ **Using Calculators for Multiple Towers** Students may use calculators to help them generate the multiples of 2-digit numbers. Students can find multiples either by skip counting on the calculator (e.g. $16 + 16 + 16 + 16\ldots$) or by adding to the previous multiple. They may use the calculator to check their multiples by using either multiplication or division. For example, "We ended at 336, and we have 21 multiples. Does $16 \times 21 = 336$? If we divide 336 by 16, do we get 21?"

❸ **Landmark Numbers** Throughout the *Investigations* curriculum, the expression *landmark* is used as an informal term to refer to numbers in our number system that serve as familiar landing places, that make for simple calculations, and that students can relate easily to other numbers. Because we have a base-ten number system, multiples of 10 are particularly useful in these ways. Students often consider the factors of 100, particularly 25 and its multiples, as landmarks or *friendly* numbers, because they are familiar with them as amounts of money.

A list of multiples helps students find their landmark multiples.

Students will continue to work on multiple towers over the next two sessions.

ONGOING ASSESSMENT: Observing Students at Work

Students generate a sequence of the multiples of a 2-digit number and reason about the number relationships in their lists.

- **Are students able to generate sequences of the multiples of 2-digit numbers?** Are they breaking up numbers in convenient ways (e.g., adding on 30 and then 6 to find the next multiple of 36)? Are they using repeated addition, skip-counting patterns, or tools such as calculators or the 300 chart?
- **Do students easily calculate the 10th multiple in the sequence and use it to find other multiples?**

As you circulate and observe students working on their multiple towers, ask them to focus on looking for patterns in the multiples.

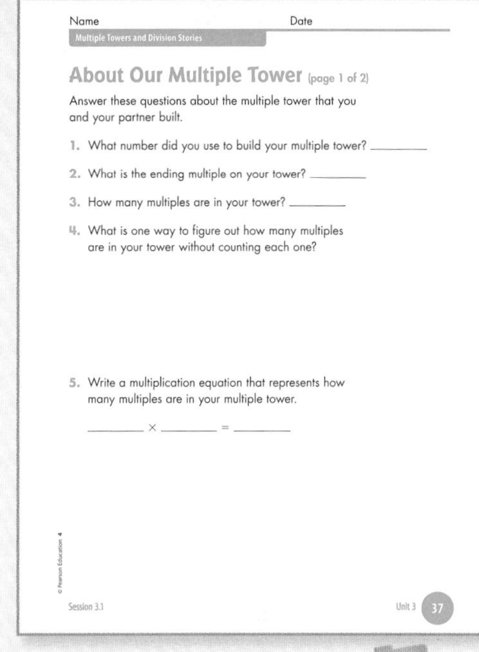
Name Date

Multiple Towers and Division Stories

About Our Multiple Tower (page 1 of 2)

Answer these questions about the multiple tower that you and your partner built.

1. What number did you use to build your multiple tower? ______
2. What is the ending multiple on your tower? ______
3. How many multiples are in your tower? ______
4. What is one way to figure out how many multiples are in your tower without counting each one?
5. Write a multiplication equation that represents how many multiples are in your multiple tower.

______ × ______ = ______

© Pearson Education 4

Session 3.1 Unit 3 37

▲ Student Activity Book, p. 37; M48 

Name Date

Multiple Towers and Division Stories

About Our Multiple Tower (page 2 of 2)

Answer these next questions without counting.

6. What is the 10th multiple? ______
7. What is the 20th multiple? ______
8. What is the 25th multiple? ______
9. How did you decide what the 20th multiple is?
10. Find each of the multiples above (10th, 20th, 25th) on your tower, and label them with a multiplication expression, such as 10 × 30.
11. What other landmark multiples can you find and label?

© Pearson Education 4

38 Unit 3 Session 3.1

▲ Student Activity Book, p. 38; M49 

DIFFERENTIATION: Supporting the Range of Learners

Intervention Help students choose a number that is most appropriate to their level of ability. Encourage the use of skip-counting tools for those who need them, as well as the use of mental strategies for those who need a greater challenge.

Remind students to break up numbers in ways that make the addition easier. For example, in a multiple tower of 36, when students reach 144, they can add on the next 36 by adding 6 first to get to 150 and then adding 30.

4 SESSION FOLLOW-UP

Daily Practice and Homework

Daily Practice: For ongoing review, have students complete *Student Activity Book* page 39.

Homework: Students use their Multiplication Cards and, if needed, the sheet Practicing with Multiplication Cards (M8) to practice and to continue to learn the multiplication combinations to 12 × 12. On *Student Activity Book* page 40, they record details about their practice. Students will be assessed on the multiplication combinations to 12 × 12 in Session 3.4.

Student Math Handbook: Students and families may use *Student Math Handbook* page 36 for reference and review. See pages 184–190 in the back of this unit.

Name Date

Multiple Towers and Division Stories — Daily Practice

Arranging Juice Cans

NOTE Students solve story problems that involve finding factors.
SMH 22

1. You have 24 juice cans. Show all of the ways you can arrange these cans into arrays. Draw the arrays.	2. List all the factors of 24.
3. Teyo has 25 juice cans. Show all of the ways he can arrange his cans into arrays. Draw the arrays.	4. List all the factors of 25.

5. Karina says, "25 has more factors than 24 because 25 is greater than 24." Do you agree or disagree with Karina? Explain.

Session 3.1 Unit 3 39

▲ Student Activity Book, p. 39 WRITING

Name Date

Multiple Towers and Division Stories — Homework

Practice with Multiplication Cards 3

NOTE Students are working on the multiplication combinations (facts) to 12 × 12. Help your child with this practice.
SMH 29–34

1. Which multiplication combinations are you practicing?

2. Write two multiplication combinations that are hard for you, and explain what helps you remember them.

Multiplication combination: ______

What helps me: ______

Multiplication combination: ______

What helps me: ______

3. How did you practice your multiplication combinations? Who helped you?

40 Unit 3 Session 3.1

▲ Student Activity Book, p. 40

Multiplying Groups of 10

Math Focus Points

- Understanding the effect of multiplying by a multiple of 10 (e.g., describing the relationship between 3×4 and 3×40)
- Representing a multiplication problem with pictures, diagrams, or models
- Comparing visual representations of multiplication situations

Today's Plan		Materials
ACTIVITY 1 **Problems About Oranges**	20 MIN PAIRS CLASS	• *Student Activity Book,* p. 41
MATH WORKSHOP 2 **Multiplying Groups of 10** 2A Multiplying by Multiples of 10: What Happens? 2B Multiple Towers	40 MIN	2A • *Student Activity Book,* pp. 42–43 • M7*; M47 (from Session 3.1) • Connecting cubes 2B • M48–M49 (from Session 3.1)* • Chart: "Starting Numbers for Multiple Towers" (from Session 3.1); adding machine tape (from Session 3.1); inch/centimeter rulers; calculators
SESSION FOLLOW-UP 3 **Daily Practice and Homework**		• *Student Activity Book,* pp. 44–46 • *Student Math Handbook,* pp. 37–38

*See *Materials to Prepare,* p. 95.

Ten-Minute Math

Counting Around the Class **Students count around the class by 15s. Ask for predictions for what the last number will be. Each student says another multiple of 15 until all students have counted once. Highlight the multiples of 15 by writing them on the board as students say them.**

How many students have counted at 120? 225? 300? What is a multiplication equation that would represent 12 people counting by 15s? ($12 \times 15 = 180$)

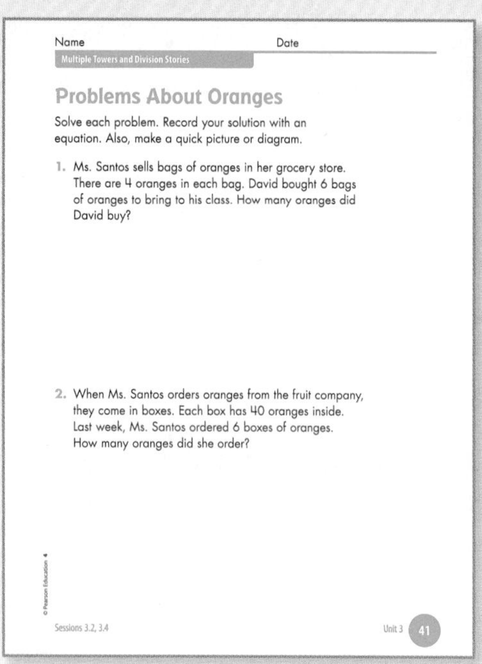
Name Date

Multiple Towers and Division Stories

Problems About Oranges

Solve each problem. Record your solution with an equation. Also, make a quick picture or diagram.

1. Ms. Santos sells bags of oranges in her grocery store. There are 4 oranges in each bag. David bought 6 bags of oranges to bring to his class. How many oranges did David buy?

2. When Ms. Santos orders oranges from the fruit company, they come in boxes. Each box has 40 oranges inside. Last week, Ms. Santos ordered 6 boxes of oranges. How many oranges did she order?

© Pearson Education 4

Sessions 3.2, 3.4 Unit 3 41

▲ Student Activity Book, p. 41

1 ACTIVITY
Problems About Oranges

Begin this session by having students solve the two related story problems on *Student Activity Book* page 41.

Give pairs of students about 5 minutes to work on these problems. They should be able to finish quickly, particularly because the first problem is a familiar multiplication combination. As students are working on the second problem, circulate and listen to what they are saying about how to solve 6×40. Make sure that they are making quick sketches of each problem situation. Look for sketches that will be useful in discussing the relationship between 6×4 and 6×40—sketches that show in some way that the product of 6×40 is 10 times the product of 6×4.

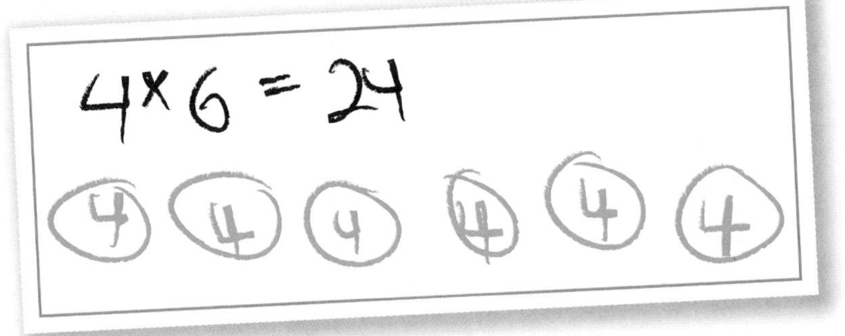

Sample Student Work

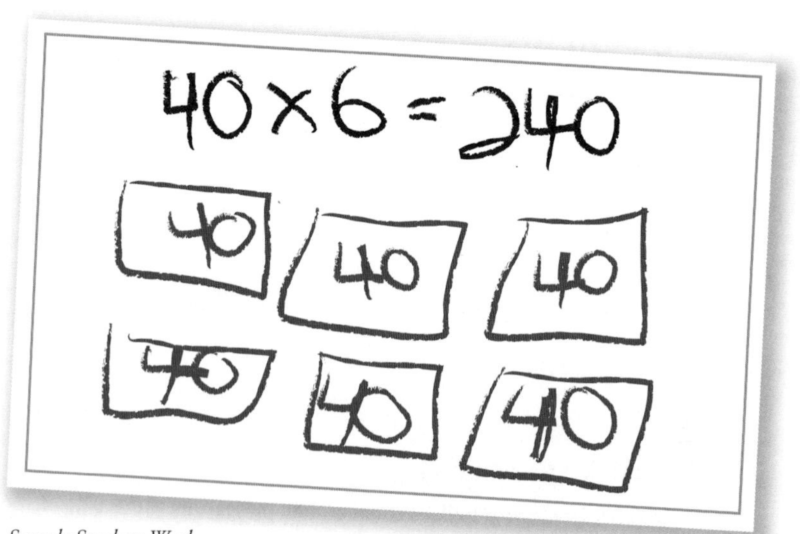

Sample Student Work

For the follow-up discussion, keep in mind that students are going to work on more problems like this and have further discussions, so they need not reach any conclusions at this time. Simply give students a chance to express their current ideas about this relationship.

When you bring the class back together, focus on the relationship between the two problems.

What equation did you write for the first problem? For the second problem? Who has a picture or diagram for the first problem? Who has one for the second problem?

Sketch a few examples on the board.

Who has something to say about the relationship between these two problems? How are they the same? How are they different? Did anyone use the first problem to help solve the second?

As students share their ideas, use students' sketches or diagrams as a way to help students visualize the relationship between the two problems.

Ramona had a picture of 6 squares with the number 4 in each square to stand for the 6 bags of oranges in the first problem. Then she had 6 squares with the number 40 in each square to stand for the 6 boxes of oranges in the second problem. How are these two situations the same? How are they different?❶

Students may bring up the idea that you can "add a zero" to the product of 6 × 4 to get the product of 6 × 40. You will have a longer discussion of this idea in Session 3.4. For now, ask students to think about why the pattern they have noticed works.❷

Yuki said that he can get the answer to a problem like 6 × 40 because he knows that the answer to 6 × 4 is 24 and then he puts a zero on 24 to make 240. Who else used that idea? I'm wondering how you know that this works. Can you do that with other numbers? What about 3 × 50 or 70 × 8? I'd like you to think about this question as you work on more problems like this in Math Workshop. Why can you solve 6 × 40 by multiplying 6 × 4 to get 24 and then changing 24 to 240?

MATH WORKSHOP

2 Multiplying Groups of 10

40 MIN

In this Math Workshop, students continue to examine what happens when a number is multiplied by a multiple of 10. They should complete their multiple towers from the last session if they haven't already, and they may have time to make a multiple tower for another number. Students will be discussing their multiple towers at the beginning of the next session. They will discuss their work on multiples of 10 at the end of Session 3.4.

Professional Development

❶ **Teacher Note:** Multiplying by Multiples of 10, p. 167

Math Note

❷ **Adding a Zero** Many students have noticed that when they multiply a multiple of 10, such as 6 × 40, they can *ignore* the zero, multiply the other digits (in this case, 6 × 4 = 24), and then "add the zero" to get their answer to the original problem. Students often develop a procedure based on this pattern without understanding why it works. In this investigation, students consider what "adding a zero" means and why it works.

Algebra Note

3 Algebraic Thinking Even though students may be working with specific numbers, such as 6 × 4 and 6 × 40, they are actually building an argument that will apply to a range of similar multiplication expressions. You can encourage this kind of algebraic thinking by asking how students' reasoning based on one set of numbers can apply to a different set. For example, "I see that you are working with 6 × 4 and 6 × 40. Could your diagram [or model or explanation] also work for 3 × 8 and 3 × 80? Explain how."

Name Date

Multiple Towers and Division Stories

Multiplying by Multiples of 10: What Happens? (page 1 of 2)

Solve these problems.

1.
5 × 6 =
50 × 6 =
5 × 60 =

2.
3 × 4 =
30 × 4 =
3 × 40 =

3.
8 × 6 =
80 × 6 =
8 × 60 =

© Pearson Education 4

42 Unit 3 Sessions 3.2, 3.3, 3.4

▲ Student Activity Book, p. 42 PORTFOLIO

PAIRS

2A Multiplying by Multiples of 10: What Happens?

Students solve sets of related problems and represent one set of problems on *Student Activity Book* pages 42–43. Have assorted math tools available: connecting cubes, Centimeter Grid Paper (M7), and 300 Charts (M47).

On these pages, your job is to find a way to explain why it works to solve a problem like 6 × 40 by first thinking of it as 6 × 4. Does this pattern always work? Why does it work? When we discuss your work on these pages in a couple of days, I want to hear what ideas you have about this and see the pictures or other representations you have used to show your ideas. 3

ONGOING ASSESSMENT: Observing Students at Work

Students examine the mathematical relationship that underlies the pattern they see when a number is multiplied by a multiple of 10.

- **Can students use one of the available tools to create a visual representation of both 3 × 4 and 3 × 40?**
- **Can students use their representations to explain the mathematical relationship between the two problems?**

As you observe students working, look for a variety of representations that can be shared during the discussion in Session 3.4. For example, for Problem 2, students might do any of the following:

- **Use connecting cubes to show groups of 4 and then groups of 40, perhaps in towers of 10**
- **Sketch three bags of 4 oranges and three boxes of 40 oranges, showing how 40 oranges are 4 groups of 10**
- **Draw arrays on grid paper, perhaps cutting them apart to show how ten arrays of 3 × 4 can be used to construct a 3 × 40 array**

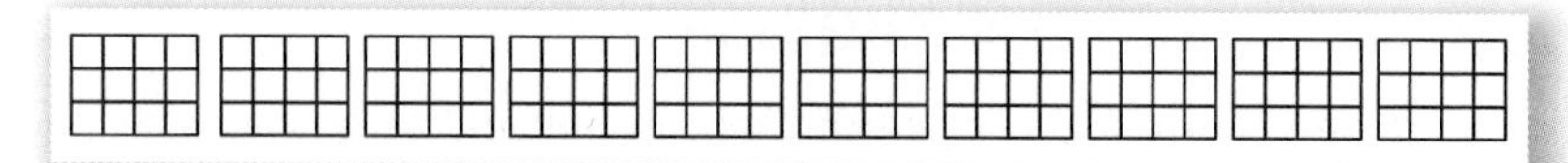

Choose pairs of students whose representations fall into the above categories and ask them to be prepared to share with the class when it is time.

DIFFERENTIATION: Supporting the Range of Learners

Intervention When students do not have a way to start problems such as 50×6, help them represent the problem with an array or a sketch of an invented story context. With which tool are students most familiar and comfortable? Can they use cubes to represent the 50 oranges in one box? Do they understand that they must then make 6 groups (or "boxes") of 50 cubes? Help these students sort out what the problem asks for and what the first step could be. For students who move through this first step quickly, offer an additional problem that matches your invented story context, such as finding the number of oranges in 13 boxes. Ask students to think about how to represent this situation. Are some tools easier to use than others in this case? Are some representations clearer than others?

2B Multiple Towers

PAIRS

Students continue to work on making their multiple towers of 2-digit numbers. For complete details of this activity, see Session 3.1, pages 100–103.

Those who are starting a new tower may choose a different number from the "Starting Numbers for Multiple Towers" list or any other 2-digit number that they are interested in exploring. Make copies of About Our Multiple Tower (M48–M49) available for pairs working on additional towers.

The calculator is a useful tool for skip counting by larger numbers.

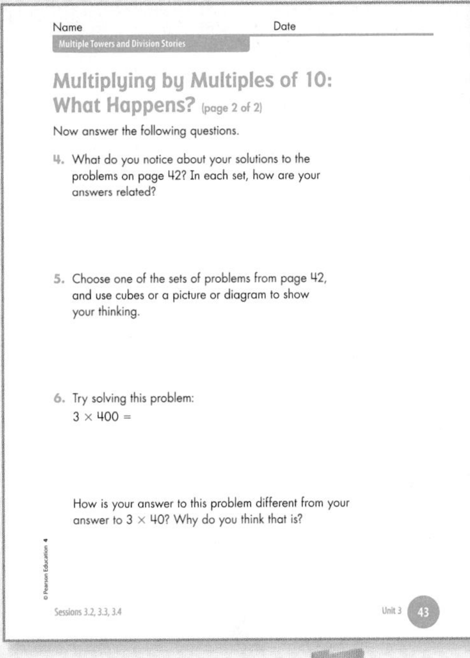

Name Date

Multiple Towers and Division Stories

Multiplying by Multiples of 10: What Happens? (page 2 of 2)

Now answer the following questions.

4. What do you notice about your solutions to the problems on page 42? In each set, how are your answers related?

5. Choose one of the sets of problems from page 42, and use cubes or a picture or diagram to show your thinking.

6. Try solving this problem:
$3 \times 400 =$

How is your answer to this problem different from your answer to 3×40? Why do you think that is?

© Pearson Education 4

Sessions 3.2, 3.3, 3.4 Unit 3 43

▲ Student Activity Book, p. 43 

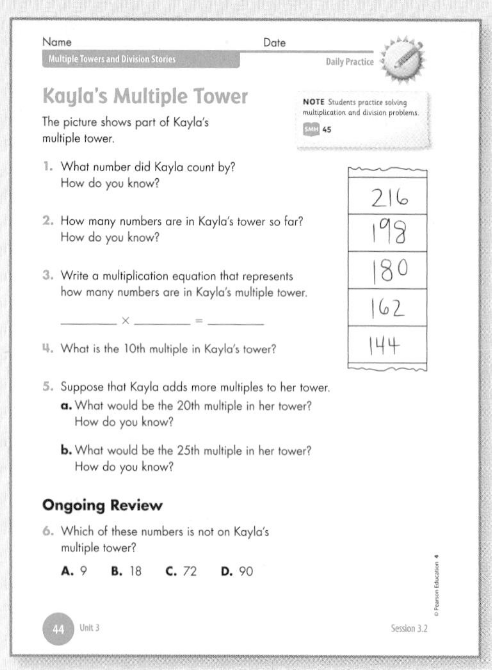
Name Date
Multiple Towers and Division Stories
Daily Practice

Kayla's Multiple Tower

The picture shows part of Kayla's multiple tower.

NOTE Students practice solving multiplication and division problems.
SMH 45

216
198
180
162
144

1. What number did Kayla count by? How do you know?
2. How many numbers are in Kayla's tower so far? How do you know?
3. Write a multiplication equation that represents how many numbers are in Kayla's multiple tower.
_______ × _______ = _______
4. What is the 10th multiple in Kayla's tower?
5. Suppose that Kayla adds more multiples to her tower.
a. What would be the 20th multiple in her tower? How do you know?
b. What would be the 25th multiple in her tower? How do you know?

Ongoing Review

6. Which of these numbers is not on Kayla's multiple tower?
A. 9 B. 18 C. 72 D. 90

© Pearson Education 4
44 Unit 3 Session 3.2

▲ Student Activity Book, p. 44

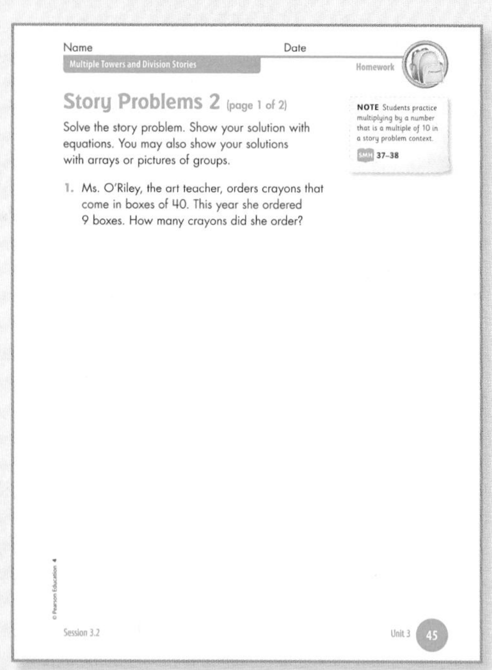
Name Date
Multiple Towers and Division Stories
Homework

Story Problems 2 (page 1 of 2)

Solve the story problem. Show your solution with equations. You may also show your solutions with arrays or pictures of groups.

NOTE Students practice multiplying by a number that is a multiple of 10 in a story problem context.
SMH 37–38

1. Ms. O'Riley, the art teacher, orders crayons that come in boxes of 40. This year she ordered 9 boxes. How many crayons did she order?

© Pearson Education 4
Session 3.2 Unit 3 45

▲ Student Activity Book, p. 45

DIFFERENTIATION: Supporting the Range of Learners

Extension Encourage students to label multiples in addition to the 10th, 20th, and 25th according to other relationships that they notice. For example, they might notice that the 12th multiple of 35 could be seen as $(10 \times 35) + (2 \times 35)$, or they may notice that the 4th multiple of 35 (140) is double the second multiple (2×70).

Additionally, some students may be interested in working with small 3-digit numbers.

3 SESSION FOLLOW-UP

Daily Practice and Homework

Daily Practice: For reinforcement of this units' content, have students complete *Student Activity Book* page 44.

Homework: On *Student Activity Book* pages 45–46, students solve one story problem and write a story for another multiplication problem with a focus on multiplying by a multiple of 10.

Student Math Handbook: Students and families may use *Student Math Handbook* pages 37–38 for reference and review. See pages 184–190 in the back of this unit.

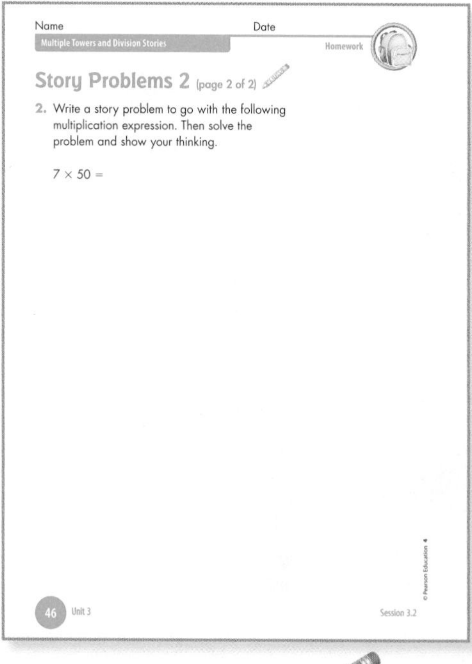
Name Date
Multiple Towers and Division Stories
Homework

Story Problems 2 (page 2 of 2)

2. Write a story problem to go with the following multiplication expression. Then solve the problem and show your thinking.

7 × 50 =

© Pearson Education 4
46 Unit 3 Session 3.2

▲ Student Activity Book, p. 46

SESSION 3.3

Multiplying 2-Digit Numbers

Math Focus Points

- Understanding the effect of multiplying by a multiple of 10 (e.g., describing the relationship between 3×4 and 3×40)
- Multiplying multiples of 10
- Comparing visual representations of multiplication situations

Today's Plan		Materials
1 DISCUSSION **Using the 10th Multiple**	15 MIN CLASS	
2 MATH WORKSHOP **Multiplying Groups of 10** 2A Multiples of 10: Related Problems 2B Story Problems About 10s 2C Multiplying by Multiples of 10: What Happens?	45 MIN	2A • *Student Activity Book,* p. 47 • Connecting cubes 2B • *Student Activity Book,* p. 48 • M7* • Connecting cubes 2C • *Student Activity Book,* pp. 42–43 • M7; M47 (from Session 3.1) • Connecting cubes
3 SESSION FOLLOW-UP **Daily Practice and Homework**		• *Student Activity Book,* pp. 49–50 • *Student Math Handbook,* pp. 37–38

*See *Materials to Prepare,* p. 95.

Ten-Minute Math

Counting Around the Class **Students count around the class by 30s.**

How are the multiples of 30 related to the multiples of 15?

Each student says another multiple of 30 until all students have counted once.

Highlight the multiples of 30 by writing them on the board as students say them.

How many students have counted at 210? 420? 480? What is a multiplication equation that would represent 9 people counting by 30s? ($9 \times 30 = 270$)

DISCUSSION

1 Using the 10th Multiple

Math Focus Points for Discussion

- Multiplying multiples of 10

Present the following problem.

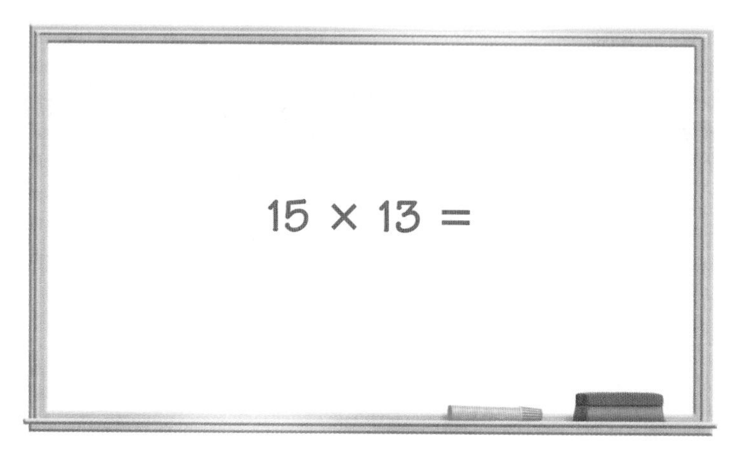

Here's a problem for you to solve before we talk about it together. Think about the work you've been doing on multiplying by 10s. How can that help you with this problem?

Give students a few minutes to solve the problem, either on their own or with a partner. Encourage students to make a representation or think of a story about the problem. Circulate while students are working and look for ways in which they are breaking the numbers apart in order to make the problem manageable.

Bring the class back together to collect students' strategies. As several students explain how they thought about and solved the problem, listen for strategies that use a multiple of 10 to solve the problem. Focus the discussion on these strategies.

[Alejandro], you solved the problem by breaking apart the 15 into 10 and 5. It was easy for you to multiply 10×13. What did you have to do to finish the problem? Did multiplying 10s help you with 5×13?

[Lucy], I noticed that you thought of the problem as a multiple tower of 13. You knew that 130 would be the 10th multiple. Did that help you find the 15th multiple?

[Marisol] and [Jake] said that they had it easy with this problem because they already made a multiple tower of 15! How did you find the 13th multiple on your tower? Did it help to break the numbers apart in some way?

Students will continue to share and discuss their strategies for solving problems with 2-digit numbers throughout this unit, with a focus on breaking problems apart in a variety of ways. Remind students to look for ways in which multiplying by 10 or multiples of 10 can help make the problems easier.

45 MIN

MATH WORKSHOP

Multiplying Groups of 10

Students work individually or in pairs, solving problems that involve multiplying by multiples of 10. They should complete all the related problems (Activity 2A) and at least one of the story problems (Activity 2B) in this session. If any students have not finished *Student Activity Book* pages 42–43 (Activity 2C), they should complete that first because they will be discussing this work at the end of the next session.

If students finish all of the Math Workshop activities, they can build more multiple towers, trying numbers they have not used before.

INDIVIDUALS

2A Multiples of 10: Related Problems

On *Student Activity Book* page 47, students solve several pairs of related problems and then write a story problem about one of the pairs.

ONGOING ASSESSMENT: Observing Students at Work

Students solve multiplication problems that involve multiples of 10.

- **Do students solve the second problem in each pair by relating it to the first?**
- **Can students create a story problem that represents one of the pairs of problems?**

Name Date

Multiple Towers and Division Stories

Multiples of 10: Related Problems

Solve each pair of multiplication problems.

1. $3 \times 9 =$ 27 $90 \times 3 =$ 270	2. $8 \times 7 =$ 56 $8 \times 70 =$ 560
3. $6 \times 6 =$ 36 $6 \times 60 =$ 360	4. $2 \times 12 =$ 24 $20 \times 12 =$ 240
5. $15 \times 2 =$ 30 $150 \times 2 =$ 300	6. $4 \times 10 =$ 40 $10 \times 40 =$ 400

7. Choose one of these problem pairs. Write a story problem to go with it.

Sessions 3.3, 3.4 Unit 3 47

▲ Student Activity Book, p. 47 WRITING

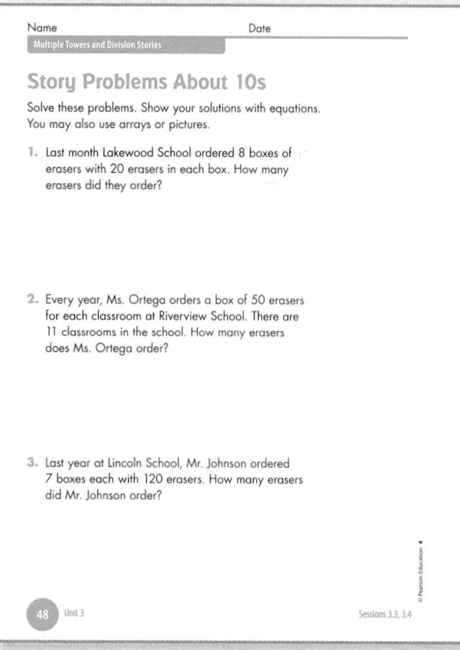
Name Date

Multiple Towers and Division Stories

Story Problems About 10s

Solve these problems. Show your solutions with equations. You may also use arrays or pictures.

1. Last month Lakewood School ordered 8 boxes of erasers with 20 erasers in each box. How many erasers did they order?

2. Every year, Ms. Ortega orders a box of 50 erasers for each classroom at Riverview School. There are 11 classrooms in the school. How many erasers does Ms. Ortega order?

3. Last year at Lincoln School, Mr. Johnson ordered 7 boxes each with 120 erasers. How many erasers did Mr. Johnson order?

© Pearson Education 4

48 Unit 3 Sessions 3.3, 3.4

▲ Student Activity Book, p. 48

DIFFERENTIATION: Supporting the Range of Learners

Intervention Writing story problems can be a challenging task for some students. Suggest that they first tell you or another student the story they have in mind, before writing it down. They may also use cubes or drawings to "act out" what they imagine is happening in the problem.

INDIVIDUALS PAIRS

2B Story Problems About 10s

On *Student Activity Book* page 48, students solve three story problems about school supply items that come packaged in multiples of 10. Students may work either individually or with a partner.

Students can sketch pictures to help them visualize story problems.

ONGOING ASSESSMENT: Observing Students at Work

Students solve story problems that involve multiples of 10.

- **Can students multiply by a multiple of 10 accurately?**
- **Can students show their thinking with equations?** Do they illustrate their thinking with visual representations (arrays, pictures, or diagrams)?

DIFFERENTIATION: Supporting the Range of Learners

Intervention For those students who need to use tools to solve these problems, provide connecting cubes in towers of 10 or grid paper for drawing arrays.

2C Multiplying by Multiples of 10: What Happens?

Students complete *Student Activity Book* pages 42–43. For complete details about this activity, see Session 3.2, page 108.

SESSION FOLLOW-UP

3 Daily Practice and Homework

Daily Practice: For ongoing review, have students complete *Student Activity Book* page 49.

Homework: On *Student Activity Book* page 50, students solve pairs of related problems with multiples of 10.

Student Math Handbook: Students and families may use *Student Math Handbook* pages 37–38 for reference and review. See pages 184–190 in the back of this unit.

Name Date

Multiple Towers and Division Stories — Daily Practice

Things That Come in Groups

Solve these problems. Write a multiplication equation for each problem. Show how you solved it.

NOTE Students practice multiplication by solving story problems.

SMH 40–43

Spiders have 8 legs.

1. How many legs do 6 spiders have? ________
   Equation: ________

2. How many legs do 12 spiders have? ________
   Equation: ________

3. How many legs do 18 spiders have? ________
   Equation: ________

© Pearson Education 4

Session 3.3 Unit 3 49

▲ Student Activity Book, p. 49

Name Date

Multiple Towers and Division Stories — Homework

Multiplying Groups of 10

Solve each pair of multiplication problems.

NOTE Students are learning how multiplying one number in a multiplication problem by 10 affects the product. Here, they solve problems with numbers that are multiples of 10.

SMH 37

1. $8 \times 4 =$ ____ $8 \times 40 =$ ____	2. $6 \times 7 =$ ____ $6 \times 70 =$ ____
3. $9 \times 5 =$ ____ $90 \times 5 =$ ____	4. $12 \times 6 =$ ____ $120 \times 6 =$ ____
5. $15 \times 4 =$ ____ $15 \times 40 =$ ____	6. $5 \times 14 =$ ____ $50 \times 14 =$ ____
7. $11 \times 3 =$ ____ $11 \times 30 =$ ____	8. $40 \times 5 =$ ____ $400 \times 5 =$ ____

© Pearson Education 4

50 Unit 3 Session 3.3

▲ Student Activity Book, p. 50

Assessment: Multiplication Combinations

Math Focus Points

- Reviewing multiplication combinations to 12 × 12
- Understanding the effect of multiplying by a multiple of 10 (e.g., describing the relationship between 3 × 4 and 3 × 40)
- Comparing visual representations of multiplication situations

Today's Plan		Materials
1 ASSESSMENT ACTIVITY **Multiplication Combinations**	10 MIN INDIVIDUALS	• M50*
2 MATH WORKSHOP **Multiplying Groups of 10** 2A Multiples of 10: Related Problems 2B Story Problems About 10s	25 MIN	2A • *Student Activity Book*, p. 47 (from Session 3.3) • Connecting cubes 2B • *Student Activity Book*, p. 48 (from Session 3.3) • M7* • Connecting cubes
3 DISCUSSION **What Does It Mean to "Add a Zero"?**	25 MIN CLASS	• *Student Activity Book*, pp. 42–43 (from Session 3.2) • Connecting cubes
4 SESSION FOLLOW-UP **Daily Practice**		• *Student Activity Book*, p. 51 • *Student Math Handbook*, pp. 29–34

*See *Materials to Prepare*, p. 95.

Ten-Minute Math

Counting Around the Class **Students count around the class by 11s. Follow the procedure given on page 105.**

How many students have counted at 110? 165? 220? What if we had 26 students in the class? What would the ending number be?

1 ASSESSMENT ACTIVITY
Multiplication Combinations

This activity provides the opportunity to assess Benchmark 5: Demonstrate fluency with multiplication combinations up to 12 × 12. In order to meet the benchmark, students should be able to solve 30 multiplication problems (representative of the combinations to 12 × 12) accurately in three minutes or less. Students who take longer than this, but who solve all but one or two of the problems accurately, partially meet the benchmark. Students who need a great deal of time to work the problems out, or who give wrong answers for many problems, do not meet the benchmark.❶ ❷

This is the year's last whole-group timed test on multiplication combinations to 12 × 12.

You will want to structure this assessment so that you learn what you need to know without leaving students frustrated that they are not allowed to finish. One approach is to have students complete as many problems as they can in three minutes, skipping around to answer the ones they "just know" first. At the end of three minutes, they stop and circle any problems they have not yet solved and then continue working. This allows students to finish, yet provides a record of which problems they needed more time to complete.

Hand out Assessment: Multiplication Combinations (M50) to each student. Tell students to solve the problems as quickly as they can because they have only three minutes to work on this sheet. Explain that you are trying to help them identify which combinations they might still need to practice, if any.❸

Name Date

Multiple Towers and Division Stories

Assessment: Multiplication Combinations

11 × 6 =	9 × 4 =	7 × 8 =
3 × 9 =	8 × 12 =	9 × 9 =
4 × 7 =	8 × 9 =	5 × 6 =
3 × 6 =	8 × 5 =	7 × 6 =
6 × 4 =	5 × 12 =	8 × 6 =
5 × 9 =	3 × 12 =	3 × 8 =
7 × 10 =	7 × 9 =	6 × 12 =
3 × 7 =	8 × 4 =	7 × 7 =
8 × 8 =	12 × 12 =	9 × 6 =
12 × 4 =	6 × 6 =	5 × 7 =

M50 Unit 3 Session 3.4

▲ Resource Masters, M50

Professional Development

❶ **Teacher Note:** Learning and Assessing Multiplication Combinations, p. 151

Teaching Notes

❷ **Further Practice** This is the final assessment for the year on multiplication combinations to 12 × 12. However, this assessment may show that some students still need to practice a few or even many combinations. Such students may retake this assessment at a later date, after they have completed more practice. All students will continue to practice, review, and, most importantly, use these combinations as they solve multiplication problems throughout the year.

❸ **Explaining the Assessment** Because timed work can make some students anxious, talk with them directly about why you want them to solve as many problems as they can in three minutes and how that will help both you and them find out which combinations they still need to work on. If students still seem anxious before the assessment, take time to discuss ways to identify those problems they can tackle easily.

ONGOING ASSESSMENT: Observing Students at Work

Students demonstrate fluency with multiplication combinations.

- **Are students able to accurately solve multiplication combinations that are presented in random order?**
- **Are there particular categories of combinations with which students need more practice (for example, the square number combinations, the ×8 combinations)?**

DIFFERENTIATION: Supporting the Range of Learners

Intervention As needed, cut apart Assessment: Multiplication Combinations (M50) so that students face fewer problems at one time. Although many students will know most of these combinations at this point, some students may need an opportunity to take this assessment more than once or to continue practicing a few facts that you can assess individually later on.

MATH WORKSHOP

Multiplying Groups of 10

25 MIN

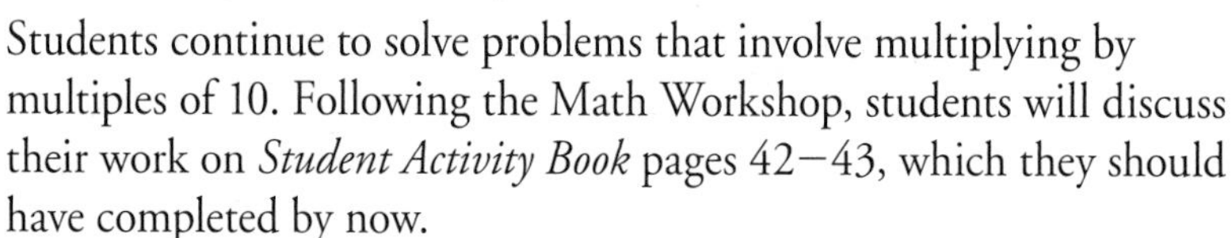

Students continue to solve problems that involve multiplying by multiples of 10. Following the Math Workshop, students will discuss their work on *Student Activity Book* pages 42–43, which they should have completed by now.

Remind students that they can build more multiple towers if they finish all of the Math Workshop activities.

2A Multiples of 10: Related Problems

INDIVIDUALS

Students work on *Student Activity Book* page 47. For complete details about this activity, see Session 3.3, page 113.

2B Story Problems about 10s

INDIVIDUALS PAIRS

Students work on *Student Activity Book* page 48. For complete details about this activity, see Session 3.3, page 114.

DISCUSSION

3 What Does It Mean to "Add a Zero"?

25 MIN CLASS

Math Focus Points for Discussion

- Understanding the effect of multiplying by a multiple of 10 (e.g., understanding the relationship between 3 × 4 and 3 × 40)
- Comparing visual representations of multiplication situations

Students should have at hand the representations they created for *Student Activity Book* pages 42–43. Write the following pairs of equations on the board and ask students to supply the products.

5 × 6 = ___	3 × 4 = ___
5 × 60 = ___	3 × 40 = ___

When people look at pairs of equations like these, I have often heard them say that there's a pattern here, and that the pattern is that we simply "add a zero." But what happens if we *really* add 6 + 0? 6 + 0 does not equal 60.

When you solve a problem like 5 × 60, in which one number is a multiple of 10, will it always work to think of the solution to 5 × 6 and then put another zero on the number? What is changing? Who thinks they can explain whether this will always work and why?

Ask students to use the representations that they made in earlier sessions to explain their thinking about this question.[4]

The goal of this discussion is for students to come away with an understanding that the "added zero" means that one of the numbers in the problem represents groups of 10s. Although 5 × 6 means 5 groups of 6 *ones,* 5 × 60 means 5 groups of 6 *tens* or (5 × 6) × 10.

Professional Development

[4] **Dialogue Box:** What Does It Mean to "Add a Zero"?, p. 183

Professional Development

5 **Teacher Note:** Multiplying by Multiples of 10, p. 167

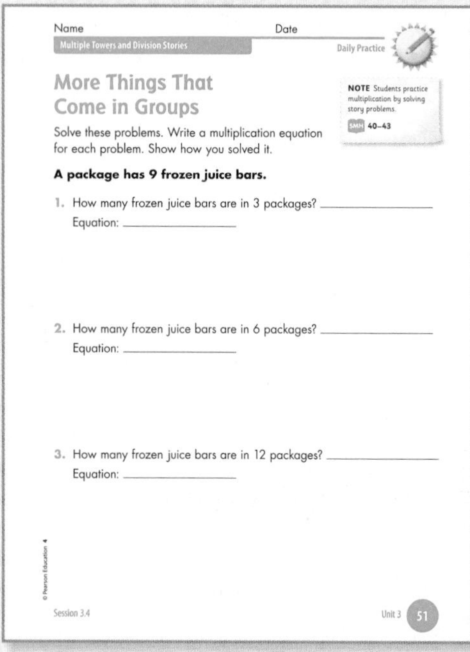
Name Date
Multiple Towers and Division Stories
Daily Practice

More Things That Come in Groups

NOTE Students practice multiplication by solving story problems.

SMH 40–43

Solve these problems. Write a multiplication equation for each problem. Show how you solved it.

A package has 9 frozen juice bars.

1. How many frozen juice bars are in 3 packages? ______
Equation: ______

2. How many frozen juice bars are in 6 packages? ______
Equation: ______

3. How many frozen juice bars are in 12 packages? ______
Equation: ______

Session 3.4 Unit 3 51

▲ Student Activity Book, p. 51

As students share their representations, ask them to point out the groups of 10 in each one. It may help students to refer back to the Problems About Oranges on *Student Activity Book* page 41 as a context for visualizing the relationships.

[Jill] and [Andrew] made their representation of 6 × 40 with cubes, and [Enrique] and [Anna] drew arrays. If we think of these as boxes of oranges, both of these show that there are 240 oranges altogether. Can we see the groups of 10 in [Jill] and [Andrew's] cube representation? Where are they in [Enrique] and [Anna's] arrays? How are these representations the same or different from their representations for 6 × 4?

Refer to the other representations in the same way. By comparing and describing representations, students are developing visual images for the groups of 10 in a multiple of 10 such as 40 and connecting images of 5 groups of 6 with images of 5 groups of 6 tens.

Conclude the discussion by asking students whether they can explain the pattern or rule in their own words. 5

SESSION FOLLOW-UP

Daily Practice

Daily Practice: For ongoing review, have students complete *Student Activity Book* page 51.

Student Math Handbook: Students and families may use *Student Math Handbook* pages 29–34 for reference and review. See pages 184–190 in the back of this unit.

INVESTIGATION 4

Mathematical Emphases

Computational Fluency Solving multiplication problems with 2-digit numbers

Math Focus Points

- Developing strategies for multiplying that involve breaking apart numbers

Whole Number Operations Understanding and using the relationship between multiplication and division to solve division problems

Math Focus Points

- Using known multiplication combinations to solve division problems

Whole Number Operations Reasoning about numbers and their factors

Math Focus Points

- Determining the effect on the product when a factor is doubled or halved

Whole Number Operations Representing the meaning of multiplication and division

Math Focus Points

- Representing a multiplication or division problem with pictures, diagrams, or models
- Using arrays to model multiplication

Strategies for Multiplication

Session	Student Activity Book	Student Math Handbook	Professional Development: Read Ahead of Time
SESSION 4.1 p. 124 **Doubles and Halves** Students examine what happens when one or both factors in a multiplication expression are doubled or halved.	52–56	43	• **Teacher Note:** Reasoning and Proof in Mathematics, p. 168
SESSION 4.2 p. 129 **Multiplication Cluster Problems** As they solve multiplication problems with larger numbers, students consider ways to break apart the problems in order to use familiar number relationships.	57–60	39	• **Teacher Note:** Multiplication Clusters and the Properties of Multiplication, p. 171; **Teacher Note:** Visualizing Arrays, p. 154
SESSION 4.3 p. 136 **Strategies for Multiplication** Students develop and practice strategies for solving multiplication problems with 2-digit numbers.	53–54, 57–58, 61–64	39; G8, G10	
SESSION 4.4 p. 144 **Strategies for Multiplication,** ***continued*** Students continue to develop and practice strategies for solving multiplication problems with 2-digit numbers.	57–58, 61–62, 65	39–43; G8, G10	
SESSION 4.5 p. 148 **End-of-Unit Assessment** Students solve these problems assessing their understanding of multiplication.	66	39–43, 50–52	• **Teacher Note:** End-of-Unit Assessment, p. 173

Ten-Minute Math See page 20 for an overview.

Quick Images: Seeing Numbers

- T38–T39, *Quick Images: Seeing Numbers*

Counting Around the Class

- No materials needed

	Materials to Gather	Materials to Prepare
	• **Connecting cubes** (as needed)	
	• **Chart paper** (as needed)	• **Chart paper** Prepare a poster that shows the following multiplication cluster: 13×2 13×4 3×8 12×8 13×8 Highlight the final problem in a second color.
	• **Connecting cubes** (as needed) • **M17–M37, Array Cards** (1 set per pair; from Session 1.2) • **Construction paper** (1 sheet per pair)	• **M40, *Small Array/Big Array* Recording Sheet** Make copies. (1 per pair, plus extras) • **M45, *Missing Factors* Recording Sheet** Make copies. (1 per pair, plus extras)
	• **M17–M37, Array Cards** (1 set per pair; from Session 1.2) • **Construction paper** (1 sheet per pair)	• **M40, *Small Array/Big Array* Recording Sheet** Make copies. (as needed) • **M45, *Missing Factors* Recording Sheet** Make copies. (as needed)
		• **M51–M52, End-of-Unit Assessment** Make copies. (1 per student)

Doubles and Halves

Math Focus Points

- Determining the effect on the product when a factor is doubled or halved
- Representing a multiplication or division problem with pictures, diagrams, or models

Vocabulary

doubled
halved

Today's Plan	Materials
ACTIVITY 1 **Ms. Santos's Apples** (30 MIN, PAIRS, CLASS)	• *Student Activity Book,* p. 52
ACTIVITY 2 **Related Problems About Doubles and Halves** (30 MIN, INDIVIDUALS)	• *Student Activity Book,* pp. 53–54 • Connecting cubes (as needed)
SESSION FOLLOW-UP 3 **Daily Practice and Homework**	• *Student Activity Book,* pp. 55–56 • *Student Math Handbook,* p. 43

Image 13
4 × (3×3)
2 × (9×2)

Image 14
5× (6 + 1)

Ten-Minute Math

Quick Images: Seeing Numbers Show *Quick Images: Seeing Numbers* (T38), Images 13 and 14, one at a time. For each pattern, ask students to write several different equations to find the total number of dots. For the first two viewings, give students 3 seconds to look at the pattern; the third time, leave the image displayed. Have two or three students explain how they saw the images (including any revisions they made) and their equations, showing how their numbers match the patterns.

ACTIVITY

30 MIN CLASS PAIRS

Ms. Santos's Apples

To begin this session, students solve the two problems on *Student Activity Book* page 52.

Through these problems, students examine how halving one factor and doubling the other in a multiplication expression results in an equivalent expression: $28 \times 6 = 14 \times 12$. In other words, students are investigating how they know that if $28 \times 6 = 168$, then $14 \times 12 = 168$.[1]

As you work on these problems, think about the relationship between them. How are these two problems the same? How are they different? What do the arrays or pictures that you draw for each problem help you see about this relationship?

Give student pairs about 10 minutes to work on the problems. Circulate and listen in order to identify what students are noticing about the two problems. Identify students who have sketches that will be useful in discussing why the number of boxes has to be doubled when the amount the box will hold (28 apples) is cut in half (14 apples).[2]

When you bring the class back together, first collect examples of the equations and pictures that students used. Students may have written division or multiplication equations. Record them all on the board. Sketch several students' representations on the board.

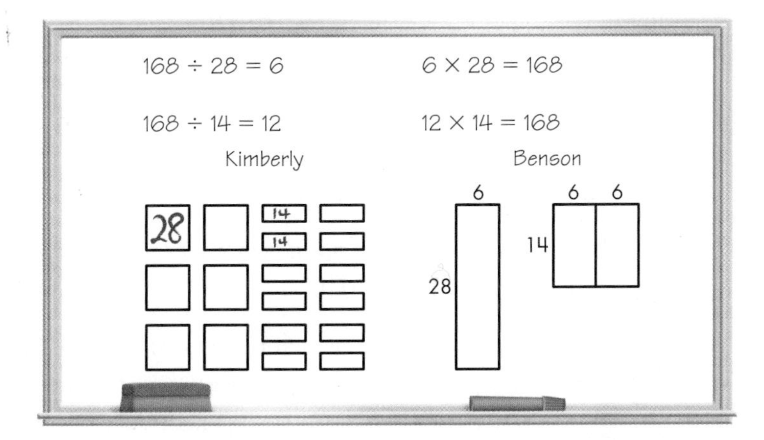

Then ask about the relationship between the two problems.

When Ms. Santos found that she could put only 14 apples in a box, how did that change the number of boxes she needed? What do you know about the numbers 28 and 14? What do you notice about your solutions to these two problems?

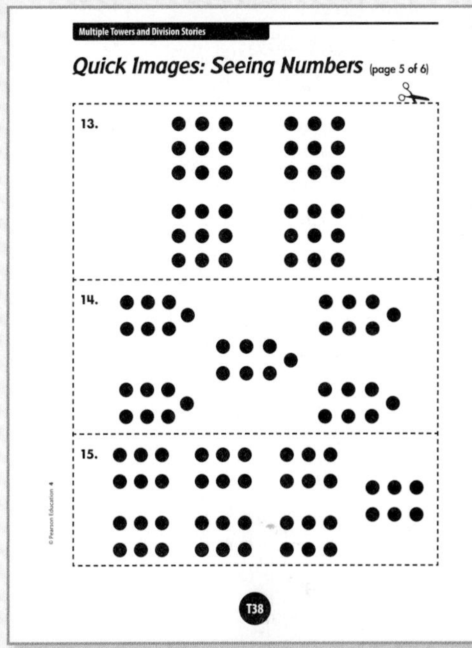

▲ Transparencies, T38

Algebra Note

[1] **Doubling and Halving** Some students may adopt doubling and halving as a useful strategy for some multiplication problems. The primary goal of this investigation is for all students to add to their understanding of how multiplication works by examining the mathematics behind this strategy and by making visual representations of why it works. This is discussed more fully in Algebra Connections in This Unit, p. 16.

Professional Development

[2] **Teacher Note:** Reasoning and Proof in Mathematics, p. 168

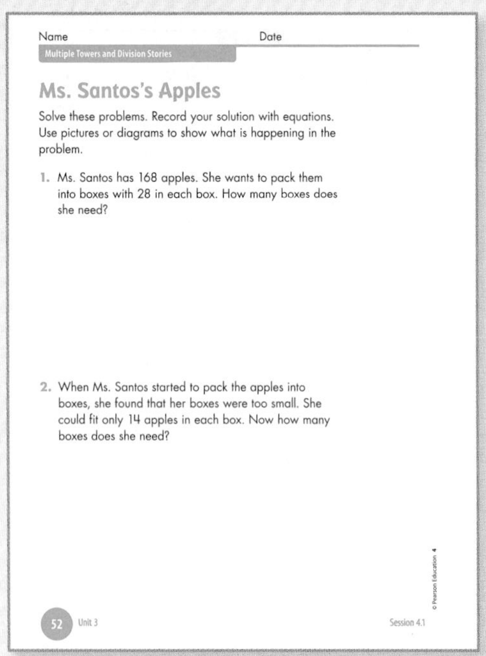
Name Date
Multiple Towers and Division Stories

Ms. Santos's Apples

Solve these problems. Record your solution with equations. Use pictures or diagrams to show what is happening in the problem.

1. Ms. Santos has 168 apples. She wants to pack them into boxes with 28 in each box. How many boxes does she need?

2. When Ms. Santos started to pack the apples into boxes, she found that her boxes were too small. She could fit only 14 apples in each box. Now how many boxes does she need?

52 Unit 3 Session 4.1

▲ Student Activity Book, p. 52

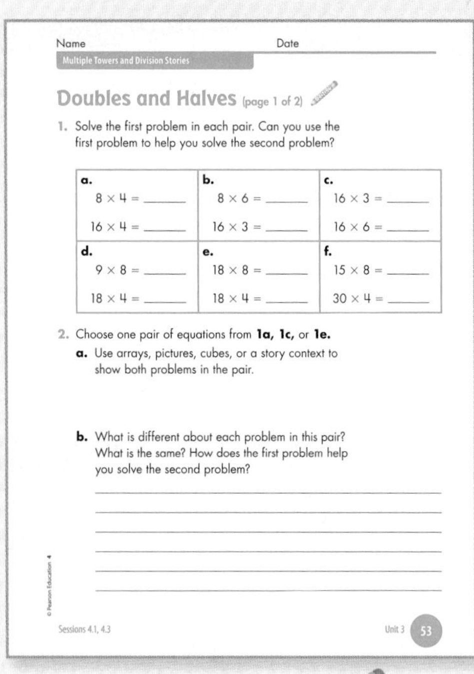
Name Date
Multiple Towers and Division Stories

Doubles and Halves (page 1 of 2)

1. Solve the first problem in each pair. Can you use the first problem to help you solve the second problem?

a.	b.	c.
$8 \times 4 =$ ___ $16 \times 4 =$ ___	$8 \times 6 =$ ___ $16 \times 3 =$ ___	$16 \times 3 =$ ___ $16 \times 6 =$ ___
d. $9 \times 8 =$ ___ $18 \times 4 =$ ___	**e.** $18 \times 8 =$ ___ $18 \times 4 =$ ___	**f.** $15 \times 8 =$ ___ $30 \times 4 =$ ___

2. Choose one pair of equations from **1a, 1c,** or **1e.**
   a. Use arrays, pictures, cubes, or a story context to show both problems in the pair.
   b. What is different about each problem in this pair? What is the same? How does the first problem help you solve the second problem?

Sessions 4.1, 4.3 Unit 3 53

▲ Student Activity Book, p. 53 WRITING

How does [Kimberly's] picture of boxes show what happens to the number of boxes?

How do [Benson's] arrays show what happens when the size of the boxes is cut in half?

Would this idea work with other numbers? What if we wanted to pack the 168 apples in even smaller boxes that hold only 7 apples? What do you think would happen to the number of boxes? Think about these ideas while you work on more problems.

Students encounter more problems with a double/half relationship in the next activity. They will then return to this more general discussion in Session 4.3.

ACTIVITY 2

30 MIN INDIVIDUALS

Related Problems About Doubles and Halves

Students next work alone on six pairs of related problems on *Student Activity Book* pages 53–54.

In problem pairs 1a, 1c, and 1e, one factor in the first problem is doubled in the second problem, resulting in a doubled product (e.g., $8 \times 4 = 32$, $16 \times 4 = 64$). In pairs 1b, 1d, and 1f, one factor in the first problem is doubled in the second problem and the second factor is halved, resulting in the same product (e.g., $8 \times 6 = 16 \times 3 = 48$). Students make representations of one pair of each type of problem in order to better visualize these relationships.

Call attention to the directions: Solve the first problem in each pair, and then use that answer in solving the second problem.

As you look at the two problems, notice whether one factor in the second problem has been doubled or halved.

Advise students to look carefully at each pair because the second problem does not always change in the same way. Encourage students to think of each problem pair in the story context of apples in boxes:

What if you still have 16 boxes, but each box has twice as many apples?

After students finish their work, they compare and discuss their answers with partners.

ONGOING ASSESSMENT: Observing Students at Work

Students solve related problems in which one factor is doubled or halved and the other factor is doubled.

- **How do students solve multiplication problems with numbers of this size?** Do they easily multiply numbers by place, multiplying the tens and then the ones?
- **Do students recognize that in each problem, one or both factors have been doubled or halved?** Do students use the first problem to solve the second? Do students understand the effect of doubling or halving one factor? Of doubling one factor and halving the other?
- **Can students make representations that show the doubling or double/half relationship?**

DIFFERENTIATION: Supporting the Range of Learners

Extension Provide students who finish easily with pairs of problems that involve more difficult numbers. For example:

64×4	60×6	12×8
128×2	120×3	4×24

Ask students who have a strong understanding of doubling and halving to try working with triples and thirds (as in the third pair above).

Name Date

Multiple Towers and Division Stories

Doubles and Halves (page 2 of 2)

3. Choose one pair of equations from **1b, 1d,** or **1f.**

   a. Use arrays, pictures, cubes, or a story context to show both problems in the pair.

   b. What is different about each problem in this pair? What is the same? How does the first problem help you solve the second problem?

54 Unit 3 Sessions 4.1, 4.3

▲ Student Activity Book, p. 54 WRITING

Name Date

Multiple Towers and Division Stories Daily Practice

Counting Around the Class 1

Solve these problems.

NOTE Students find the multiples of a given number and solve multiplication problems.

SMH 25

1. Mr. Bugwadia's class counted by 10s. Each person said one number. The first person said 10, the second said 20, and the third said 30.
   How many people counted to get to 200? ______
   How do you know?

2. Ms. Tan's class counted by 20s. Each person said one number. The first person said 20, the second said 40, and the third said 60.
   a. How many people counted to get to 420? ______
   How do you know?
   b. When Ms. Tan's class counted by 20s, did anyone say the number 300? ______
   How do you know?

© Pearson Education 4

Session 4.1 Unit 3 55

▲ Student Activity Book, p. 55

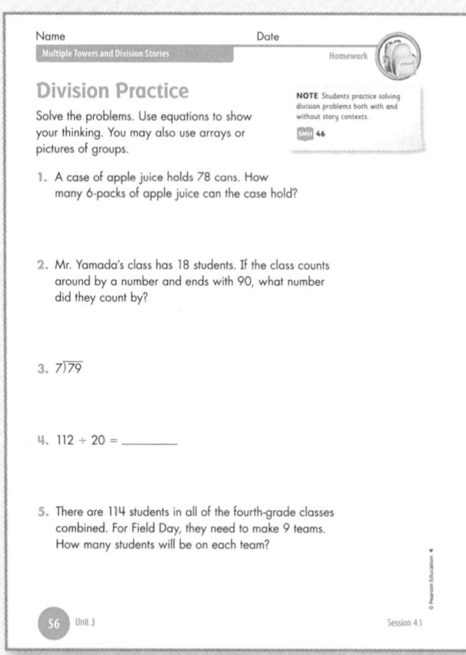
Name Date

Multiple Towers and Division Stories Homework

Division Practice

Solve the problems. Use equations to show your thinking. You may also use arrays or pictures of groups.

NOTE Students practice solving division problems both with and without story contexts.

SMH 46

1. A case of apple juice holds 78 cans. How many 6-packs of apple juice can the case hold?

2. Mr. Yamada's class has 18 students. If the class counts around by a number and ends with 90, what number did they count by?

3. $7\overline{)79}$

4. 112 ÷ 20 = ______

5. There are 114 students in all of the fourth-grade classes combined. For Field Day, they need to make 9 teams. How many students will be on each team?

© Pearson Education 4

56 Unit 3 Session 4.1

▲ Student Activity Book, p. 56

3 SESSION FOLLOW-UP
Daily Practice and Homework

Daily Practice: For ongoing review, have students complete *Student Activity Book* page 55.

Homework: On *Student Activity Book* page 56, students solve a variety of division problems, including some that result in a remainder.

Student Math Handbook: Students and families may use *Student Math Handbook* page 43 for reference and review. See pages 184–190 in the back of this unit.

Multiplication Cluster Problems

Math Focus Points

- Developing strategies for multiplying that involve breaking apart numbers
- Using arrays to model multiplication

Today's Plan			Materials
ACTIVITY 1 Introducing Multiplication Cluster Problems	20 MIN	CLASS	• Chart paper (multiplication cluster)*
ACTIVITY 2 Multiplication Cluster Problems	25 MIN	INDIVIDUALS	• *Student Activity Book,* pp. 57–58
ACTIVITY 3 Representing Cluster Problems with Arrays	15 MIN	CLASS	• Chart paper (as needed)
SESSION FOLLOW-UP 4 Daily Practice and Homework			• *Student Activity Book,* pp. 59–60 • *Student Math Handbook,* p. 39

*See *Materials to Prepare,* p. 123.

Ten-Minute Math

Quick Images: Seeing Numbers Show *Quick Images: Seeing Numbers* (T38–T39), Images 15 and 16, one at a time. For each pattern, ask students to write several different equations to find the total number of dots. For the first two viewings, give students 3 seconds to look at the pattern; the third time, leave the image displayed. Have two or three students explain how they saw the images (including any revisions they made) and their equations, showing how their numbers match the patterns.

▲ Transparencies, T39

ACTIVITY

Introducing Multiplication Cluster Problems

20 MIN CLASS

For the next few days, you'll be solving sets of multiplication problems that are related to one another. We call these "multiplication cluster problems." Let's start with this set.

Show the poster you have prepared that lists a multiplication cluster with the final problem 13×8.

$13 \times 2 =$

$13 \times 4 =$

$3 \times 8 =$

$12 \times 8 =$

Final problem: $13 \times 8 =$

In this kind of problem set, all of the problems are related in some way to the final problem—in this case, 13×8—even though they might not all be related to one another. For example, 12×8 is not closely related to 13×4, but it is related in a different way to 13×8, the final problem you are trying to solve in this cluster.

Give students a few minutes to work on this cluster. Explain that they are to solve the first four problems. To solve the final problem, they choose one or more problems in the cluster to help them.

When they have finished, ask students to share the ways they used problems in the cluster. Record their strategies on a new piece of chart paper. Leave space either below or beside each strategy because you will be adding arrays to this chart later in the session.

This cluster suggests several possibilities for solving 13×8. The following are several strategies that students might describe.

In the first stategy, one of the factors is doubled each time, which doubles the product.

In the second strategy, 13 is broken apart by place value. Students use 3×8 from the cluster and then add 10×8, which is not in the cluster.

In the third strategy, some students "just know" that $12 \times 8 = 96$. They then add one more 8 to solve 13×8.

Leave the solution strategies for 13×8 posted so that students can use them as a model during the next activity.

$13 \times 2 = 26$
$13 \times 4 = 52$
$13 \times 8 = 104$

$3 \times 8 = 24$
$10 \times 8 = 80$
$13 \times 8 = 104$

$12 \times 8 = 96$
$96 + 8 = 104$
$13 \times 8 = 104$

25 MIN INDIVIDUALS

ACTIVITY 2

Multiplication Cluster Problems

Students work on *Student Activity Book* pages 57–58. In the space beside each set of cluster problems that they solve, students explain which problems they used in solving the final problem and how they used them.①

Advise students that they will have more time to work on these cluster problems as part of the Math Workshop in the next session.

ONGOING ASSESSMENT: Observing Students at Work

Students choose strategies for solving multiplication problems by considering ways to use number relationships that they know.

- **Do students recognize the relationships between the problems in the set and the final problem to be solved?**
- **Are students able to break the numbers of the final problem into more manageable parts?**

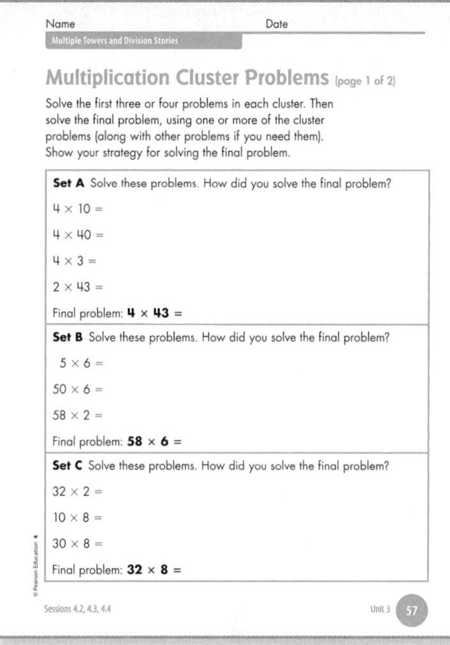

Name Date

Multiple Towers and Division Stories

Multiplication Cluster Problems (page 1 of 2)

Solve the first three or four problems in each cluster. Then solve the final problem, using one or more of the cluster problems (along with other problems if you need them). Show your strategy for solving the final problem.

Set A Solve these problems. How did you solve the final problem?
$4 \times 10 =$
$4 \times 40 =$
$4 \times 3 =$
$2 \times 43 =$
Final problem: $4 \times 43 =$

Set B Solve these problems. How did you solve the final problem?
$5 \times 6 =$
$50 \times 6 =$
$58 \times 2 =$
Final problem: $58 \times 6 =$

Set C Solve these problems. How did you solve the final problem?
$32 \times 2 =$
$10 \times 8 =$
$30 \times 8 =$
Final problem: $32 \times 8 =$

© Pearson Education 4

Sessions 4.2, 4.3, 4.4 Unit 3 57

▲ Student Activity Book, p. 57

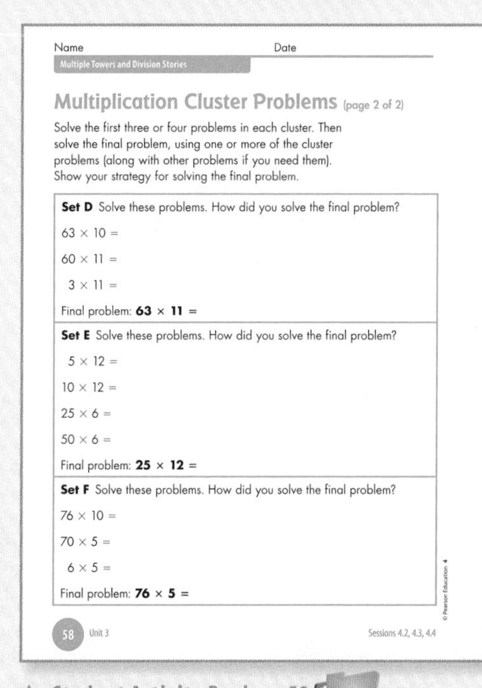

Name Date

Multiple Towers and Division Stories

Multiplication Cluster Problems (page 2 of 2)

Solve the first three or four problems in each cluster. Then solve the final problem, using one or more of the cluster problems (along with other problems if you need them). Show your strategy for solving the final problem.

Set D Solve these problems. How did you solve the final problem?
$63 \times 10 =$
$60 \times 11 =$
$3 \times 11 =$
Final problem: $63 \times 11 =$

Set E Solve these problems. How did you solve the final problem?
$5 \times 12 =$
$10 \times 12 =$
$25 \times 6 =$
$50 \times 6 =$
Final problem: $25 \times 12 =$

Set F Solve these problems. How did you solve the final problem?
$76 \times 10 =$
$70 \times 5 =$
$6 \times 5 =$
Final problem: $76 \times 5 =$

© Pearson Education 4

58 Unit 3 Sessions 4.2, 4.3, 4.4

▲ Student Activity Book, p. 58

Professional Development

① **Teacher Note:** Multiplication Clusters and the Properties of Multiplication, p. 171

Professional Development

❷ **Teacher Note:** Visualizing Arrays, p. 154

- **Are students multiplying multiples of 10 easily?**
- **Are students using knowledge about doubling or halving factors to solve problems?**

DIFFERENTIATION: Supporting the Range of Learners

Intervention Problem sets A and B on page 57 build on the work in Investigation 3. These clusters involve multiplying a multiple of 10 (e.g., 4×40 and 50×6) and familiar factor pairs. Multiplying multiples of 10 may still feel new to some students. You may want to provide additional problem sets for students to gain more practice before going on to other clusters. Some students may find arrays, pictures, or story contexts helpful in thinking about the relationship between, for example, 4 groups of 3 and 4 groups of 3 *tens*.

ACTIVITY

15 MIN CLASS

3 Representing Cluster Problems with Arrays

Direct students' attention back to the chart showing their solution strategies for 13×8.

Let's go back and look again at the ways you solved 13×8. Let's see how we can use arrays to show how you used the problems in the cluster. Pick the strategy you used, and draw arrays to show how it worked.

After students have worked for a few minutes, choose one of the strategies to focus on, perhaps breaking 13 apart by place value.

I'm going to start by showing just the final problem, 13×8, as an array. I'll draw the shape and write the dimensions, and we'll imagine all the squares that make up this array. How many rows are in this array? How many squares in each row?❷

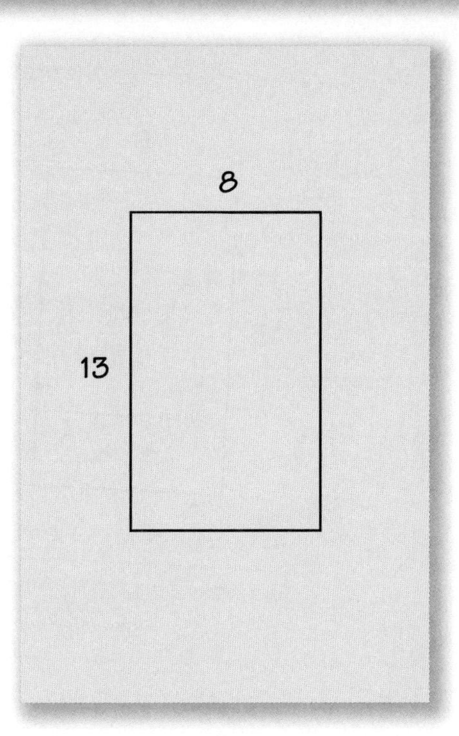

[Richard] says that if we drew in all the squares, there would be 13 rows with 8 squares in each row. You could also think about Ms. Santos's fruit stand. If this were her display of apples, what would it look like?

In the second strategy on the chart, 13 was broken into two parts, 10 and 3, and each part multiplied by 8. Ask students to imagine how these two arrays would look.

Now, how would you break up this array? Draw it on your paper with just the shape and the dimensions, the way I did here. Then break it up to show the different parts of this strategy.

Give students a minute to work on this. Then ask for a volunteer to come up to the chart and show how 10×8 and 3×8 combine to make 13×8.

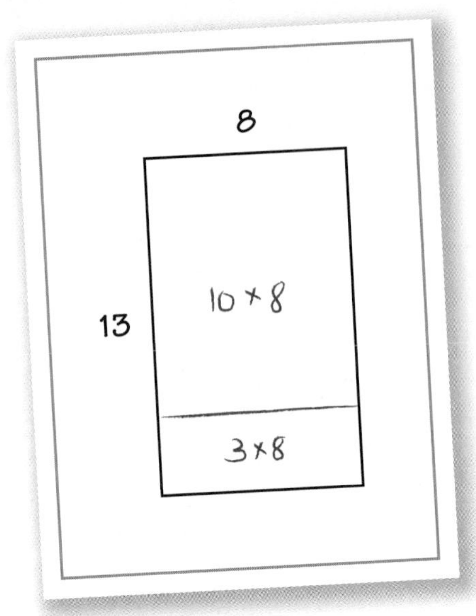

Sample Student Work

If this were a combination of arrays that you could make when playing *Small Array/Big Array,* what equation would you write for this?

Write the equation on the chart below the array.

$$(10 \times 8) + (3 \times 8) = 13 \times 8$$

If you think about Ms. Santos's apples, what part of her display does this 10 × 8 rectangle show? What part does the 3 × 8 rectangle show?

The work that you've been doing with small arrays and big arrays can help you think about these cluster problems, too. Sometimes imagining the solution to a multiplication problem as an array can help you see whether you have all of the parts of the problem.

You might spend a few more minutes on this, asking students for the arrays that represent another solution to 13 × 8. Invite students to choose one of the cluster problems that they solved in their *Student Activity Books* and to use arrays to represent the solution on another sheet of paper.

Breaking up arrays helps students explain how they used cluster problems to solve a final problem.

SESSION FOLLOW-UP

Daily Practice and Homework

Daily Practice: For reinforcement of this unit's content, have students complete *Student Activity Book* page 59.

Homework: On *Student Activity Book* page 60, students find either the missing factor or the missing product in a set of equations. These problems provide both multiplication and division practice with 2-digit numbers. Encourage students to use mental strategies for as many problems as they can.

Student Math Handbook: Students and families may use *Student Math Handbook* page 39 for reference and review. See pages 184–190 in the back of this unit.

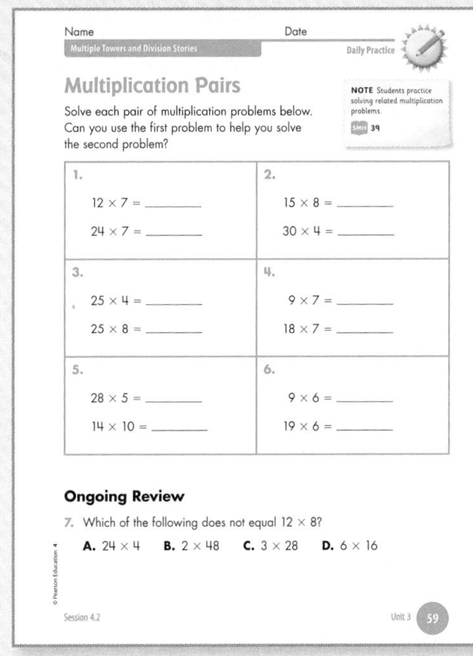

Name Date

Multiple Towers and Division Stories — Daily Practice

Multiplication Pairs

Solve each pair of multiplication problems below. Can you use the first problem to help you solve the second problem?

NOTE Students practice solving related multiplication problems.

SMH 39

1. $12 \times 7 =$ ____ $24 \times 7 =$ ____	2. $15 \times 8 =$ ____ $30 \times 4 =$ ____
3. $25 \times 4 =$ ____ $25 \times 8 =$ ____	4. $9 \times 7 =$ ____ $18 \times 7 =$ ____
5. $28 \times 5 =$ ____ $14 \times 10 =$ ____	6. $9 \times 6 =$ ____ $19 \times 6 =$ ____

Ongoing Review

7. Which of the following does not equal 12×8?

A. 24×4 **B.** 2×48 **C.** 3×28 **D.** 6×16

© Pearson Education 4

Session 4.2 Unit 3 59

▲ Student Activity Book, p. 59

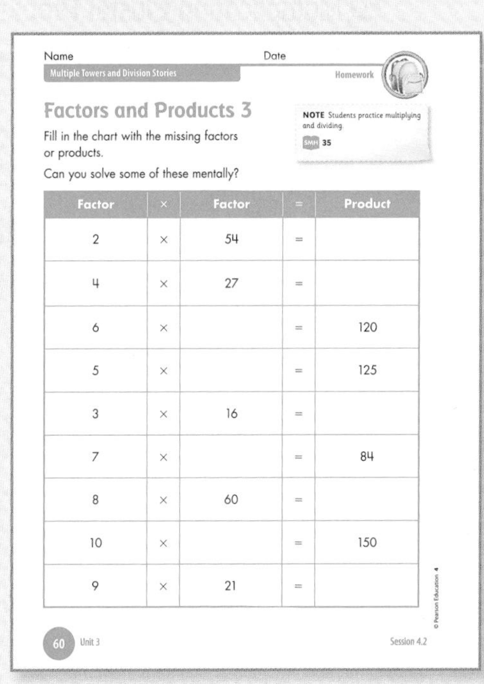

Name Date

Multiple Towers and Division Stories — Homework

Factors and Products 3

Fill in the chart with the missing factors or products.

Can you solve some of these mentally?

NOTE Students practice multiplying and dividing.

SMH 35

Factor	×	Factor	=	Product
2	×	54	=	
4	×	27	=	
6	×		=	120
5	×		=	125
3	×	16	=	
7	×		=	84
8	×	60	=	
10	×		=	150
9	×	21	=	

© Pearson Education 4

60 Unit 3 Session 4.2

▲ Student Activity Book, p. 60

Strategies for Multiplication

Math Focus Points

- Determining the effect on the product when a factor is doubled or halved
- Developing strategies for multiplying that involve breaking apart numbers

Today's Plan		Materials
1 DISCUSSION **Double and Half**	30 MIN, CLASS, PAIRS	• *Student Activity Book,* pp. 53–54 (from Session 4.1) • Connecting cubes (as needed)
2 MATH WORKSHOP **Strategies for Multiplication** 2A Multiplication Cluster Problems 2B More Multiplication Problems 2C Array Card Games	30 MIN	2A • *Student Activity Book,* pp. 57–58 (from Session 4.2) 2B • *Student Activity Book,* pp. 61–62 2C • M40* (from Session 2.3); M45* (from Session 2.4); M17–M37 (from Session 1.2) • Construction paper
3 SESSION FOLLOW-UP **Daily Practice and Homework**		• *Student Activity Book,* pp. 63–64 • *Student Math Handbook,* pp. 39; G8, G10

*See *Materials to Prepare,* p. 123.

Ten-Minute Math

Quick Images: Seeing Numbers Show *Quick Images: Seeing Numbers* (T39), Images 17 and 18, one at a time. For each pattern, ask students to write several different equations to find the total number of dots. For the first two viewings, give students 3 seconds to look at the pattern; the third time, leave the image displayed. Have two or three students explain how they saw the images (including any revisions they made) and their equations, showing how their numbers match the patterns.

1 DISCUSSION

Double and Half

Math Focus Points for Discussion

- Determining the effect on the product when a factor is doubled or halved

Refer students back to their work on Doubles and Halves, *Student Activity Book* page 53. Write the problems from 1c on the board, and spend about 10 minutes discussing doubling one factor in a multiplication expression.

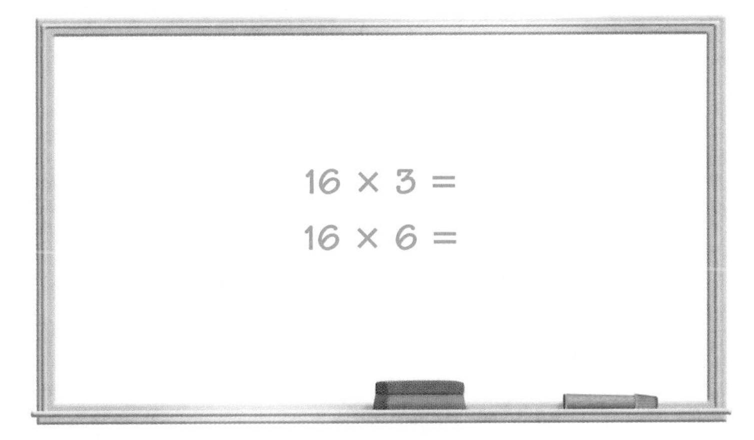

Let's look again at these two problems. How are they related to each other? How are the two answers related?

Collect a few responses that express why the product is doubled when one factor is doubled. Then ask students to share story contexts or representations from their previously completed work that show why this is true.

If no one suggests using an array, introduce the idea yourself by drawing an unmarked array of 16×3 on the board, followed by a divided 16×6 array.

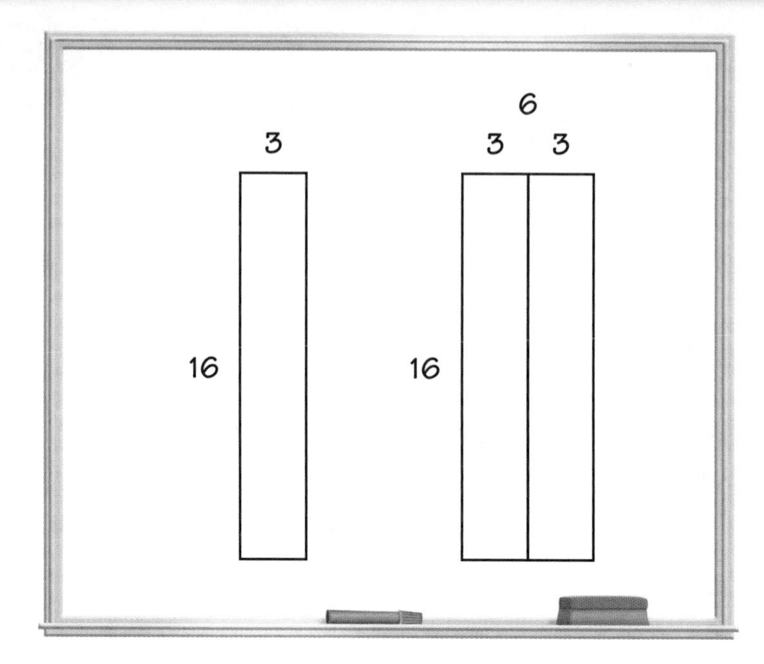

We can use arrays to show how these two problems are related. How much bigger is the 16 × 6 array? Can you find the 16 × 3 array inside the 16 × 6 array?

Introducing a story context can also help students visualize the relationship between 16 × 6 and 16 × 3.

Who can think of a story problem for 16 × 6? . . . [Andrew], you thought of 16 × 6 as 16 bags with 6 marbles in each bag, and you said that there were 96 marbles in all. How could we use [Andrew's] story about marbles to talk about 16 × 3? What would 16 × 3 mean? . . . [Kimberly], you said that it's half. How do you know that it's half? Can you explain that by using the bags of marbles idea?

After about 10 minutes, shift the discussion to doubling one factor and halving another. Direct students' attention to the problems in 1f.

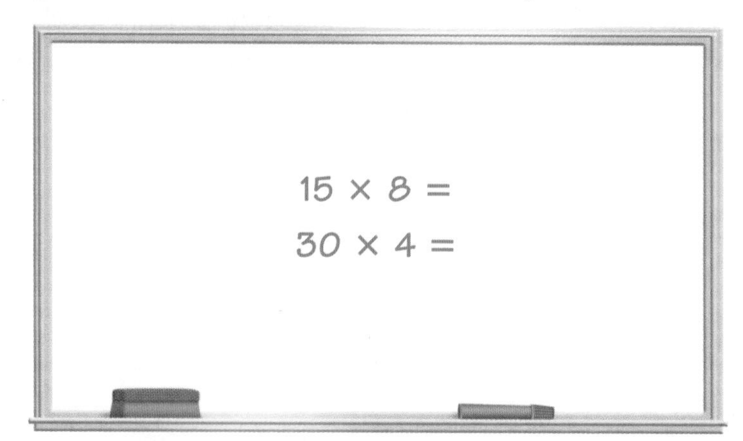

What about these two problems? How did you solve them? . . . [Lucy] says that she solved 15 × 8 by doing 30 × 4 in her head. Would that give her the correct answer?

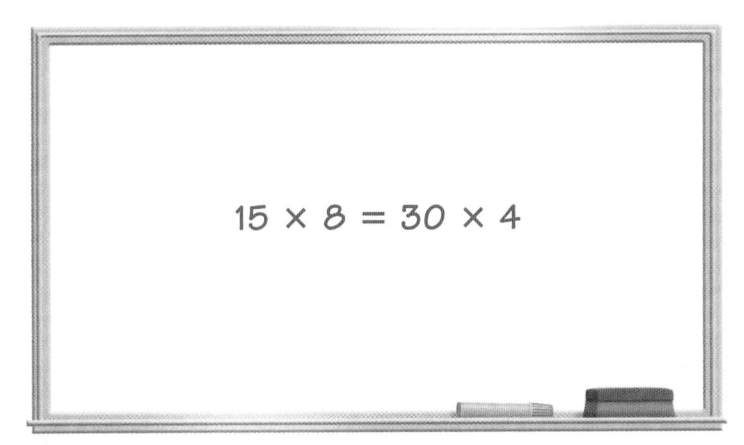

Is this equation true? Why or why not? Talk about this with your partner for a few minutes. You can make drawings, use cubes, or think of a story context to show each other your thinking about why this is or is not true.

Give students a few minutes to discuss this question. Students who chose this problem to represent in their earlier work on *Student Activity Book* page 54 can turn to their representations. As you circulate and listen to them make their arguments, encourage individual students to make representations that support their thinking.

[Tonya], would it help to use an array to show what you mean about cutting the 30 in half?

If students are drawing arrays, remind them that they can make unmarked arrays as you did for the cluster problems in the last session.

[Derek], what do you mean when you say that 15 groups of 8 "turns into" 30 groups of 4? Can you show us using cubes or explain by talking about Ms. Santos's apples?

Bring the class back together for a discussion. Ask other students to share their representations.

Professional Development

➊ **Teacher Note:** Reasoning and Proof in Mathematics, p. 168

Algebra Note

➋ **Creating Equivalent Expressions** Doubling one factor and halving another factor in order to create an equivalent multiplication expression is one case of a more general property of multiplication. In this case, one factor is multiplied by 2 and the other factor is divided by 2. Some students may notice that they can create equivalent expressions in other ways besides doubling and halving. For example, $15 \times 50 = 5 \times 150$: 15 is divided by 3 and 50 is multiplied by 3 to create the equivalent expression 5×150. Another example is $15 \times 50 = 3 \times 250$, using 5 as the number to divide 15 and multiply 50. These strategies are discussed more fully in Algebra Connections in This Unit, page 16.

Many of you are saying that when you double one factor and cut the other in half, the product stays the same. Who can show how this works? Why is it true for 8×15 and 4×30? Is it true for other numbers? How do you know? Does your picture work only for 8×15? Could it work for two other numbers?➊

Sometimes this strategy can be used when you're solving multiplication problems with harder numbers. In this equation, I think 30×4 is easier to solve in my head than 15×8. So when I see 15×8, I might change it to make it easier. Let's try a few more of these together.

Doubling and halving the numbers is often a useful strategy for more difficult problems.

Is there a way you can use doubling and halving to make any of these problems easier to solve? Remember that the idea is to make the problem easier, not harder!➋

Suggest that students try doubling and halving as they work on multiplication during the Math Workshop activities for the rest of this session and the next.

MATH WORKSHOP

Strategies for Multiplication

In this two-day Math Workshop, students solve a variety of multiplication problems (story problems, cluster problems, and "just number" problems). They also revisit the two Array Card games from earlier in the unit, *Missing Factors* and *Small Array/Big Array*. Students should spend time on all three activities.

Watch to see which strategies students are using most effectively at this point in the year. In particular, notice how students are breaking apart 2-digit numbers to make problems easier to solve and whether students can accurately recombine the parts of the problem.

Consider using this first day to check in with individual students. Then, on the second day, you might pull together a small group to work on a few problems, focusing on an aspect of the process that students are having difficulty understanding. By the end of this unit, students should be able to solve 2-digit by 1-digit multiplication problems. Later in the year, they will be revisiting multiplication strategies and working with larger numbers.

2A Multiplication Cluster Problems

INDIVIDUALS

Students continue working on *Student Activity Book* pages 57–58. For complete details about this activity, see Session 4.2, pages 130–131.

DIFFERENTIATION: Supporting the Range of Learners

Intervention For students who are not easily making the connections between the smaller problems and the final one, ask explicit questions about these connections.

- What part of 23 × 4 is 20 × 4?
- How does solving 20 × 4 help you solve 23 × 4?
- What is left for you to solve?

Use a story context, such as Ms. Santos's apples, to talk through the problem.

Let's say that we need to pack 23 boxes with 4 apples in each box. Which multiple of 4 do you know that can help you figure out the number of apples we need? How many apples would be in 10 boxes? In 20 boxes?

2B More Multiplication Problems

INDIVIDUALS

On *Student Activity Book* pages 61–62, students solve story problems as well as "just number" multiplication problems.

Encourage students to use equations and to identify their answers as they show their solutions. Students may also draw unmarked arrays and diagrams to visualize the groups in some of the problems. At this point

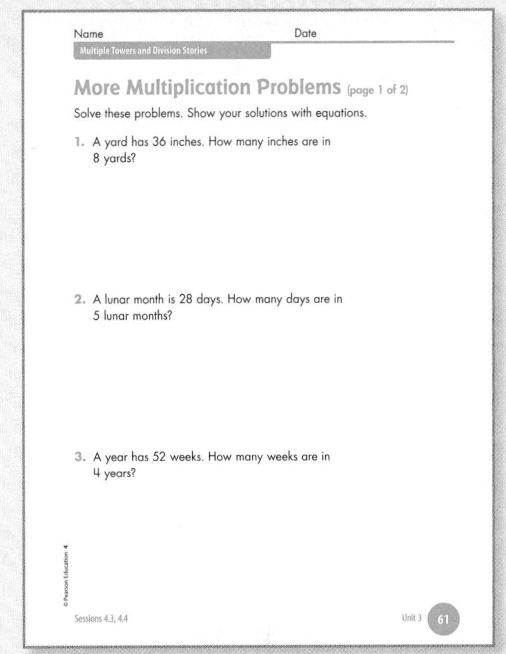

Name Date

Multiple Towers and Division Stories

More Multiplication Problems (page 1 of 2)

Solve these problems. Show your solutions with equations.

1. A yard has 36 inches. How many inches are in 8 yards?
2. A lunar month is 28 days. How many days are in 5 lunar months?
3. A year has 52 weeks. How many weeks are in 4 years?

© Pearson Education 4

Sessions 4.3, 4.4 Unit 3 61

▲ Student Activity Book, p. 61

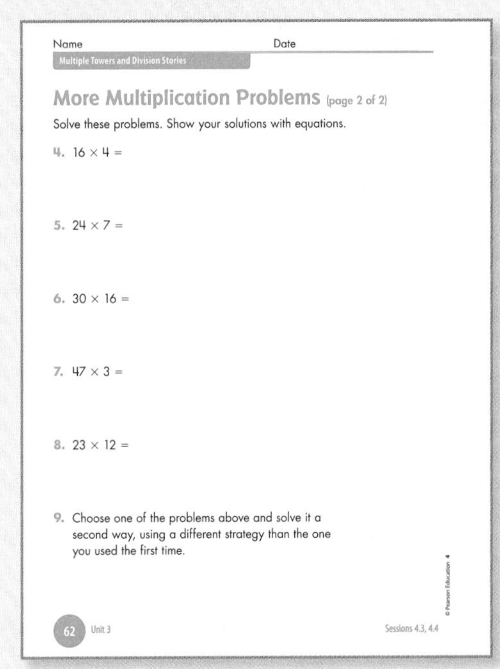

Name Date

Multiple Towers and Division Stories

More Multiplication Problems (page 2 of 2)

Solve these problems. Show your solutions with equations.

4. 16 × 4 =
5. 24 × 7 =
6. 30 × 16 =
7. 47 × 3 =
8. 23 × 12 =
9. Choose one of the problems above and solve it a second way, using a different strategy than the one you used the first time.

© Pearson Education 4

62 Unit 3 Sessions 4.3, 4.4

▲ Student Activity Book, p. 62

in fourth grade, however, students should not be relying on exact representations to solve the problem, drawing every object in each group and counting them or adding them all up.

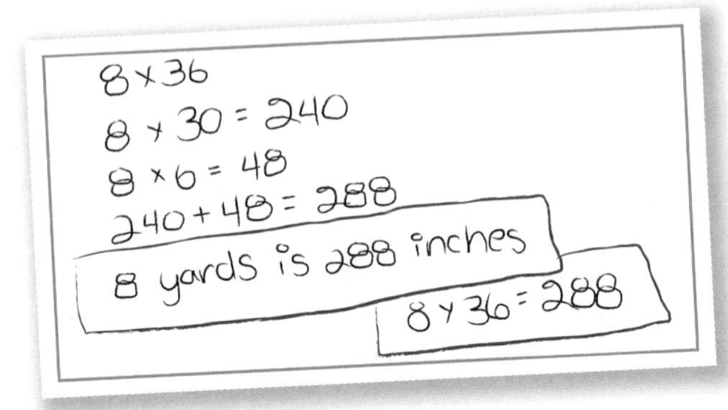

Sample Student Work

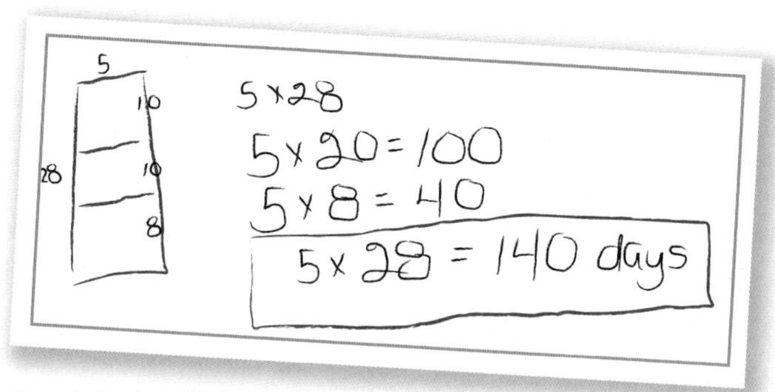

Sample Student Work

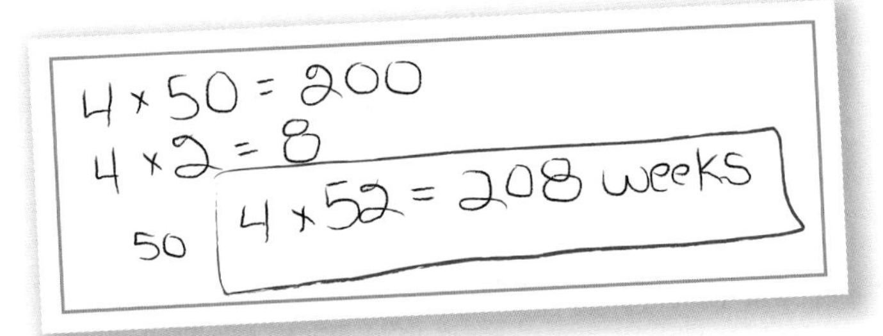

Sample Student Work

ONGOING ASSESSMENT: Observing Students at Work

Students develop and practice strategies for solving problems with 2-digit numbers.

- **How are students breaking apart these 2-digit numbers to make the problems easier to solve?** Do they break the numbers apart by place value? Do they use other familiar number relationships (e.g., breaking 16 into 12 + 4 because students know combinations of 12)?

- **Do students accurately recombine all parts of the problem to get the final product?**
- **Do students use doubling and halving to create an easier equivalent problem?**

As you observe students working on these problems, ask questions that focus on how students are breaking apart the numbers.

- Why did you decide to break apart the numbers this way? Did that give you two problems that you could solve easily?
- What number relationships do you know that can help you decide how to break apart these numbers?

Look for a variety of strategies for Problem 2 (28×5) that would be useful to bring up in the discussion at the end of Session 4.4. Ask students to be prepared to talk with the whole class about their strategies.

2C Array Card Games

PAIRS

Students choose either *Small Array/Big Array* or *Missing Factors* to play with a partner. You may help students decide which game to play, judging from what they need to work on most. Students who are practicing the multiplication combinations should play *Missing Factors,* and students who are developing ideas about breaking apart numbers should play *Small Array/Big Array.* However, all students can benefit from spending more time playing both of these games in order to strengthen their understanding of multiplication and division.

For complete details about *Small Array/Big Array,* see Session 1.3, pages 43–44.

For complete details about *Missing Factors,* see Session 2.4, page 80.

3 SESSION FOLLOW-UP

Daily Practice and Homework

Daily Practice: For ongoing review, have students complete *Student Activity Book* page 63.

Homework: On *Student Activity Book* page 64, students use the problems in the cluster to solve 7×34.

Student Math Handbook: Students and families may use *Student Math Handbook* pages 39, G8, and G10 for reference and review. See pages 184–190 in the back of this unit.

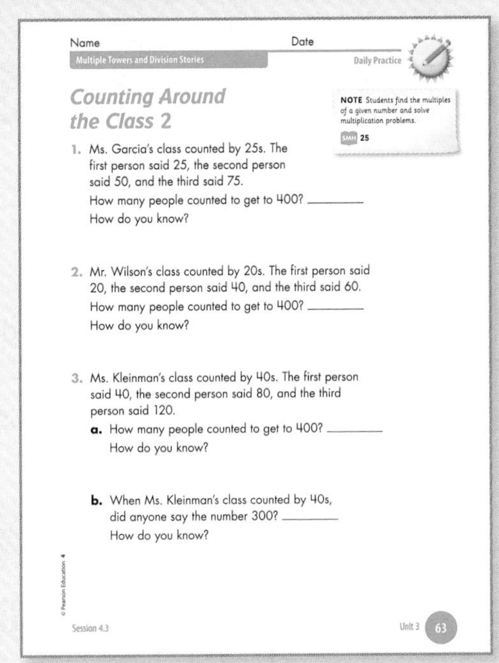

Name Date

Multiple Towers and Division Stories — Daily Practice

Counting Around the Class 2

NOTE Students find the multiples of a given number and solve multiplication problems. SMH 25

1. Ms. Garcia's class counted by 25s. The first person said 25, the second person said 50, and the third said 75.
   How many people counted to get to 400? ______
   How do you know?
2. Mr. Wilson's class counted by 20s. The first person said 20, the second person said 40, and the third said 60.
   How many people counted to get to 400? ______
   How do you know?
3. Ms. Kleinman's class counted by 40s. The first person said 40, the second person said 80, and the third person said 120.
   a. How many people counted to get to 400? ______
   How do you know?
   b. When Ms. Kleinman's class counted by 40s, did anyone say the number 300? ______
   How do you know?

Session 4.3 Unit 3 63

▲ Student Activity Book, p. 63

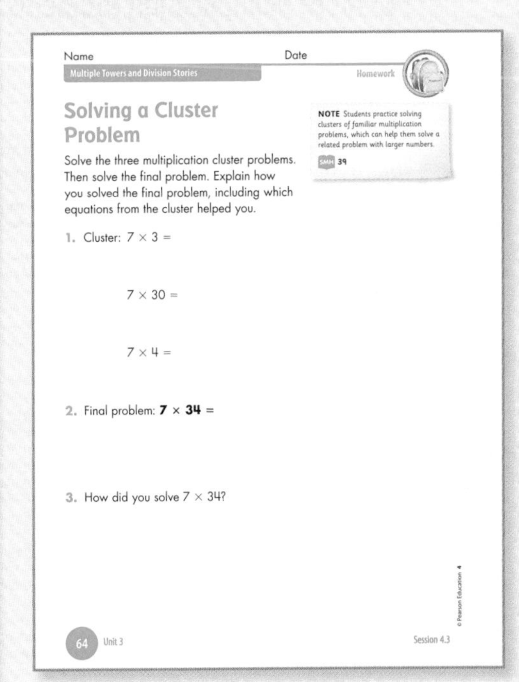

Name Date

Multiple Towers and Division Stories — Homework

Solving a Cluster Problem

NOTE Students practice solving clusters of familiar multiplication problems, which can help them solve a related problem with larger numbers. SMH 39

Solve the three multiplication cluster problems. Then solve the final problem. Explain how you solved the final problem, including which equations from the cluster helped you.

1. Cluster: $7 \times 3 =$
   $7 \times 30 =$
   $7 \times 4 =$
2. Final problem: $\mathbf{7 \times 34 =}$
3. How did you solve 7×34?

64 Unit 3 Session 4.3

▲ Student Activity Book, p. 64

Strategies for Multiplication, *continued*

Math Focus Points

- Determining the effect on the product when a factor is doubled or halved
- Developing strategies for multiplying that involve breaking apart numbers

Today's Plan		Materials
1 MATH WORKSHOP **Strategies for Multiplication** 1A Multiplication Cluster Problems 1B More Multiplication Problems 1C Array Card Games	40 MIN	1A • *Student Activity Book,* pp. 57–58 (from Session 4.2) 1B • *Student Activity Book,* pp. 61–62 (from Session 4.3) 1C • M40* (from Session 2.3); M45* (from Session 2.4); M17–M37 (from Session 1.2 • Construction paper (1 sheet per pair)
2 DISCUSSION **Comparing Our Strategies**	20 MIN CLASS	• *Student Activity Book,* p. 61 (from Session 4.3)
3 SESSION FOLLOW-UP **Daily Practice**		• *Student Activity Book,* p. 65 • *Student Math Handbook,* pp. 39–43; G8, G10

*See *Materials to Prepare,* p. 123.

Ten-Minute Math

Counting Around the Class **Ask questions about a class that is counting by 60s.** When the class finished counting, the last number was 1,200. How many students are in that class? What number did the 6th person say? What number did the 9th person say? **Collect answers as well as explanations about how students found their answer.**

MATH WORKSHOP

40 MIN

Strategies for Multiplication

Students continue to solve a variety of multiplication problems. Make sure that everyone completes *Student Activity Book* page 61 (Activity 1B) because the class will be discussing their work on Problem 2 during the last 20 minutes of this session.

1A Multiplication Cluster Problems

INDIVIDUALS

Students work on *Student Activity Book* pages 57–58. For complete details about this activity, see Session 4.2, pages 130–131.

1B More Multiplication Problems

INDIVIDUALS

Students work on *Student Activity Book* pages 61–62. For complete details about this activity, see Session 4.3, pages 141–142.

1C Array Card Games

PAIRS

Students choose one of two familiar Array Card games to play with a partner.

For complete details about *Small Array/Big Array,* see Session 1.3, pages 43–44.

For complete details about *Missing Factors,* see Session 2.4, pages 80–81.

Missing Factors *provides ongoing practice with multiplication and division combinations to* 12×12 *(*$144 \div 12$*).*

DISCUSSION

2 Comparing Our Strategies

Math Focus Points for Discussion

- Developing strategies for multiplying that involve breaking apart numbers

Bring the class together to discuss their work on *Student Activity Book* page 61, Problem 2. Refer to your observation notes and call on those students that you identified to share their strategies with the class. Strategies should include the following:

- Breaking the numbers apart by place
  $(20 \times 5) + (8 \times 5)$
- Breaking the numbers apart in some other way
  $(25 \times 5) + (3 \times 5)$
- Creating an equivalent problem that is easier to solve
  $(28 \times 5 = 14 \times 10)$

As you record the equation for each strategy, ask the other students to consider how that strategy compares to the one that they used.

Enrique's Strategy	Jill's Strategy
28 = 20 + 8	28 × 2 = 56
20 × 5 = 100	28 × 4 = 112 (56 + 56 = 112)
8 × 5 = 40	
100 + 40 = 140	112 + 28 = 140

Did anyone solve the problem the same way that Enrique did, by breaking the 28 apart into 20 and 8? Did anyone break the 28 apart differently?

[Jill], it looks like you broke the 5 apart instead of the 28. First you multiplied two 28s, which made it easy to multiply four 28s, and then you added one more 28. Did anyone else think of it the same way as [Jill] did?

After several strategies have been recorded, ask the class to consider them all and discuss similarities and differences. Referring back to the context of the problem—days in a lunar month—can help students hold on to a visual image of what's happening in each of these strategies.

Remember that the problem was about 5 groups of 28, if we think of each lunar month as a group of 28 days. Where are these 5 groups, or 5 months, in [Enrique's] strategy? Where are the 5 groups in [Jill's] strategy?❶

Let students know that they will continue to practice, examine, and compare their strategies for multiplication as their fourth-grade year goes on. They will revisit all of these ideas in the unit *How Many Packages? How Many Groups?* later in the year.

Teaching Note

❶ **Discussing Strategies** Determining similarities and differences in their strategies can be a challenging task for fourth graders because it is often difficult for them to articulate what they are noticing. In the examples given here, Enrique keeps the 5 groups, but adds together 5 groups of 20 and 5 groups of 8. Jill has broken the 5 groups into 2 groups, plus 2 more groups, plus 1 more group. They have each chosen a different factor to break apart. In both cases, all the groups are accounted for, which is a fundamental multiplication concept, based on the distributive property.

3 SESSION FOLLOW-UP
Daily Practice

Daily Practice: For ongoing review, have students complete *Student Activity Book* page 65.

Student Math Handbook: Students and families may use *Student Math Handbook* pages 39–43 and G8, G10 for reference and review. See pages 184–190 in the back of this unit.

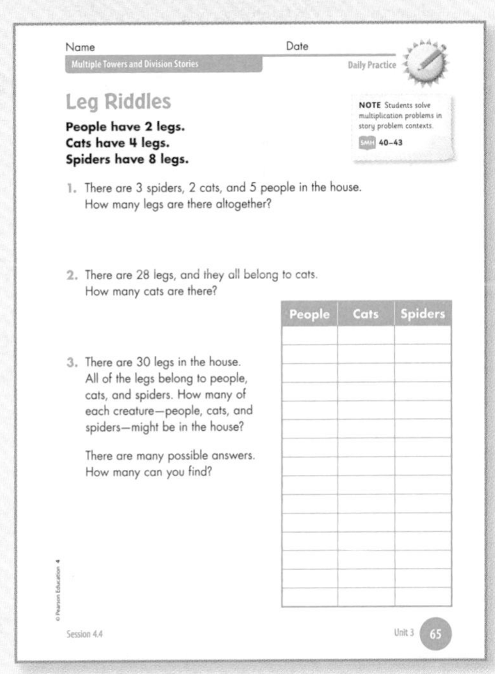

Name Date

Multiple Towers and Division Stories — Daily Practice

Leg Riddles

People have 2 legs.
Cats have 4 legs.
Spiders have 8 legs.

NOTE Students solve multiplication problems in story problem contexts.

SMH 40–43

1. There are 3 spiders, 2 cats, and 5 people in the house. How many legs are there altogether?

2. There are 28 legs, and they all belong to cats. How many cats are there?

3. There are 30 legs in the house. All of the legs belong to people, cats, and spiders. How many of each creature—people, cats, and spiders—might be in the house?

   There are many possible answers. How many can you find?

People	Cats	Spiders

© Pearson Education 4

Session 4.4 Unit 3 65

▲ Student Activity Book, p. 65

End-of-Unit Assessment

Math Focus Points

- Solving division problems by making groups of the divisor
- Using known multiplication combinations to solve division problems
- Developing strategies for multiplying that involve breaking apart numbers

Today's Plan	Materials
1 ASSESSMENT ACTIVITY **End-of-Unit Assessment** 60 MIN INDIVIDUALS	• M51–M52*
2 SESSION FOLLOW-UP **Daily Practice**	• *Student Activity Book*, p. 66 • *Student Math Handbook,* pp. 39–43, 50–52

*See *Materials to Prepare*, p. 123.

Ten-Minute Math

Counting Around the Class **Ask questions about a class that is counting by 75s.** When the class finished counting, the last number was 1,500. How many students are in that class? What number did the 5th person say? What number did the 11th person say? **For each question, collect answers as well as explanations about how students found their answer.**

1 ASSESSMENT ACTIVITY
End-of-Unit Assessment

60 MIN INDIVIDUALS

This End-of-Unit Assessment (M51–M52) addresses four of the five benchmarks for this unit.❶

Problems 1 and 2 ask students to solve multiplication problems, one involving a multiple of 10 (23×6 and 17×20). These problems address Benchmark 1: Multiply 2-digit numbers by 1-digit and small 2-digit numbers (e.g., 12, 15, 20), using strategies that involve breaking the numbers apart; and Benchmark 4: Multiply by 10 and by multiples of 10.

Problem 3 asks students to solve a division problem with a remainder ($91 \div 8$) and to create a story context to represent that problem. This problem addresses Benchmark 2: Solve division problems (2-digit and small 3-digit numbers divided by 1-digit numbers), including some that result in a remainder; and Benchmark 3: Use story problems, pictures, or concrete models to represent division situations.

Students work individually to solve the three assessment problems. Remind students to use story contexts and visual representations to help them understand and solve each problem.

Most students will not need the entire 60 minutes to complete this assessment. When they finish, suggest that students quietly return to the Math Workshop activities from previous sessions in this unit or to any unfinished work.

DIFFERENTIATION: Supporting the Range of Learners

Intervention If some students are unclear about what they are to figure out, help them by restating the problem.

- Problem 1 is asking you to figure out how many there are in 6 groups of 23.
- For Problem 2, can you picture 17 boxes of oranges? Inside each box are 20 oranges. How many oranges are there in all of the boxes together?

If some students have an answer but are having trouble writing their strategy, encourage them to explain their thinking aloud. Help them choose words, mathematical expressions, and images to put their thoughts in writing.

Professional Development

❶ Teacher Note: End-of-Unit Assessment, p. 173

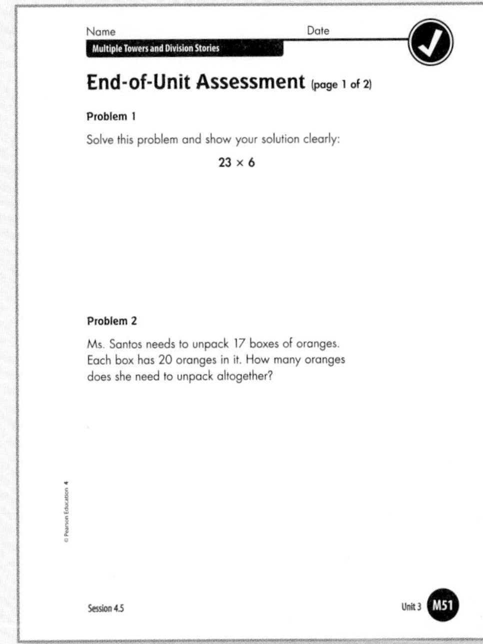

Name Date

Multiple Towers and Division Stories

End-of-Unit Assessment (page 1 of 2)

Problem 1

Solve this problem and show your solution clearly:

23×6

Problem 2

Ms. Santos needs to unpack 17 boxes of oranges. Each box has 20 oranges in it. How many oranges does she need to unpack altogether?

© Pearson Education 4

Session 4.5 Unit 3 M51

▲ Resource Masters, M51

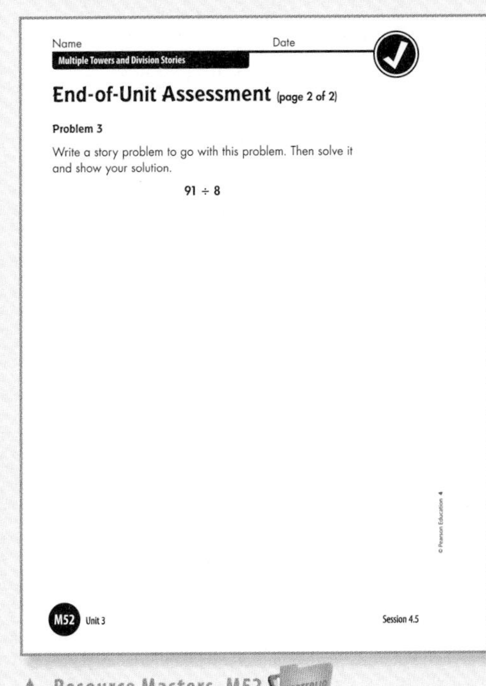

Name Date

Multiple Towers and Division Stories

End-of-Unit Assessment (page 2 of 2)

Problem 3

Write a story problem to go with this problem. Then solve it and show your solution.

$91 \div 8$

© Pearson Education 4

M52 Unit 3 Session 4.5

▲ Resource Masters, M52

Name Date

Multiple Towers and Division Stories

Daily Practice

Sunken Treasure

NOTE Students solve division problems in a real-world context.

SMH 50–52

Solve the problems. Use another sheet of paper if you need to. Show equations, pictures, and diagrams. Decide what to do with any extras.

1. These are gold coins found at the site of a shipwreck. If a scuba diver could carry 18 of these coins to the surface in one trip, how many trips would it take to carry 108 coins?
2. If a scuba diver could carry 36 coins to the surface in one trip, how many trips would it take to carry 108 coins?
3. If five scuba divers found a total of 108 coins and were allowed to share them equally, how many coins would each scuba diver get?
4. If the five scuba divers were allowed to share only half of the 108 coins, how many coins would they each get?

66

▲ Student Activity Book, p. 66

Some students need ongoing support in learning to record their strategies for themselves.

SESSION FOLLOW-UP

2 Daily Practice

Daily Practice: For enrichment, have students complete *Student Activity Book* page 66. This page provides real-world problems involving the math content of this unit.

Student Math Handbook: Students and families may use *Student Math Handbook* pages 39–43, 50–52 for reference and review. See pages 184–190 in the back of this unit.

UNIT 3

Multiple Towers and Division Stories

Teacher Notes

In Part 6 of *Implementing Investigations in Grade 4,* you will find a set of Teacher Notes that addresses topics and issues applicable to the curriculum as a whole rather than to specific curriculum units. They include the following:

Computational Fluency and Place Value

Computational Algorithms and Methods

Representations and Contexts for Mathematical Work

Foundations of Algebra in the Elementary Grades

Discussing Mathematical Ideas

Racial and Linguistic Diversity in the Classroom: What Does Equity Mean in Today's Math Classroom?

Dialogue Boxes

Learning and Assessing Multiplication Combinations

Students began working on the multiplication combinations in Grade 3, learning combinations with products to 50. They continued on to the rest of the combinations (to 12×12) in the first Grade 4 unit, *Factors, Multiples, and Arrays.* In this unit, students practice and review multiplication combinations to 12×12 as homework, making use of these combinations as they solve multiplication problems in class. The goal is for all students to become fluent with multiplication combinations by the end of this unit. To meet this goal, however, some students will need additional practice during the unit, and some will need continuing practice after the unit is completed. This Teacher Note provides recommendations for supporting students in this ongoing practice.

Why Do We Call Them *Combinations*?

The pairs of factors from 1×1 through 12×12 are traditionally referred to as "multiplication facts"—those multiplication combinations with which students are expected to be fluent. The *Investigations* curriculum follows the National Council of Teachers of Mathematics (NCTM) convention of calling these expressions *combinations* rather than *facts. Investigations* does this for two reasons. First, naming *only* particular addition and multiplication combinations as *facts* seems to give them elevated status, more important than other critical parts of mathematics. In addition, the word *fact* implies that something cannot be learned through reasoning. For example, it is a fact that the first president of the United States was George Washington, and it is a fact that Rosa Parks was born in Alabama in 1913. If these facts are important for us to know, we can remember them or use reference materials to look them up. However, the product for the multiplication combination 6×7 can be determined in many ways; it is logically connected to our system of numbers and operations. If we forget the product, but understand what multiplication is and know some related multiplication combinations, we can find the product through reasoning. For example, if we know that $5 \times 7 = 35$, we can add one more 7 to determine that the product of 6×7 is 42. If we know that $3 \times 7 = 21$, we can reason that the product of 6×7 would be twice that, $2 \times (3 \times 7) = 42$.

The term *facts* does convey a meaning that is generally understood by some students and family members, so you will need to decide whether to use the term *facts* along with *combinations* in certain settings in order to make your meaning clear.

Fluency with Multiplication Combinations

Like NCTM, this curriculum supports the importance of students learning the basic combinations through a focus on reasoning about number relationships: "Fluency with whole-number computation depends, in large part, on fluency with basic number combinations—the single digit addition and multiplication pairs and their counterparts for subtraction and division. Fluency with basic number combinations develops from well-understood meanings for the four operations and from a focus on thinking strategies. . . ." (*Principles and Standards for School Mathematics*, pages 152–153)

Fluency means that combinations are quickly accessible mentally, either because they are immediately known or because the calculation that is used is so effortless as to be essentially automatic (in the way that some adults quickly derive one combination from another).

Helping Students Learn the Multiplication Combinations

A. Students Who Know Their Combinations to 50

Students who know their combinations to 50, as well as the combinations that involve multiplying by 10 up to 100 (6×10, 7×10, 8×10, 9×10, 10×10), can work on learning the most difficult combinations. Here is one way of sequencing this work.

1. Learning the remaining combinations with products to 100. There are 6 difficult facts to learn (other than the $\times 11$ and $\times 12$ combinations, which are, in fact, not as difficult as these, and are discussed below). These six difficult combinations are: 6×9 (and 9×6), 7×8 (and 8×7), 7×9 (and 9×7), 8×8, 8×9 (and 9×8), and 9×9. Note that knowing that multiplication is commutative is crucial for learning all the multiplication combinations. The work with Array Cards supports this understanding. See **Teacher Note:** Representing Multiplication with Arrays, page 117, Unit 1 in *Factors, Multiples, and Arrays.*

Students can work on one or two of these most difficult multiplication combinations each week. Make sure that they use combinations they do know to help them learn ones they don't know—for example, $8 \times 7 = 2 \times (4 \times 7)$, or $9 \times 7 = (10 \times 7) - 7$. They can write these related multiplication combinations as "start with" hints on the Multiplication Cards. If most of your class needs to work on the same few hard combinations, you might want to assign the whole class to focus on two of these each week.

2. Learning the ×11 and ×12 combinations. We consider these combinations to be in a different category. Historically, these combinations were included in the list of "multiplication facts." However, when we are dealing with 2-digit numbers in multiplication, an efficient way to solve them is through applying the distributive property, breaking the numbers apart by place as you would with any other 2-digit numbers. We include them here because some local or state frameworks still require knowing multiplication combinations through 12×12. In addition, 12 is a number that occurs often in our culture, and it is useful to know the $\times 12$ combinations fluently. Most students learn the $\times 11$ combinations easily because of the pattern (11, 22, 33, 44, 55, . . .) created by multiplying successive whole numbers by 11. They should also think through why this pattern occurs: $3 \times 11 = (3 \times 10) + (3 \times 1) = 30 + 3 = 33$. They should think through why $11 \times 10 = 110$ and $11 \times 11 = 121$ by breaking up the numbers. Students can learn the $\times 12$ combinations by breaking the 12 into a 10 and 2, e.g., $12 \times 6 = (10 \times 6) + (2 \times 6)$. Some students may also want to use doubling or adding on to known combinations: $12 \times 6 = 2 \times (6 \times 6)$, or $12 \times 6 = (11 \times 6) + 6$.

B. Students Who Need Review and Practice of Combinations to 50

Students who have difficulty learning the multiplication combinations often view this task as overwhelming—an endless mass of combinations with no order and reason. Bringing order and reason to students' learning of these combinations in a way that lets them have control over their progress is essential. Traditionally, students learned one "table" at a time (e.g., first the $\times 2$ combinations, then the $\times 3$ combinations, the $\times 4$ combinations, and so on). However, the multiplication combinations can be grouped in other ways to support learning related combinations.

First, make sure that students know all multiplication combinations that involve $\times 0$, $\times 1$, $\times 2$, $\times 5$, and $\times 10$ (up to 10×10) fluently. (Students worked with the $\times 0$ combinations in Grade 3.) Note that, although most fourth graders can easily count by 2, 5, and 10, the student who is fluent does not need to skip count to determine the product of multiplication combinations involving these numbers.

When students know these combinations, turn to those that they have not yet learned. Provide a sequence of small groups of combinations that students can relate to what they already know. There are a number of ways to do this.

1. Learning the ×4 combinations. Work on the ×4 combinations that students do not yet know: 3×4, 4×4, 6×4, 7×4, 8×4, and 9×4. Help students think of these as doubling the ×2 combinations. So, $4 \times 6 = (2 \times 6) + (2 \times 6)$, or $4 \times 6 = 2 \times (2 \times 6)$. Students may verbalize this idea as "4 times 6 is 2 times 6 and another 2 times 6," or "to get 4 times 6, I double 2×6." Doubling is also useful within the ×4 combinations; for example, when students know that $3 \times 4 = 12$, then that fact can be used to solve 6×4: $6 \times 4 = (3 \times 4) + (3 \times 4)$. Getting used to thinking about doubling with smaller numbers will also prepare students for using this approach with some of the harder combinations.

2. Learning the square numbers. Next, students learn or review the four remaining combinations that produce square numbers less than 50: 3×3, 5×5, 6×6, and 7×7. These are often easy for students to remember. If needed, use doubling or a known combination for "start with" clues during practice (e.g., 6×6 is double 3×6; 5×5 is 5 more than 4×5). Students can also build these combinations with tiles or draw them on grid paper to see how they can be represented by squares.

3. Learning the remaining combinations with products to 50. Finally, learn or review the six remaining combinations with products to 50: 3×6 through 3×9, 7×6, and 8×6. First, relate them to known combinations (e.g., double 3×3 or halve 6×6 to get 3×6), and then practice them.

Assessing Students' Knowledge of Multiplication Combinations

In Investigation 3 of this unit, students are assessed on their fluency with the multiplication combinations. For this assessment, students are expected to be able to solve 30 problems that are representative of the set of combinations to 12×12, with accuracy, in three minutes. If they can solve them all within that time limit, students are either accessing these combinations from memory or they are able to make a very quick calculation that is almost automatic. Some students may take longer than others to reach this level of fluency. You can expect to have students in your class who may need to do this assessment more than once. They will continue to identify combinations they still need to work on and will practice those with their Multiplication Cards. These students may also use Array Cards for practice, either by laying them out factor side up and identifying the products or by playing *Missing Factors*. You may have other favorite practice methods or activities that you want to suggest for particular students. Also, enlist parents or other family members to help with this practice.

In this unit, students also begin to work on division problems that are counterparts to the multiplication combinations. They will continue to work on these in the next multiplication and division unit, *How Many Packages? How Many Groups?* In the meantime, as students work on solving division problems, help them relate division expressions to the multiplication combinations they know; for example, what multiplication combination can help you solve $24 \div 6$?

Fluency Benchmarks for Learning Facts Through the Grades

Addition: Fluent by end of Grade 2, with review and practice in Grade 3

Subtraction: Fluent by end of Grade 3, with review and practice in Grade 4

Multiplication: Fluent with multiplication combinations with products to 50 by the end of Grade 3; up to 12×12 by the middle of Grade 4, with continued review and practice

Division: Fluent by end of Grade 5

Teacher Note

Visualizing Arrays

In order to use rectangular arrays to visualize breaking up a multiplication problem, students must be able to see that the lengths of the sides of the rectangle represent factors, and the area represents the product. Evidence from research and practice indicates that fully understanding this relationship takes time and experience. As adults, we are so familiar with the relationship between the area of a rectangle and the length of its sides that we may not realize that the relationship is not necessarily obvious to students.

As students are learning to visualize how a rectangular array represents multiplication, they use arrays that show all the individual units of the area. Students can describe the area in terms of the dimensions of the rectangle. For example, in this rectangle, there are 8 rows with 12 squares in each row.

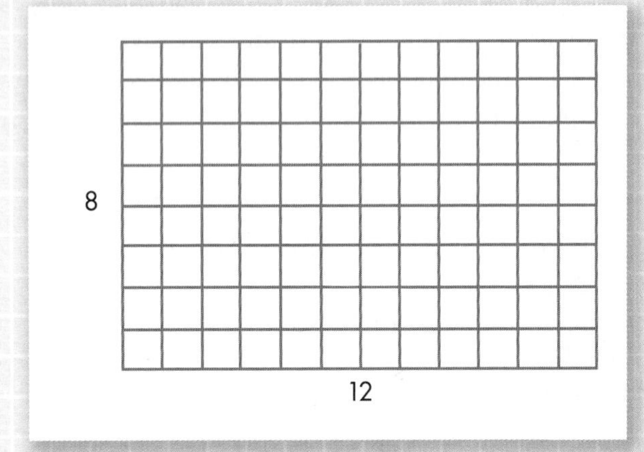

In order to help students visualize a rectangular array to represent any multiplication problem, you will introduce unmarked arrays (arrays without a grid of units) in Investigation 1. Thus, for the problem 8×12, you can draw an unmarked array like this:

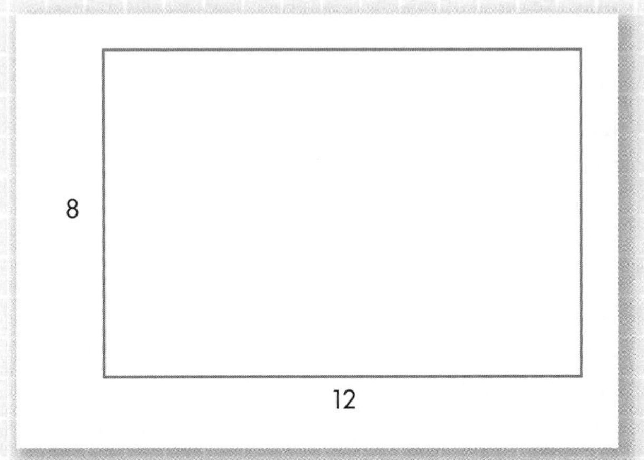

Students can use the unmarked array to help them think through the ways they might break up the array to help them solve the problem.

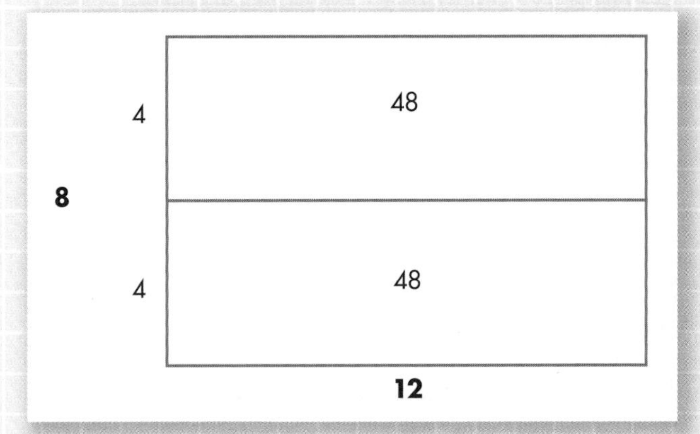

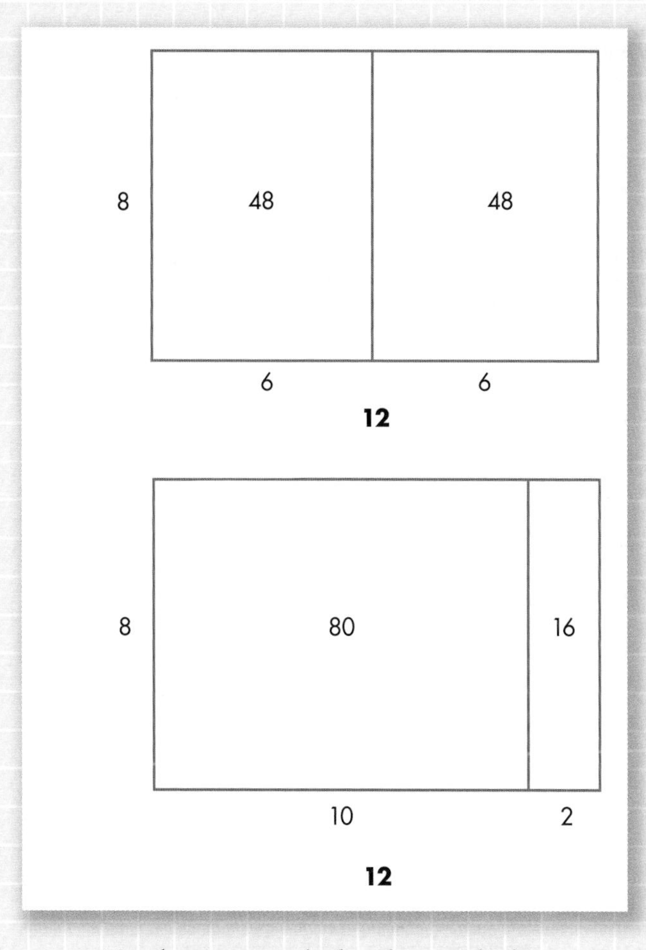

As a transition between marked and unmarked arrays, you can add tick marks along two sides of the rectangle.

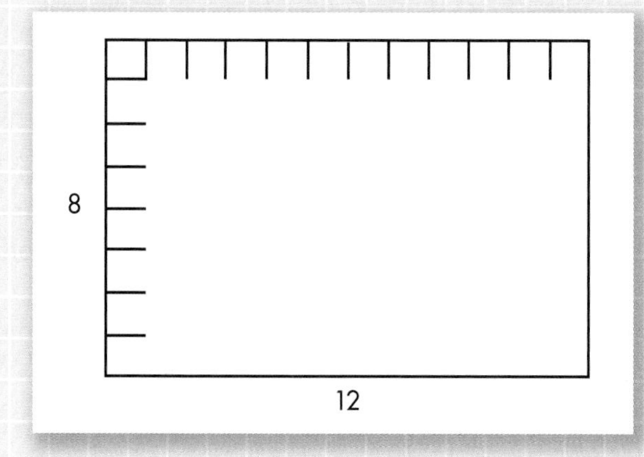

At first, you should present unmarked arrays with sides drawn to fairly closely represent the relative proportion of the numbers in the multiplication expression, as in the first array for 8 × 12 above. Students are learning to use and visualize arrays, so using correct proportions in the diagram helps some students visualize how the array represents multiplication. Eventually, when students are more confident about sketching an unmarked array to help them think through how to solve a problem, you and your students may sketch the arrays without trying to be as accurate about showing the relative length of the sides.

It is essential that students thoroughly understand how an array represents a multiplication (or division) expression before they use an unmarked array to solve problems. For a multiplication expression such as 8 × 12, they must be able to explain where the 8 is in the representation, where the 12 is, and why the area of the rectangle is the product of these two numbers.

Teacher Note

Playing *Small Array/Big Array*

The Array Card game *Small Array/Big Array* has a complex set of rules that become familiar through practice. It is important that you play this game yourself ahead of time to ensure that you understand it thoroughly and can help students as they learn to play. See *Small Array/Big Array* (M38–M39) for full directions.

Sample Game

Here's an example of a demonstration game that a teacher and student played to help the class learn the rules. This demonstration version uses only 3 center cards. Here are the center cards at the beginning of the game:

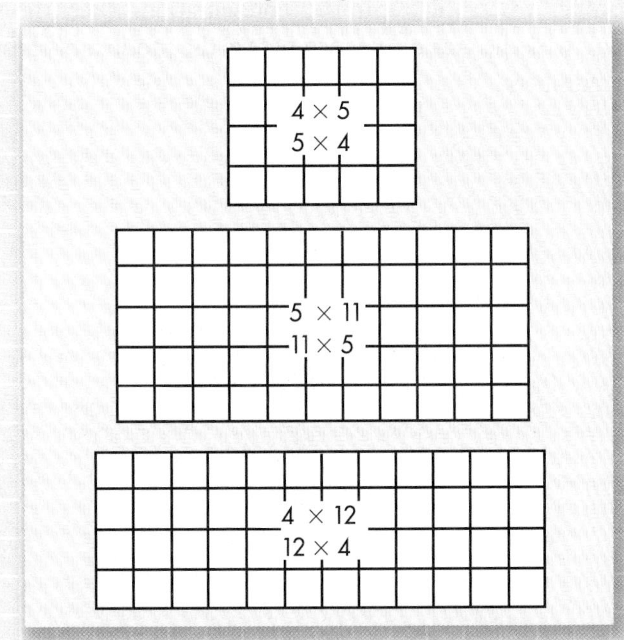

Round 1

Player A (teacher) has a 4 × 7 array among her set of cards. She matches it to the 4 × 12 center card.

Player B (student) has a 3 × 11 array in his set of 10 cards. He matches it to the 5 × 11 center card.

Round 2

Player A doesn't have any more cards with dimensions that match the center cards. She puts the 4 × 5 card from the center onto the 4 × 12 array, completing this match. She collects the match and records it as follows:

1. $4 \times 12 = (4 \times 7) + (4 \times 5)$
   $48 = 28 + 20$

Player A discards one of her cards, 3 × 10, to the center, to replace the 4 × 5 center card that she used. Because she also collected a match on this turn, she draws the top card from the deck, 2 × 8, and replaces the big array that she collected, keeping 3 cards in the center.

Now the cards in the center are:

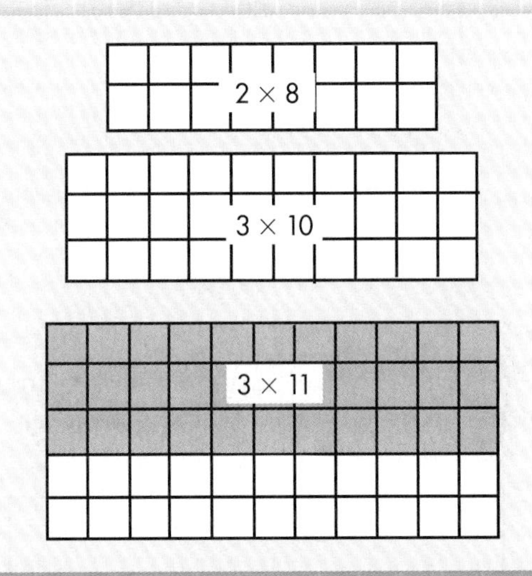

Player B has a 1 × 11 array, which he places on the 5 × 11 array in the center. He recognizes that only a 1 × 11 array can complete the 5 × 11 array. Because there is not another 1 × 11 Array Card in the set, the match is counted as complete. Player B collects this match and records it. The 5 × 11 center card is replaced by a card from the pile.

Common Incorrect Moves

In this game, each small array played on a big array must have one dimension in common with the big array. After one dimension of the big array has been matched, the next array cards played *must match that same dimension.* One way to help students think about this is to say that each new array card must match one of the sides completely.

A common incorrect move occurs when students do not follow this rule. For example, in this game, one player has placed her 3×12 array on top of an 8×12 array in the center, using the common side length of 12. The next player fits his 5×5 array in part of the remaining space, leaving a space that can be filled with a 5×7 array.

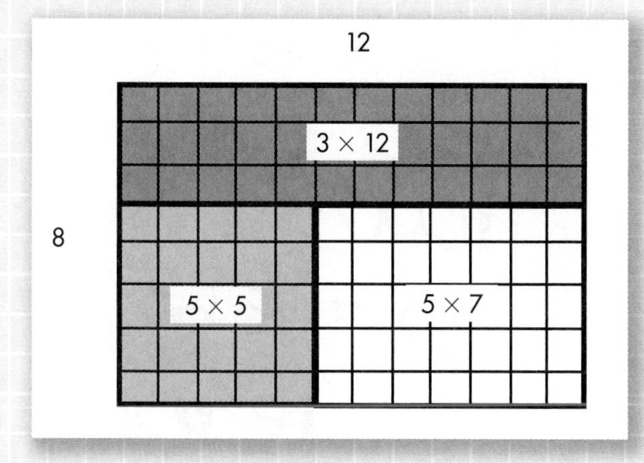

An equation that describes this *Small Array/Big Array* match is

$$8 \times 12 = (3 \times 12) + (5 \times 5) + (5 \times 7)$$

Although the equation is correct mathematically, this arrangement of small arrays is not as helpful for students at this stage. Students need to think through how they can apply the distributive property of multiplication to solve the problem. In later work on more difficult multiplication problems, students will break up both of the numbers in the problem. However, in this unit, breaking up both dimensions can weaken the connection between the array model and students' ideas about multiplication as involving equal groups.

Keeping one dimension common in the big array and its matching small arrays helps students visualize ways to break up one of the numbers in a multiplication problem. For example, if an array has 8 rows with 12 units in each row, students can find the number of squares by first finding how many are in 3 of those groups and then finding how many are in the remaining 5 groups, or 8 groups altogether: $8 \times 12 = (3 \times 12) + (5 \times 12)$. A story context can also be connected to the rectangular array: "I need 8 dozen bagels, but the bagel shop has only 3 dozen left. So I buy those and then go to the supermarket to buy 5 dozen more." Although it is possible to modify this story context so that it can be represented by the more complex equation—$8 \times 12 = (3 \times 12) + (5 \times 5) + (5 \times 7)$—the connection is much more convoluted. For these reasons, it is important to emphasize the rule that one dimension of each small array must match the same dimension of the big array.

Below is another typical incorrect play. In this case, even though the small array 6×4 does have one side that matches a dimension of the big array, the card is placed so that the two sides of 6 are not parallel.

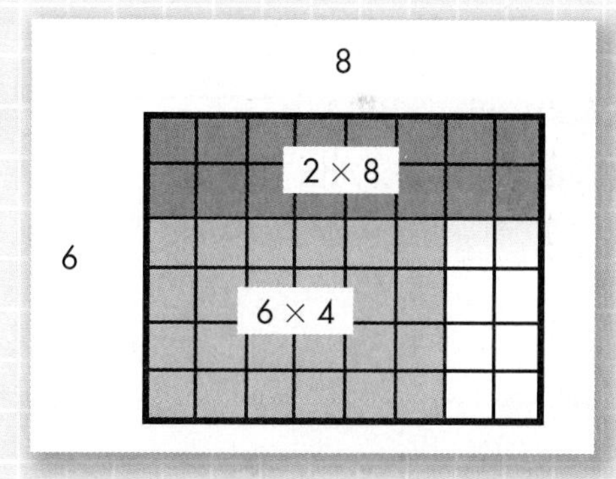

It is likely that as they play, students will need reminders about matching one full dimension of the arrays.

Teacher Note

Assessment: Solving 18 × 7

Problems 1 and 2

Benchmark addressed:

Benchmark 1: Multiply 2-digit numbers by 1-digit and small 2-digit numbers (e.g., 12, 15, 20), using strategies that involve breaking the problems apart.

In order to meet the benchmark, students' work should show that they can:

- Break apart the problem in a reasonable way in order to create problems that can be easily solved (see examples that follow).
- Accurately solve each smaller problem.
- Accurately combine the products of each smaller problem.
- Represent their solutions by dividing the array of 18 × 7 and accurately labeling the smaller arrays that are created.

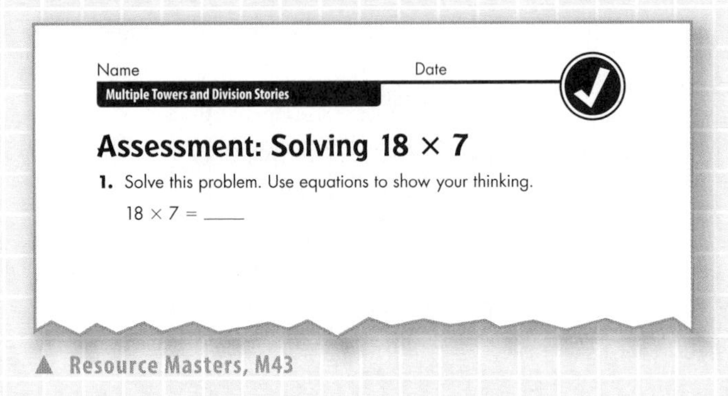
Name Date
Multiple Towers and Division Stories
Assessment: Solving 18 × 7
1. Solve this problem. Use equations to show your thinking.
18 × 7 = ____

▲ Resource Masters, M43

Meeting the Benchmark

Students who meet the benchmark may break apart the problem in a variety of ways, as shown in the examples that follow. All of these students solve all parts of the problem accurately, combine the parts, and represent their thinking clearly.

Cheyenne broke 18 apart by place value.

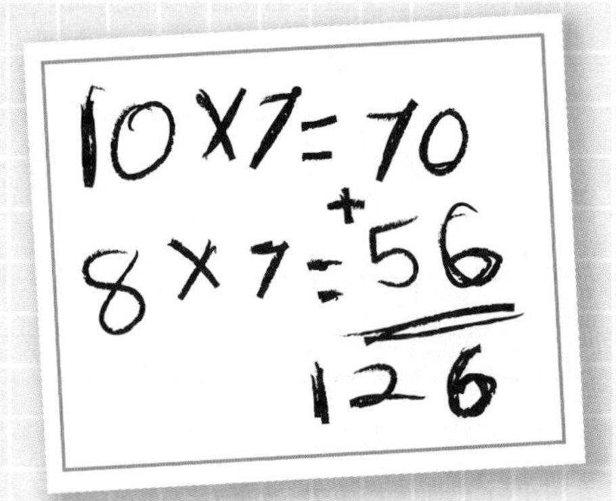

Cheyenne's Work

Yuki broke the problem apart in the same way and drew this array to represent his solution.

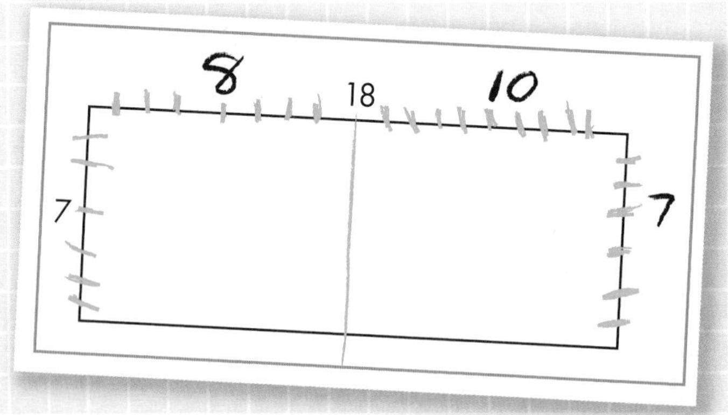

Yuki's Work

Helena broke 18 in half.

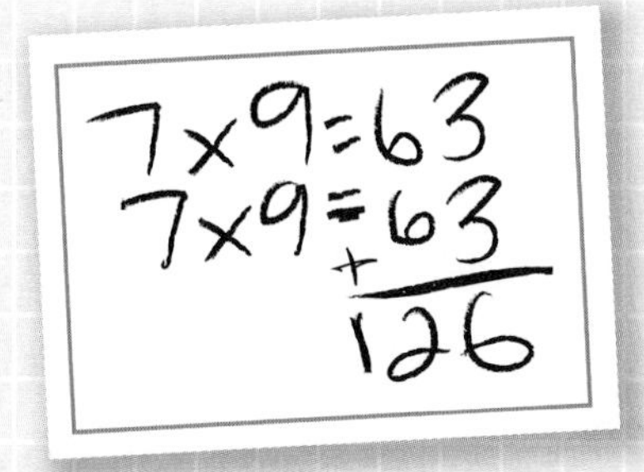

Helena's Work

Both Helena and Cheyenne use clear and concise notation to show their work.

This is Nadeem's array for the same strategy Helena used.

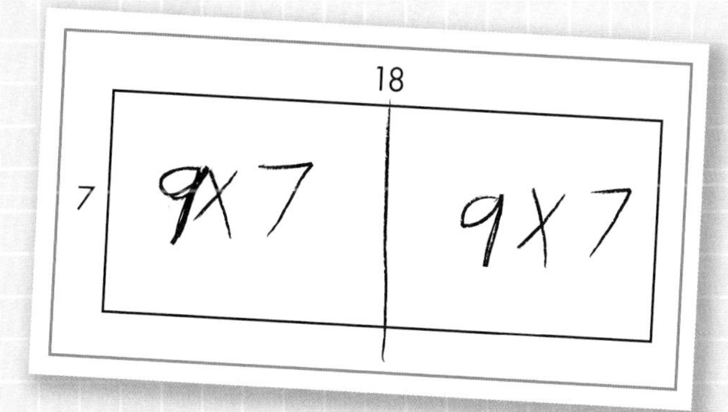

Nadeem's Work

Derek knew some multiples of 18. He broke the 7 apart to create two problems that he knew how to solve.

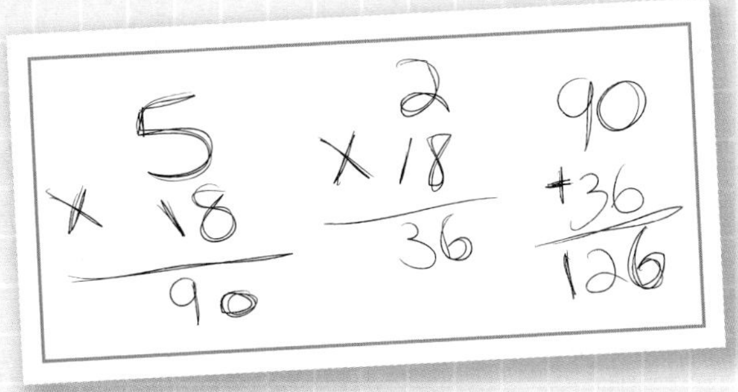

Derek's Work

Partially Meeting the Benchmark

Some students may break apart the problem correctly, but make errors in computation. For example, Anna used Cheyenne's strategy but incorrectly solved 8×7 as 63, probably confusing the product of 8×7 with the product of 9×7. She needs to review any multiplication combinations that she does not know.

Other students may be able to easily and correctly solve the problem but may not be able to represent their solution accurately on the array of 18×7. It is not necessary that students use arrays as their primary means of visualizing multiplication relationships, but they should be able to make sense of this representation. Have these students use Array Cards to construct a variety of array combinations for 18×7, and then ask students how they can match these arrays to different ways of breaking apart the problem.

Not Meeting the Benchmark

Sometimes a student breaks apart a problem in a way that does not help solve it. For example, Bill broke 18×7 into 18×3 and 18×4 but had difficulty solving either of these smaller problems. He seems to know that he should break up one factor of the problem, but does not know why he is doing so or how to follow through and solve the problem. For a student like Bill, check first that the student can interpret the multiplication expression by creating a story context for it. Then determine whether the student can, from that context, think of a multiplication combination related to the problem.

If some students are *not* breaking apart one of the factors in order to solve a problem of this size (for example, they are adding 18 seven times or drawing tally marks and counting), continue to work with them throughout this unit on such activities as *Small Array/Big Array* and on solving multiplication problems by breaking apart one of the factors. Use story contexts to help students identify the part of the problem that has been solved and the part that remains.

Two Kinds of Division: Sharing and Grouping

In this unit, students encounter two kinds of division situations. Consider these two problems.

I have 18 balloons for my party. After the party is over, I'm going to divide them evenly between my sister and me. How many balloons will each of us get?

I have 18 balloons for my party. I'm going to tie them together in bunches of 2 to give to my friends. How many bunches can I make?

Each of these problems is a division situation—a quantity is broken up into equal groups. The problem and the solution for each situation can be written in standard notation as $18 \div 2 = 9$. These two situations are actually quite different, however. In the first situation, the number of groups of balloons is given. The question is this: How many balloons will be in each group? In the second situation, the number of balloons in each group is given, and the question is this: How many groups will there be? Each problem involves equal groups of balloons, but the results of the actions look different.

I have 18 balloons and 2 people. How many balloons for each person?

I have 18 balloons to put into bunches of 2. How many bunches?

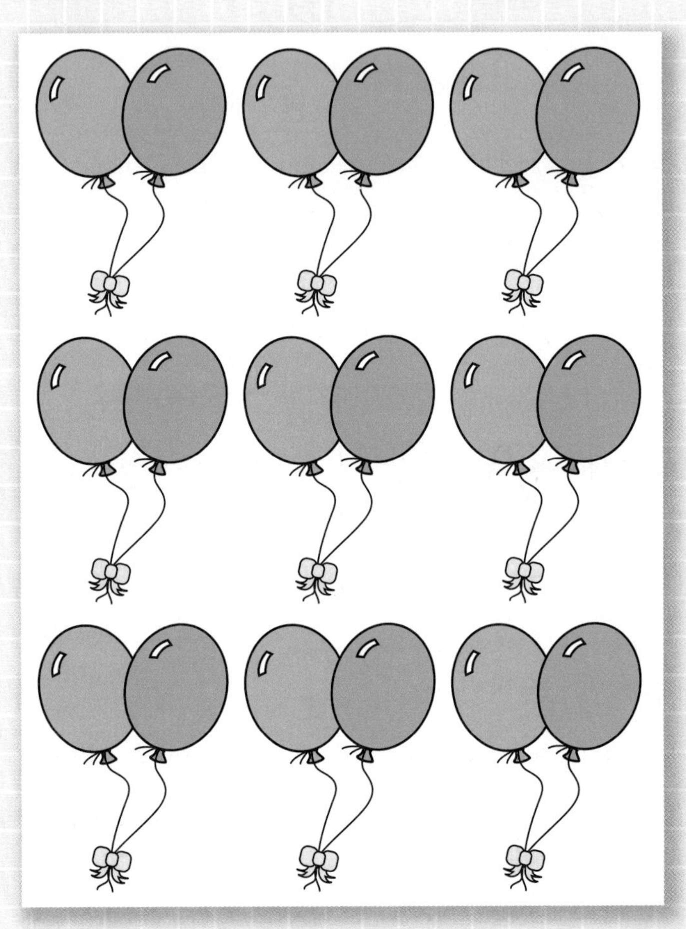

The solution to each problem is 9, but in the first problem, 9 is the number of balloons per person (the number in each group). In the second problem, 9 is the number of bunches of balloons (the number of groups).

The first situation is probably the one with which your students are most comfortable because it can be solved by dealing out. That is, the action to solve the problem might be as follows: one for you, one for me, one for you, one for me, until all the balloons are given out. In this situation, division is used to describe *sharing.* A more formal term for this kind of problem is *partitive* division—a division situation in which something is distributed and the problem is to determine *how many are in each group.*

In the second situation, the action to solve the problem is making groups—that is, making a group of 2, then another group of 2, and another, and so on, until no balloons are left. In this situation, division is used to describe *grouping.* This situation is sometimes called *measurement division* because the total amount is measured out into equal groups. The formal term for this kind of division situation is *quotative* division—a problem in which the question is *how many equal groups* can be made.

By working with a variety of problems in this unit, students learn to recognize both of these actions as division situations and to develop an understanding that both can be written in the same way: $18 \div 2 = 9$. Depending on the context, help students interpret the notation as either of these questions: If 18 is divided into 2 groups, how many are in each group? or How many groups of 2 are in 18?

As students become more flexible with division, they will understand that they can solve a sharing problem by thinking of it as grouping, or a grouping problem by thinking of it as sharing—whichever way makes it easier to solve. Here is an example:

How many people are on each team if I make 25 equal teams from 100 people?

To solve this problem, it is easy to think, "How many groups of 25 are in 100?" even though the problem is not about groups of 25, but about 25 groups. The numerical answer to this grouping question is also the numerical answer to the sharing problem. Some of your students may soon have an intuitive understanding that they can solve a division problem by thinking about it either way. Students can draw on what they know about multiplication—that 4 teams of 25 is the same number of people as 25 teams of 4 ($4 \times 25 = 25 \times 4$). This understanding is based on the commutative property of multiplication.

Teacher Note

What Do You Do with the Remainders?

Depending on the situation or context of a division problem, remainders affect the solution to the problem in a variety of ways. Consider the following problems involving $44 \div 8$ and the ways that students look at the remainder in each context.

There are 44 people taking a trip in some small vans. Each van holds 8 people. How many vans do they need?

Andrew: There are 5 vans with 4 people left. You can't leave any people behind, and you can't take half a van, so you'd need 6 vans to take everyone.

If 8 people share 44 crackers equally, how many crackers does each person get?

Ramona: Each person can get 5 crackers. Keep 4 crackers for another day. $44 \div 8 = 5$ crackers per person with 4 extras.

Steve: Each person can get $5\frac{1}{2}$ crackers. $44 \div 8 = 5\frac{1}{2}$.

If 8 people share 44 balloons equally, how many balloons does each person get?

Venetta: Each person gets 5 balloons. They can't split the four balloons left over, so they will have to decide what to do with them. Maybe they could give them to their teacher. 44 divided by 8 equals 5 with 4 balloons left over.

There are 44 students going to see a movie. Each row holds 8 people. How many rows do they fill up?

Derek: There are 40 people who will fill up 5 rows. Then 4 people have to sit in row 6. 44 divided by 8 equals 5 rows, with 4 more people in another row.

Noemi: You will fill up 5 rows and half of another row. $44 \div 8 = 5\frac{1}{2}$ or 5.5.

On Sunday, 8 friends earned $44 by washing people's cars. They want to share the money equally. How much does each person get?

Emaan: First, each person gets $5. That uses up $40. Then you can split the $4 that's left and give each person $0.50, so each person gets $5.50.

Each of these problems involves dividing 44 by 8. If the problem is presented numerically, the quotient can be written as 5 R4 or $5\frac{1}{2}$ or 5.5. If the problem is given in a context, however, the context determines the answer. Some division problems require whole number solutions, as in the contexts about vans and balloons. Notice that in the van problem, the whole number answer must be greater than the actual numerical quotient, and in the balloon problem, the whole number answer is less than the numerical quotient. In other contexts, a solution can involve fractions or decimals.

By solving problems such as these, students learn to consider the remainder in the context of the problem and to give a solution that makes sense for that problem.

The Relationship Between Multiplication and Division

Multiplication and division are related operations. For example, here is a set of linked multiplication and division equations.

$8 \times 3 = 24$ $3 \times 8 = 24$

$24 \div 8 = 3$ $24 \div 3 = 8$

After students have become fluent with multiplication combinations to 12×12, they can use these to solve related division equations (sometimes refered to as "division facts") by considering which factor pairs equal a given product. Students often think of a problem such as $24 \div 3 = \_\_\_\_$ as a "missing factor" problem. Using the relationship between multiplication and division, they transform $24 \div 3 = \_\_\_\_$ into $3 \times \_\_\_\_ = 24$. Then they use the multiplication combinations they know to solve the problem: "3 groups of what equal 24? I know that's 3 times 8. So 24 divided by 3 is 8."

The multiplication equations show the multiplication of two factors to equal a product. The division equations show that product divided by one of the factors to equal the other factor. Some problem situations that your students encounter in this unit can be described as both multiplication and division.

For example:

I have a supply of 336 treats for my dog. If I give her 14 treats every week, how many weeks will the supply last?

The quantities in this problem are 336 treats, 14 treats per week, and a number of weeks to be determined. This problem can be written in standard notation as either multiplication or division.

$336 \div 14 = \_\_\_\_$ or $\_\_\_\_ \times 14 = 336$

After the answer to the problem has been found, both division and multiplication equations can be written to show the relationship of the three quantities.

336 treats divided into groups of 14 (14 treats per week) results in 24 groups (weeks):

$$336 \div 14 = 24$$

14 per group (14 treats per week) in 24 groups (weeks) equals 336 treats:

$$24 \times 14 = 336$$

When students solve a problem like this one, they might write either a division equation or a multiplication equation to express the answer and its relationship to the quantities in the problem. Both notations represent the problem, depending on whether the student is thinking of the problem as a division problem or as a multiplication problem with a missing factor. Students should be able to read and interpret both of these notations, explaining what each number in the equation represents and relating the equation to the original problem.

Assessment: Writing and Solving a Division Problem

Problem 1

Benchmark addressed:

Benchmark 3: Use story problems, pictures, or concrete models to represent division situations.

In order to meet the benchmark, students' work should show that they can:

- Understand division as splitting a quantity into equal groups;
- Write a story problem in which 104 is divided into groups of 8 or into 8 groups, with a corresponding question about either the number of groups or the number in each group.

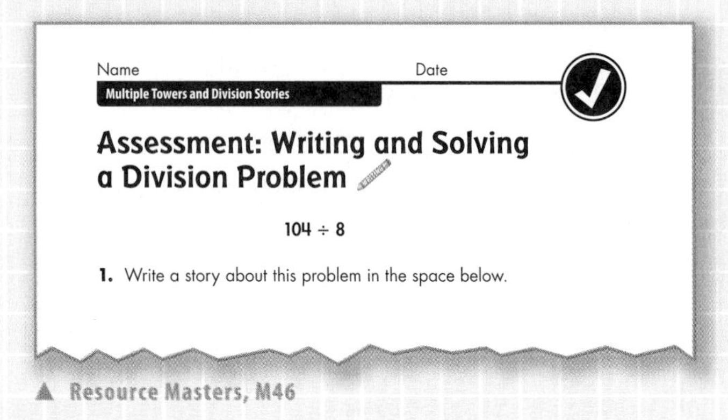
Name Date

Multiple Towers and Division Stories

Assessment: Writing and Solving a Division Problem

104 ÷ 8

1. Write a story about this problem in the space below.

▲ Resource Masters, M46

Meeting the Benchmark

At this point in fourth grade, students should be able to represent 104 ÷ 8 as a story problem.

For example, Nadeem wrote:

"There are 104 kids at the school field day. They are making teams of 8 for the games. How many teams do they make?"

Amelia wrote:

"There are 8 girls and they want to share 104 jelly beans. How many jelly beans will each girl get?"

Problem 2

Benchmark addressed:

- **Benchmark 2:** Solve division problems (2-digit and small 3-digit numbers divided by 1-digit numbers), including some that result in a remainder. **Note:** The problem in this assessment does not involve a remainder, but the End-of-Unit Assessment does include a problem with a remainder.

In order to meet the benchmark, students' work should show that they can:

- Accurately solve 104 ÷ 8 and give a correct answer in terms of the problem context;
- Use strategies that involve making groups of the divisor (for example, using known multiplication combinations such as $5 \times 8 = 40$ or $10 \times 8 = 80$) or efficiently dividing parts of the dividend (for example, 80 ÷ 8 and 24 ÷ 8).

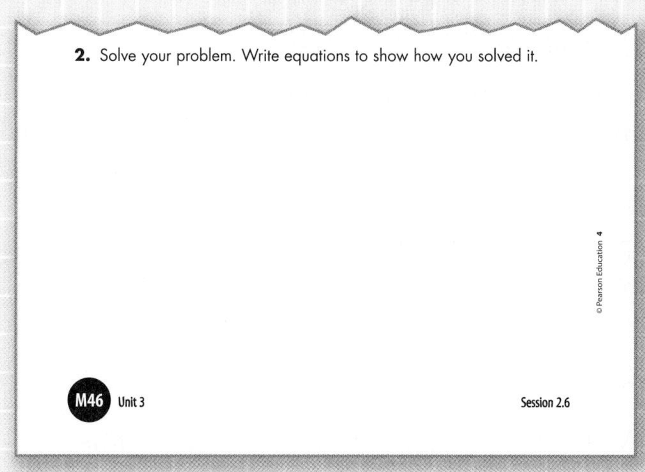
2. Solve your problem. Write equations to show how you solved it.

© Pearson Education 4

M46 Unit 3 Session 2.6

▲ Resource Masters, M46

Meeting the Benchmark

Sabrina broke the dividend (104) into 10 groups of 8 plus 3 groups of 8.

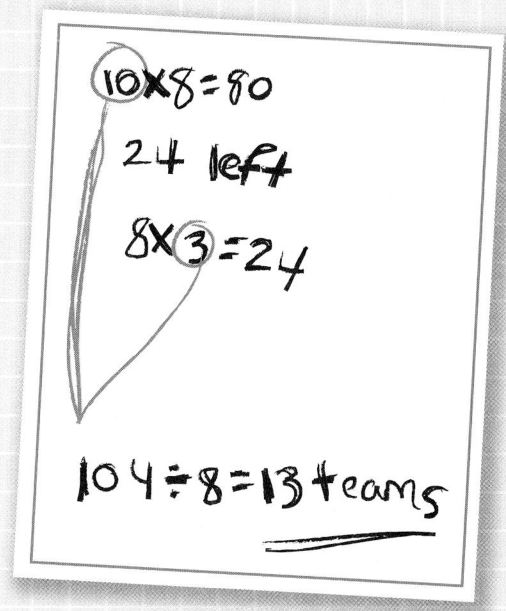

Sabrina's Work

Jill used the known combination 12 × 8 to solve this problem.

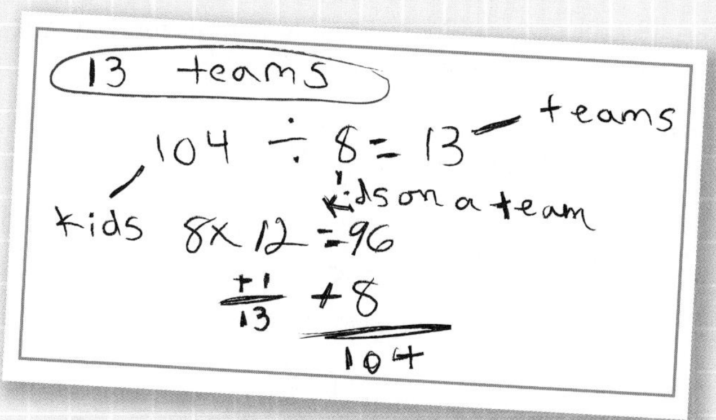

Jill's Work

Notice how Jill carefully labels each number to correspond with her context.

Although using multiplication to solve division problems is stressed in Investigation 2, some students break up the dividend and divide each part by the divisor. For example, Marisol thought of the problem this way:

$$104 \div 8 = (80 \div 8) + (24 \div 8)$$
$$= 10 + 3 = 13$$

Partially Meeting the Benchmark

Students who partially meet the benchmark recognize the groups of the divisor in the dividend but solve the problem in a less efficient way, by skip counting or listing all of the combinations involving 8 until they reach 104, for example.

Luke, for example, skip counted to determine the number of 8s in 104.

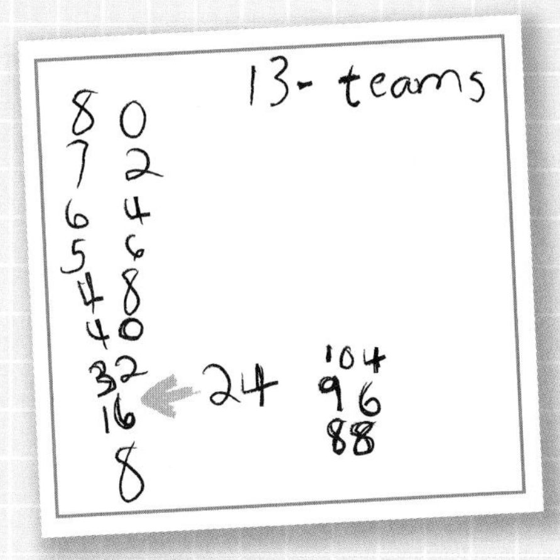

Luke's Work

Steve listed the multiplication combinations for 8 in order.

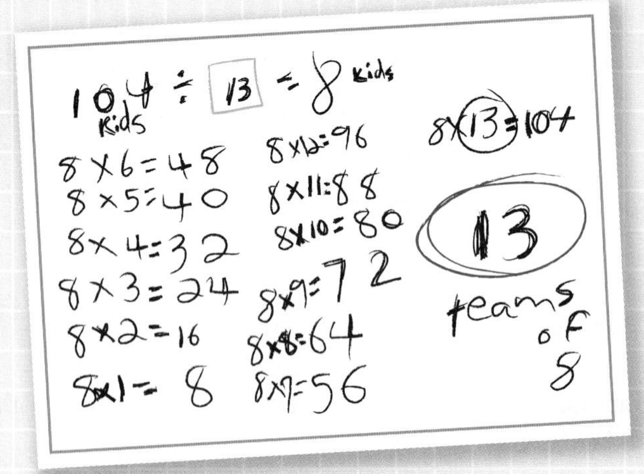

Steve's Work

Continue to work with students like these to help them move to a more efficient use of groups of the divisor. For example, tell them: "I see you counted by 8 [or, wrote the combinations involving 8] to figure out the number of 8s in 104. Is there a multiplication combination with 8 as a factor that will get you part of the way there? Do you know 5 × 8 or 10 × 8? How could these combinations help you?"

Some students use efficient strategies but make minor computation errors. Help these students find ways to double-check their work.

Not Meeting the Benchmark

Students who are directly modeling the problem with tallies, marks, or objects and counting these objects do understand something about division but do not meet the benchmark at this point in fourth grade. Ask these students questions to help them see the groups of 8 in the representations they made and to connect these groups to known combinations. These students may need to do some or all of the following:

- Work on their multiplication combinations
- Work on division problems with smaller numbers to develop the idea of removing groups of the divisor
- Use story contexts to talk through the concept of division as removing groups of groups

Multiplying by Multiples of 10

One of the traditional mathematical "tricks" that help with hard multiplication was this "rule": When you multiply by 10, just add a 0; when you multiply by 100, add two 0s; and so on. Many students notice that when they multiply a multiple of 10 such as 6×40, they can "ignore" the 0, multiply the other digits (in this case, $6 \times 4 = 24$), and then "add a 0" to get an answer to the original problem. In this unit, students consider what "adding a 0" means and why it works. Although this pattern is a very useful one, it is critical that students grasp the underlying mathematical relationships in order to develop a solid understanding of multiplying by multiples of 10.

Our number system is based on powers of 10: ones, tens, hundreds, thousands, and so forth. The value of a digit in each place in a number in this system is 10 times greater than the value of the same digit to its right.

$8 \times 1 = 8$ ones $= 8$

$8 \times 10 = 8$ tens $= 80$

$8 \times 100 = 8$ hundreds $= 800$

$8 \times 1{,}000 = 8$ thousands $= 8{,}000$

As the numbers in the last column increase, students see the addition of a 0 each time. In fact, what is happening is multiplication, not addition: Each number is 10 times greater than the previous number.

This progression becomes more difficult to see when multiplying multiples of 10, for example, 3×40. One way for you to think about how the product of 3×4 is related to the product of 3×40 is to look at the following series of equations:

$$3 \times 4 = 12$$
$$(3 \times 4) \times 10 = 12 \times 10$$
$$(3 \times 4) \times 10 = 120$$
$$3 \times (4 \times 10) = 120$$
$$3 \times 40 = 120$$

This series demonstrates, through use of the associative property, that multiplying (3×4) by 10 is equivalent to multiplying 3×40. Therefore, the product of 3×40 is 10 times the product of 3×4.

Students are not likely to understand the relationship between 3×4 and 3×40 in this way, although some of them may be able to articulate that 3×40 is 10 times 3×4 because 40 is 10 times 4. For students, using arrays and other representations to show this relationship provides the best opportunity for them to see how multiplying by 10 and by multiples of 10 works. Consider the following two representations:

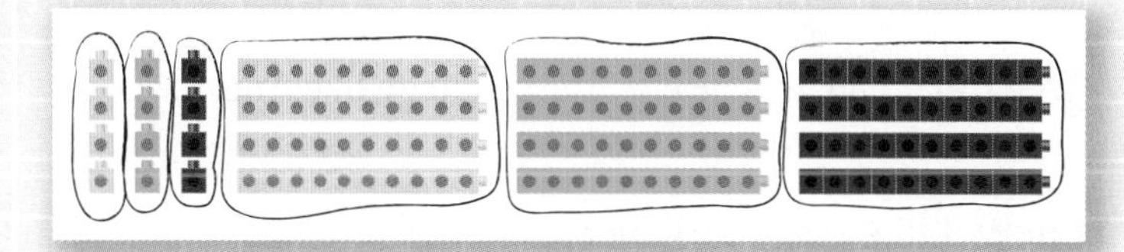

In this first representation, there are 12 cubes arranged in 3 groups of 4 cubes each: $3 \times 4 = 12$. Next to it are 3 groups with 4 towers of cubes in each group. There are 10 cubes in each tower. So there are 3×4 or 12 towers of cubes. Because each tower has 10 cubes, the total number of cubes is 12×10, or 120. In the first picture, there are 12 ones, or 12; in the second, there are 12 tens, or 120.

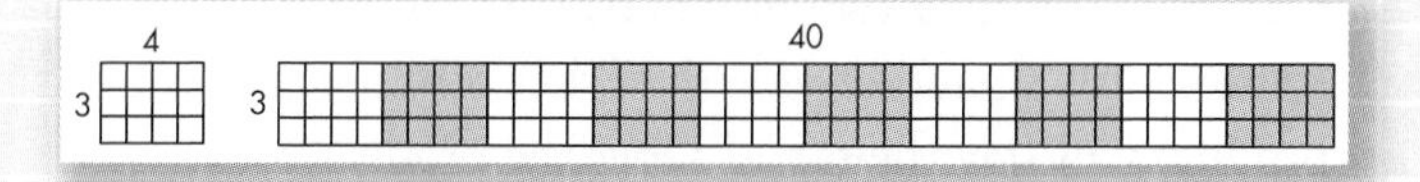

The second representation uses arrays to represent this relationship. The 3×4 array shows 3 rows of 4 squares. Ten of these smaller arrays are put together to create the 3×40 array. Now there are 3 rows of (4×10) squares. The 3×40 array has an area 10 times as large as the 3×4 array.

By visualizing and discussing representations such as these, students can develop a sound basis for understanding the "add a 0" rule.

Teacher Note

Reasoning and Proof in Mathematics

As students find strategies to perform calculations, they frequently make claims about numerical relationships. Part of the work of fourth grade involves helping students strengthen their ability to verbalize those claims and to consider questions such as these: Does this claim hold for *all* numbers? How can we know? Finding ways to answer these questions provides the basis for making sense of formal proof when it is introduced years from now. Consider the following vignette, in which a fourth-grade class is discussing methods for solving multiplication problems.

Andrew: When I did 12 × 25, I cut the 12 in half and doubled the 25 to make it 6 × 50. I can do 6 × 50 in my head. It's 300.

Teacher: Did anyone else use a strategy like Andrew's on any of the problems?

Lucy: I did. I was working on 14 × 15. I did the same kind of thing. I changed it to 7 × 30 and that's 210.

Teacher: Let's look at this. Are you saying that 12 × 25 = 6 × 50? And that 14 × 15 = 7 × 30?

Sabrina: The product stays the same. You cut one number in half and you double the other, so the answer is the same.

Teacher: Are you saying that this *always* works—that when you multiply two numbers, you can cut one number in half and double the other number, and the product will stay the same? Does the product stay the same no matter what the numbers?

Sabrina: I think so.

Teacher: Can we find a way to use diagrams or cubes to show what is happening and why the product stays the same? You may begin with the examples we have seen, but you also must show how your argument will work for *all* numbers.

In this class, Sabrina made an assertion—mathematicians call such an assertion a *conjecture*—that the product of two numbers remains the same if you divide one of the numbers by 2 and double the other number. The teacher has challenged the class to find a way to show that this conjecture is true—not just for the examples they have noted, but for *all* pairs of numbers. If they can find a proof, they have what mathematicians call a *theorem* or *proposition*.

Let us return to the Grade 4 classroom to see how the students responded to their teacher's challenge to justify their conjecture.

Noemi: I made a diagram to show it.

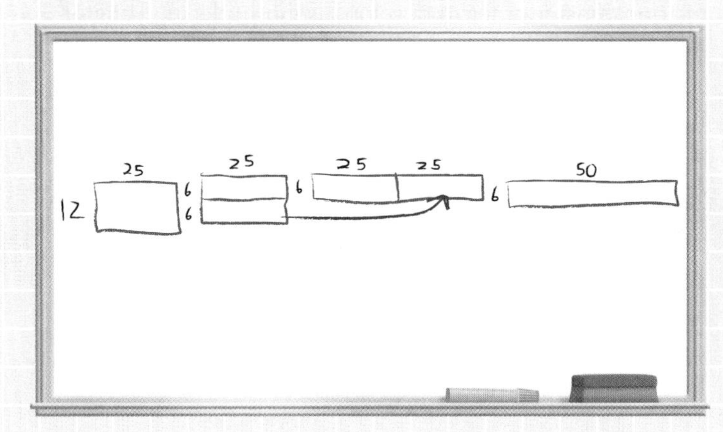

Noemi: For Andrew's example, the first rectangle is 12 by 25. Then he cut the 12 in half and moved the bottom rectangle to make a rectangle that is 6 by 50. The first rectangle has the same area as the last one because they're both made up of the same two smaller rectangles. So like Andrew says, 12 × 25 = 6 × 50.

Lucy: Noemi's picture works for my example too. You can think of the first rectangle as 14 × 15 and the last rectangle as 7 × 30.

Noemi: It doesn't matter what the numbers are. If you cut one in half, you would always have a rectangle on the bottom to move, and when you move that rectangle, you make a rectangle that is twice as long. It works for all numbers.

Noemi has presented a model of multiplication to show how she knows that 12 × 25 = 6 × 50. Lucy sees that the same representation can be used to show $14 \times 15 = 7 \times 30$. Noemi then points out that, in fact, it doesn't matter what the numbers are. The model applies to *any* two numbers that are multiplied (provided that they are positive).

Note: The fact that Sabrina's conjecture has been shown to be true—if you double one factor and halve the other, you maintain the same product—does not necessarily mean that this doubling/halving strategy makes all multiplication easier. If both numbers are odd (e.g., 17×13), halving and doubling will result in one number that includes a fractional part (e.g., $34 \times 6\frac{1}{2}$). This is not a strategy one would choose to solve all multiplication problems. However, if both numbers are even, halving and doubling to create an equivalent problem can often lead to a simpler computation. Just as important, exploring *why* doubling and halving (and tripling and thirding, etc.) work provides an opportunity to learn more about the properties of multiplication and about developing mathematical justification.

Students in Grades K–5 can work productively on developing justifications for mathematical ideas, as Noemi does here. But what is necessary to justify an idea in mathematics? First we'll examine what "proof" is in the field of mathematics and then return to what kind of justification students can do in fourth grade.

What Is "Proof" in Mathematics?

Throughout life, when people make a claim or assertion, they are often required to justify the claim, to persuade others. A prosecutor who claims that a person is guilty must make an argument, based on evidence, to convince the jury of this claim. A scientist who asserts that the earth's atmosphere is becoming warmer must marshal evidence, usually in the form of data and accepted theories and models, to justify the claim. Every field, including the law, science, and mathematics, has its own accepted standards and rules for how a claim must be justified to persuade others.

When students in Grades K–5 are asked to give reasons why their mathematical claims are true, they often say things like this: "It worked for all the numbers we could think of." "I kept on trying and it kept on working." "We asked the sixth graders and they said it was true." "We asked our parents." These are appeals to particular instances and to authority. In any field, there are appropriate times to turn to authority (a teacher or a book, for example) for help with new knowledge or with an idea that we don't yet have enough experience to think through for ourselves. Similarly, particular examples can be very helpful in understanding some phenomenon. However, neither an authoritative statement nor a set of examples is sufficient to prove a mathematical assertion about an infinite class (say, all whole numbers).

In mathematics, a *theorem* must start with a mathematical assertion, which has explicit hypotheses ("givens") and an explicit conclusion. The proof of the theorem must show how the conclusion follows logically from the hypotheses. For instance, the fourth graders asserted that the product of two numbers remains the same if you divide one of the numbers by 2 and double the other number. In later years, their theorem might be stated as: If m and n are numbers, $m \times n = (\frac{m}{2}) \times (n \times 2)$. The proof of this claim consists of a series of steps in which one begins with the hypothesis—m and n are numbers—and follows a chain of logical deductions ending with the conclusion—$m \times n = (\frac{m}{2}) \times (n \times 2)$. Each deduction must be justified by an accepted definition, fact, or principle, such as the commutative or associative property of multiplication.

For example, to show that $m \times n = (m \times \frac{1}{2}) \times (n \times 2)$, we can develop this set of steps:

$$\begin{aligned} m \times n &= [m \times (\tfrac{1}{2} \times 2] \times n \\ &= [(m \times \tfrac{1}{2}) \times 2] \times n \\ &= (m \times \tfrac{1}{2}) \times (2 \times n) \end{aligned}$$

In this series of steps, the associative property of multiplication is applied twice. The associative property can be written with symbolic notation as $(a \times b) \times c = a \times (b \times c)$; regrouping the factors does not affect the product. For example, in the series of steps above, $m \times (\frac{1}{2} \times 2)$ can be regrouped as $(m \times \frac{1}{2}) \times 2$. It may help to look at how this works with one of the examples from the classroom dialogue:

$$\begin{aligned}12 \times 25 &= [12 \times (\tfrac{1}{2} \times 2)] \times 25\\ &= [(12 \times \tfrac{1}{2}) \times 2] \times 25\\ &= (12 \times \tfrac{1}{2}) \times (2 \times 25) = 6 \times 50\end{aligned}$$

The model for such a notion of proof was first established by Euclid, who codified what was known of ancient Greek geometry in his *Elements,* written about 300 B.C. In his book, Euclid begins with the basic terms and postulates of geometry and, through hundreds of propositions and proofs, moves to beautiful and surprising theorems about geometric figures. What is remarkable is that, in each mathematical realm, you can get so far with such simple building blocks.

What Does Proof Look Like in Fourth Grade?

One does not expect the rigor or sophistication of a formal proof, or the use of algebraic symbolism, from young children. Even for a mathematician, precise validation is often developed *after* new mathematical ideas have been explored and are solidly understood. When mathematical ideas are evolving and there is a need to communicate the sense of *why* a claim is true, then informal means of justification are appropriate. Such a justification can include the use of visual displays, concrete materials, or words. The test of the effectiveness of such a justification is this: Does it rely on logical thinking about the mathematical relationships rather than on the fact that one or a few specific examples work?

This informal approach to mathematical justification is particularly appropriate in Grade K–5 classrooms, where mathematical ideas are generally "under construction" and where sense-making and diverse modes of reasoning are valued. Noemi's argument offers justification for the claim that if you halve one factor and double the other, the product remains the same. The product of the numbers m and n is represented by the area of a rectangle with dimensions m and n. Noemi then cuts the vertical dimension in half, making two rectangles, each having dimensions $(\frac{m}{2})$ and n. One of these rectangles is moved and then connected with the other to create a rectangle with dimensions $(\frac{m}{2})$ by $2 \times n$. The area of this new rectangle must be the same as the original, therefore $(\frac{m}{2}) \times (2 \times n) = m \times n$. Noemi's argument establishes the validity of the claim not only for particular numbers, but for any numbers, and easily conveys why it is true.

An important part of Noemi's justification is her statement that it does not matter what the numbers are. She understands that the process she describes with her model will guarantee that the original rectangle will have the same area as the final rectangle whose length is double that of the original and whose width is half that of the original. It is important to note that when students make such claims of generality—*this is true for all numbers*—the phrase *all numbers* refers to the numbers they are using. In this vignette, Noemi's reasoning about multiplication takes place in the context of whole numbers. We might see that Noemi's argument applies equally well to positive values that include rational numbers, but Noemi and her classmates will need to revisit this argument when the domain of numbers they are working with expands beyond whole numbers.

To support the kind of reasoning illustrated in the vignette, encourage students to use cubes, number lines, and other representations to explain their thinking. The use of representations offers a reference for the student who is explaining his or her reasoning, and it also allows more classmates to follow that reasoning. If it seems that students may be thinking only in terms of specific numbers, you might ask such questions as these: Will that work for other numbers? How do you know? Will the explanation be the same?

Multiplication Clusters and the Properties of Multiplication

Multiplication clusters are sets of problems that help students think about using what they know to solve harder problems. For example, what do you know that helps you solve 12×3? If you know that $3 \times 3 = 9$, you can double the product of 3×3 to get the product of 6×3 and then double again to get the product of 12×3. You might also start with 10×3. If you know that $10 \times 3 = 30$, then you can start with 30 and add two more 3s to get 36. As students work with multiplication clusters, they learn to think about all the number relationships they know that might help them solve a problem.

The multiplication clusters in this unit are designed to help students make sense of multiplying 2-digit numbers. Many of the clusters build an understanding of pulling apart multiplication problems into manageable subproblems, solving the smaller problems, and then putting the parts back together. This process is based on an important characteristic of multiplication called the *distributive property.* In this unit, students are not expected to learn the name of the property, but it is a core idea of the unit.

Here is an example:

$$6 \times 23 = (6 \times 10) + (6 \times 10) + (6 \times 3)$$

In this example, 23 is broken apart into $10 + 10 + 3$, and *each part* is multiplied by 6 in order to construct the solution to 6×23. The number does not have to be split into 10s and 1s.

Here is another example:

$$8 \times 12 = (4 \times 12) + (4 \times 12)$$

or

$$8 \times 12 = (8 \times 6) + (8 \times 6)$$

In each case, one of the factors is split up into parts, and each part is multiplied by the other factor in order to maintain equivalence to the original expression.

Other clusters build on ideas about halving and doubling that are developed in this unit. See **Teacher Note:** Reasoning and Proof in Mathematics?, page 168, for more about students' understanding of creating an equivalent multiplication problem by halving one factor and doubling the other.

As students solve the first few problems in each cluster, they use familiar multiplication combinations. Students say "I just knew it" for some of the problems because these single-digit multiplication combinations are part of their known repertoire. They also make use of multiplying by 10 and by multiples of 10, another essential tool in solving harder multiplication problems. See **Teacher Note:** Multiplying by Multiples of 10, page 167, for more about the ways students develop understanding of this idea.

Here are examples of student work on two multiplication clusters from the *Student Activity Book* pages 57–58.

Set C Solve these problems. How did you solve the final problem?

$32 \times 2 = 64$

$10 \times 8 = 80$

$30 \times 8 = 240$

Final problem: $\mathbf{32 \times 8} = 256$

I broke the 32 into 30 + 2. I already solved 30 x 8 = 240 & I need 2 more groups of 8 which is 16.

240 + 16 = 256

Sample Student Work

Set D Solve these problems. How did you solve the final problem?

$63 \times 10 = 630$

$60 \times 11 = 660$

$3 \times 11 = 33$

Final problem: $\mathbf{63 \times 11} = 693$

I knew 63 x 10 = 630 + I need to add one more group of 63 which makes 693.

Sample Student Work

Multiplication clusters help students learn how to look at a problem and build a strategy to solve it that is based on the number relationships they know. At first, students work on clusters of problems that are provided to help them solve a 2-digit problem, such as 4×43 or 58×6. They solve all the problems in the cluster and then decide which one(s) will most help them think about the solution to the final problem. Students may add to the cluster any other problems that help them solve the final one. Later in the unit, students create their own cluster of problems to help them solve a multiplication problem. In later units of *Investigations,* in both Grades 4 and 5, students spend more time creating their own clusters of problems as well as using a variety of given problems to solve multiplication and division problems.

End-of-Unit Assessment

This final assessment focuses on four of the five benchmarks for the unit. (The fifth benchmark, "Know multiplication combinations to 12 × 12 fluently," was the focus of the assessment activity Multiplication Combinations in Session 3.4.)

At this point in Grade 4, students' work on multiplication is focused on solving problems by breaking apart the numbers to create multiplication problems that are easier to solve and then recombining the products of those problems. The focus for division is on understanding that groups of the divisor can be removed in groups from the number being divided.

Problem 1

Benchmark addressed:

Benchmark 1: Multiply 2-digit numbers by 1-digit and small 2-digit numbers (e.g., 12, 15, 20), using strategies that involve breaking the numbers apart.

In order to meet the benchmark, students' work should show that they can:

- Interpret the problem as 6 groups of 23 or 23 groups of 6;
- Accurately solve the problem by using multiplication (e.g., students should not be adding or counting groups).

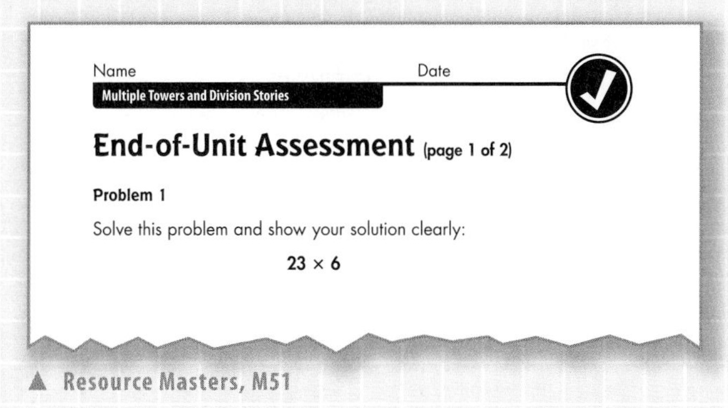
Name Date
Multiple Towers and Division Stories
End-of-Unit Assessment (page 1 of 2)
Problem 1
Solve this problem and show your solution clearly:
23 × 6

▲ Resource Masters, M51

Meeting the Benchmark

Students who meet the benchmark can break the problem into smaller problems that they know how to solve. They solve each part correctly and accurately combine all the parts for the solution.

Ramona breaks 23 into tens and ones, 20 + 3, and multiplies each part by 6. She then combines the two parts to solve the problem (20 × 6 = 120, 3 × 6 = 18, 120 + 18 = 138). Many fourth graders should be able to complete these calculations mentally, simply recording each part to keep track.

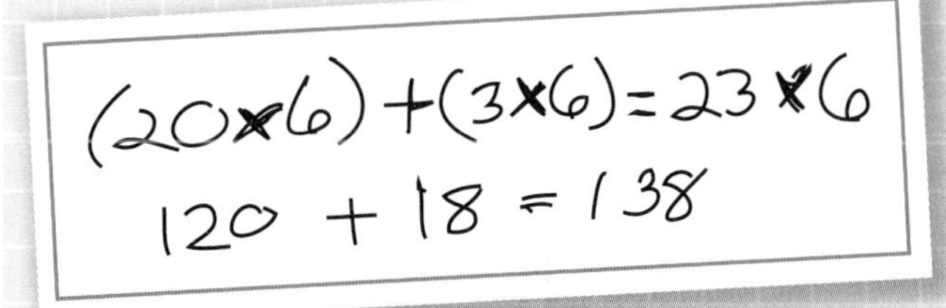

Ramona's Work

Some students break the 6 into 3 + 3. Luke, for example, multiplied 23 × 3 = 69. He knew that 23 × 6 = (23 × 3) + (23 × 3), so he added 69 + 69 to get his final answer.

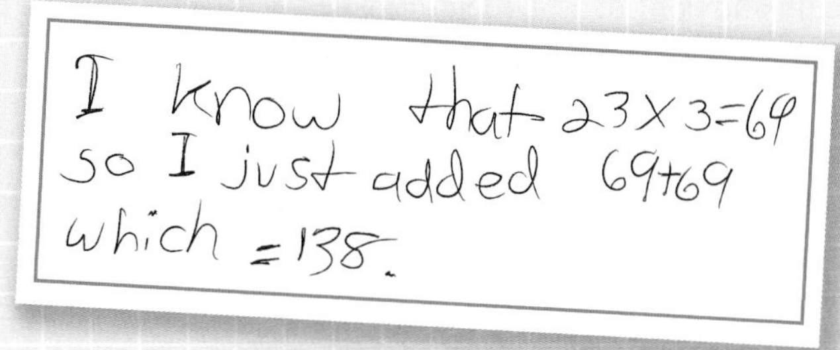

Luke's Work

Partially Meeting the Benchmark

Some students still use addition to solve a multiplication problem (e.g., adding up groups of 23), as they may have done when multiplying in Grade 3. These students understand what the multiplication expression 23×6 represents and have a strategy for finding the correct answer.

Alejandro drew 6 circles of 23 and then added 23 six times.

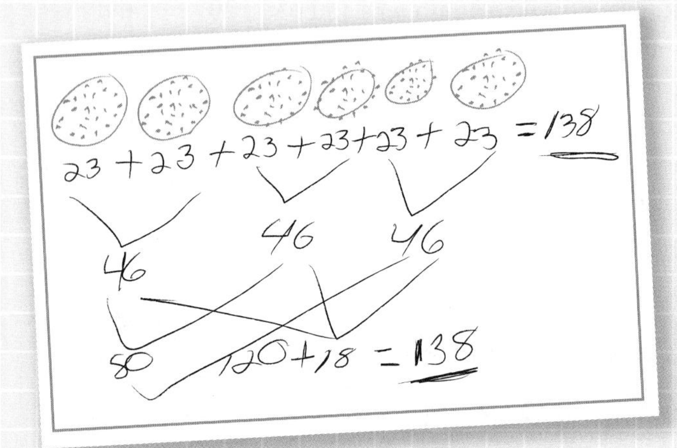

Alejandro's Work

Work with these students to identify multiplication combinations they know that are related to the problem they are trying to solve. In this example, does Alejandro know that $3 \times 20 = 60$ or that $6 \times 20 = 120$? Some fourth graders continue to add because they are more secure and confident with addition. However, they do know multiplication combinations that can help them solve a problem such as this one and need to be supported to do so. Other students need more work on their basic multiplication combinations and on multiplying multiples of 10.

Not Meeting the Benchmark

Some students may not understand the meaning of multiplication as equal groups (e.g., solving $23 + 6$ instead of 23×6). These students should solve and create story problems to clarify what a multiplication expression such as 23×6 represents: How many yogurts are in 23 six-packs?

Other students may understand the problem but cannot break apart the problem in any useful way. They may set up 23 groups of 6 cubes and count them 1 by 1. These students should be encouraged to create any groups that make sense to them. Ask them questions such as these:

"Do you know what 2 groups of 6 are? 10? 20? Can you find groups of 23 instead? How many do you need?"

These students may need more work on their basic multiplication combinations and on multiplying multiples of 10.

Problem 2

Benchmarks addressed:

Benchmark 1: Multiply 2-digit numbers by 1-digit and small 2-digit numbers (e.g., 12, 15, 20), using strategies that involve breaking the numbers apart.

Benchmark 4: Multiply by 10 and multiples of 10.

In order to meet the benchmarks, students' work should show that they can:

- Interpret the problem as a multiplication situation;
- Break the problem apart in a useful and efficient way, solve the parts, and combine them to find the correct answer;
- Multiply by multiples of 10.

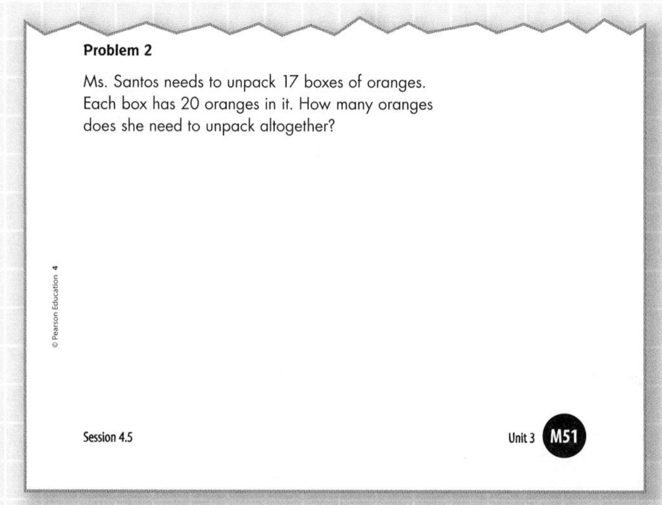

Problem 2

Ms. Santos needs to unpack 17 boxes of oranges. Each box has 20 oranges in it. How many oranges does she need to unpack altogether?

© Pearson Education 4

Session 4.5 Unit 3 M51

▲ Resource Masters, M51

Meeting the Benchmarks

Students who meet the benchmarks interpret this problem as multiplication and have efficient ways to break the numbers in the problem apart, using multiplication by 10 or 20.

Richard started with $17 \times 10 = 170$ and then doubled 170 to get the correct answer of 340.

Jill knew that 17×20 can also be written as $17 \times 2 \times 10$. She multiplied $17 \times 2 = 34$ and then $34 \times 10 = 340$.

Derek broke 17 into 10 and 7 and multiplied each piece by 20.

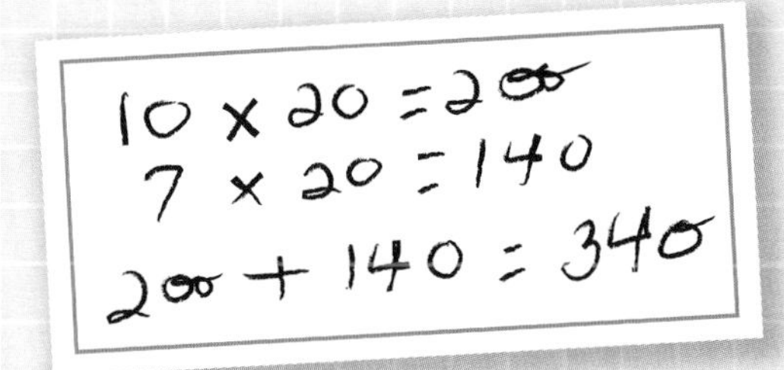

Derek's Work

Some students might use doubling or halving to create the equivalent problem 34×10, which they then solve directly, applying what they know about multiplying by 10.

Partially Meeting the Benchmarks

Some students interpret the problem correctly as 17×20 and understand how to break apart the numbers to make them easier to solve, but make a computation error (e.g., add $170 + 170$ incorrectly).

Not Meeting the Benchmarks

Multiplying by 10 and multiples of 10 is a necessary tool for efficiently solving multiplication and division problems. Some students do not break apart the problem in useful ways or use knowledge of multiplication by 10s. They may multiply 2 groups (or some other amount) of 17 and add these until they have 20 groups of 17. Alternatively, they may solve 17×10 by adding up groups of 17 instead of readily knowing that product.

Problem 3

Benchmarks addressed:

Benchmark 2: Solve division problems (2-digit and small 3-digit numbers divided by 1-digit numbers), including some that result in a remainder.

Benchmark 3: Use story problems, pictures, or concrete models to represent division situations.

In order to meet the benchmarks, students' work should show that they can:

- Interpret division notation and understand how it relates to a context;
- Solve a division problem accurately by using groups of the divisor or splitting the dividend into parts;
- Make sense of the effect of the remainder on the solution to the story problem.

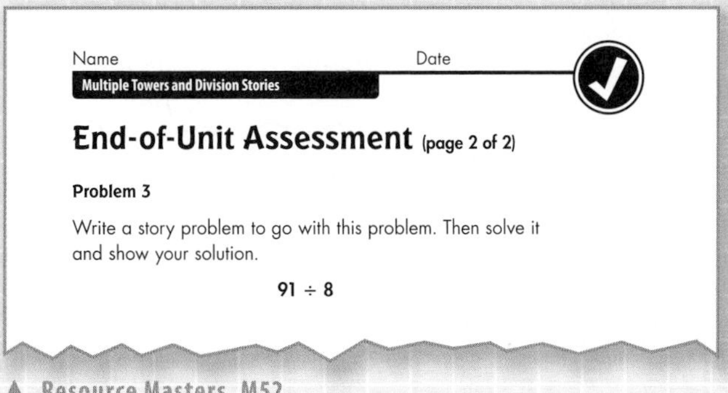
Name Date

Multiple Towers and Division Stories

End-of-Unit Assessment (page 2 of 2)

Problem 3

Write a story problem to go with this problem. Then solve it and show your solution.

$91 \div 8$

▲ Resource Masters, M52

Meeting the Benchmarks

All students should be able to write a story problem in which 91 of something is split into either 8 groups or groups of 8. Here are two examples of story problems that can be represented by 91 ÷ 8:

I have 91 muffins and 8 friends. How many muffins will each friend get?

There are 91 people who need to fit into cars that hold 8 passengers. How many cars do we need?

The following students all used groups of the divisor to solve a story problem similar to the muffin problem above. They used multiplication combinations they knew to help them find how many groups of 8 there are in 91.

Andrew first multiplied 8 × 10.

8 X 10 = 80
80 + 11 = 91
8 fits into 11 once with 3 left over. So the answer is 11 with 3 left over.

Andrew's Work

Helena used 8 × 8 = 64 as a first step.

8x8=64
91-64=27
I know that 8x3=24 and that is really close to 27. So 8 fits in 11 times with 3 left over.

Helena's Work

Alejandro uses yet another familiar fact, 8 × 11.

8 x 11 = 88
I only need 3 more to get to 91.
11 R3

Alejandro's Work

Some students divide, starting with 80 ÷ 8, or they know that 88 ÷ 8 is the closest division by 8 that results in a whole number.

88 ÷ 8 = 11
there's no more 8's in 91. So the answer is 11 remainder 3.

Steve's Work

If students choose a story problem similar to the problem about cars above, they should be able to take into account how the remainder affects the answer to the problem. So, for example, if cars are involved, they might write:

8x11 = 88
I only need 3 more to get to 91.
So we need 11 cars, but there are 3 more people so we need another car for them.

Kimberly's Work

Partially Meeting the Benchmarks

Some students understand that they can use multiplication combinations they know but miscalculate them. For example, a student might solve 8 × 12 incorrectly, thus arriving at the wrong answer.

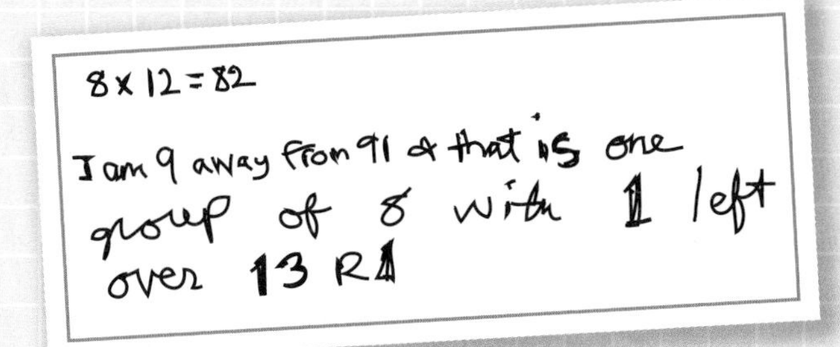

Marisol's Work

This student can interpret the division expression and can use multiplication to solve a division problem, but she needs to work on basic multiplication combinations and on double-checking his work.

Some students subtract 8s or groups of 8. For example, Noemi knows that she is trying to figure out how many 8s will fit into 91. She keeps subtracting 8 until she has no more to distribute, as follows:

$$91 - 8 = 83$$

$$83 - 8 = 75$$

$$75 - 8 = 67$$

$$67 - 8 = 59 \ldots$$

She continues all the way to 3 and then counts up the number of 8s she has subtracted, getting the correct answer, 11 R3. Noemi can interpret the division expression 91 ÷ 8. However, at this point in Grade 4, students should be able to solve a division problem with numbers of this magnitude by using a strategy based on larger groups of 8s.

Not Meeting the Benchmarks

Students who are directly modeling the problem with tallies, marks, or objects and counting these objects do understand something about division but do not meet the benchmark at this point in fourth grade.

Jill's work is an example of this strategy.

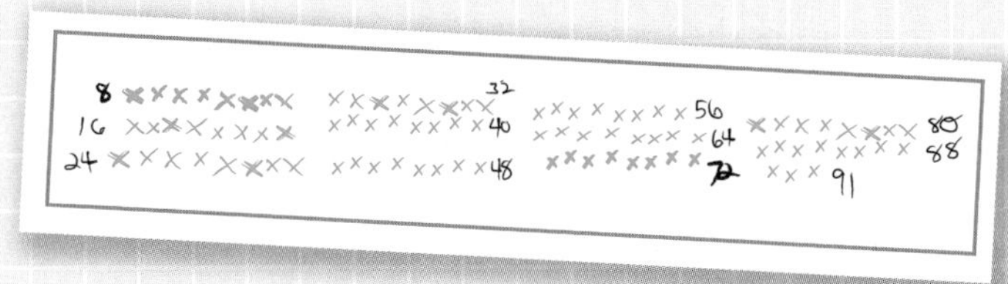

Jill's Work

This strategy may work to arrive at the correct answer but, it is inefficient and prone to error. In addition, use of this approach indicates that students do not have an understanding of how to use groups of 8 to help them solve the problem.

These students may need to do some or all of the following:

- Work on their multiplication combinations
- Work on division problems with smaller numbers to develop the idea of removing groups of the divisor
- Use story contexts to talk through division as removing groups of groups

Solving 17×6

Students have been working in pairs to think of ways that they can solve the problem 17×6 by breaking it into smaller problems. As the teacher watched them work, she noticed that they came up with a number of different ways to break up the problem. She lists some of these on the board and then brings the students together for a discussion.

$(17 \times 2) + (17 \times 2) + (17 \times 2)$

$(6 \times 11) + (6 \times 3) + (6 \times 3)$

$(17 \times 1) + (17 \times 1) + (17 \times 1) + (17 \times 1) + (17 \times 1) + (17 \times 1)$

$(6 \times 10) + (6 \times 7)$

Teacher: Here are some of the ways I noticed you using to break 17×6 into easier problems. All of these are correct, and I'm wondering how you chose ways to break up 17×6 that helped you solve the problem. Were you thinking of smaller problems that you already knew to help you solve 17×6? What did you do to make this problem easier?

Richard: I started with 17×2 because I knew that the answer is 34. Then all I had to do was add $34 + 34 + 34$.

Venetta: I think $6 \times 11 = 66$ is easy, and then all I had to do was add 6 more 6s. I did 3 groups of 6 and then 3 more groups of 6.

Teacher: Many of you know the multiples of 11 and 3×6. Who can tell me another way that made it easy for you?

Steve: 17×1.

Teacher: It is easy. What do you have to do next to finish solving the problem?

Steve: You still have to add six 17s together. That might take a long time. But it would work!

Teacher: That's right, it would work, but you're pointing out that it leaves you with some fairly difficult addition. One question everyone can think about when you're breaking problems apart is this: What do you know that can help you solve a pretty big chunk of the problem? Here's another question: Do you need to break the problem apart into many pieces, or can you find an efficient way to use only two or three pieces? When you look at all the ways that are listed here, which do you think are both easy and efficient ways to solve the problem?

Cheyenne: I think 6×10 plus 6×7 is pretty efficient because I know most of the 10 times tables. The 7s are a little harder, but 6×7 is easy for me.

Teacher: Exactly. You all know multiples of 10, and you can do 6×7 in your head. You can be more efficient when you use what you already know.

By asking students to compare different ways they broke problems apart, this teacher helps students consider how to use what they know to solve more difficult problems easily and efficiently. These students understand how to break a multiplication problem into smaller problems. Some students are also using their knowledge of the commutativity of multiplication—they find it easier to think of 17×6 as 6×17. It is important that students understand that there are many ways to break up a multiplication problem. As the teacher points out, all of their methods are correct. However, they can also think about which ways of breaking up the problem are most helpful.

Venetta knows how to solve 6×11; she also knows that she needs "6 more 6s," which she thinks of as 3 groups of 6 and another 3 groups of 6. However, breaking 6×17 into these three parts leaves her with the addition problem, $66 + 18 + 18$, which might not be easy to solve.

Steve also notices that he has not made the problem easier to solve when he breaks it up into $(17 \times 1) + (17 \times 1) + (17 \times 1) + (17 \times 1) + (17 \times 1) + (17 \times 1)$.

Cheyenne breaks the problem into two parts that are each easy for her to solve. She has to add only two numbers to find the solution to the original problem. Another student, who knows all the 12s multiplication combinations well, might break the problem into $(12 \times 6) + (5 \times 6)$, which also results in a relatively easy addition to complete the problem.

As students continue to solve problems with larger numbers by breaking them into smaller problems, this teacher encourages them to use problems that they can solve easily, such as multiplication combinations they know and multiplying by 10. She will continue to ask them to compare solution methods and to think about which ways are easy and efficient to carry out.

Dialogue Box

What Do You Do with the Extras?

The students in this classroom are working on *Student Activity Book* pages 21–22. The teacher listens to students as they work on Problem 1.

There are 44 people taking a trip in some small vans. Each van holds 8 people. How many vans will they need?

Lucy: It can't be 6 vans. No, there'd be 48 people. 2 vans are 16 people, $16 + 16$ is 32. 32 plus 8 is 40. There will be 5 vans. That's weird, though. 5 vans with 8 people and 1 van with 4 people.

Lucy writes on her paper:

5 vans will have 8 people.
1 van will have 4 people.

Teacher: How did you decide on your answer?

Lucy: 5×8 is 40, and that's the closest thing under 44 that's a multiple of 8. So 5 vans will have 8 people, and 1 van will have 4.

Teacher: What would the division equation for that be?

Lucy: $44 \div 8$. The answer would be 5 with 1 left over. No, 5 with 4 left over.

Teacher: 4 what?

Lucy: 5×8 is 40. Then there are 4 people left. There are 5 vans but 4 extra people.

As the teacher observes the students working, she recognizes that they are having difficulty sorting out the difference between the answer to the question posed in Problem 1 and the way to complete the division equation $44 \div 8 =$ ____. She decides to stop the class to discuss this issue.

Derek: There are two ways you could deal with this problem. You could just take 5 vans and leave the 4 people behind or you could take 1 extra van using only 4 spaces.

The students agree that it would not be fair to leave 4 people behind.

Teacher: Derek said that you could have 5 full vans with 8 people and 1 van with the 4 extra people. So what would be the answer to the question "How many vans will they need?"

Amelia: They would need 6 vans if they want to take all the people, but 6 isn't the answer to $44 \div 8$.

Teacher: What do you mean, that 6 is not the answer to $44 \div 8$?

Lucy: It can't be, because 6 is the answer to $48 \div 8$.

Ramona: I got 5 with a remainder of 4.

Abdul: You can also say $5\frac{1}{2}$, like with the cracker problem.

Teacher: Are you saying that these answers are correct?

The teacher records:

5 R4 $\quad 44 \div 8 = 5\frac{1}{2}$

Ramona, Abdul, and others: Yes.

Teacher: So $5\frac{1}{2}$, or 5 remainder 4, is the answer to $44 \div 8$, but is it the answer to how many vans they need?

Abdul: No. You can't drive a half van and it's not fair to leave 4 people behind, so they need 6 vans.

Teacher: Sometimes in problems about real situations, the answer to the question being asked is not the same as the number you would write to complete the division equation. I have one more question for you: If the answer to the problem is 6 vans, can I write this?

The teacher records: $44 \div 8 = 6$

Various students: No. Yes. No.

Teacher: Lucy said something before about $48 \div 8 = 6$.

Enrique: Right, you can't say $44 \div 8 = 6$ because $48 \div 8 = 6$. They can't both be 6.

Marisol: They wouldn't be equal. It's 6 vans, but it's not really 6 because one of the vans has only half the people.

In this discussion, the teacher helps students sort out how the answer to the problem about vans is not the same as the number needed to complete the equation $44 \div 8 =$ ____. By considering different division situations, students gain experience in attending carefully to the question posed in the problem. When a problem involves whole objects that cannot be broken into parts, the answer to the question in the problem cannot include a fraction or decimal. Sometimes, as in the van problem, the result of the division must be rounded up to the next whole number: 6 vans are needed. Sometimes, as in a situation involving sharing 44 balloons among 8 people, the result of the division must be rounded down: each person cannot have more than 5 balloons, if each person is to have an equal number of balloons.

The teacher's primary focus in this discussion is on finding the solution to a division problem posed in a context. The teacher also noticed that quite a few students had written the incorrect equation, $44 \div 8 = 6$, on their papers. She raises the question about whether this equation is correct at the end of the discussion, hoping that some students will be able to build on Lucy's observation that $48 \div 8 = 6$. She knows that she will need to return to this idea.

Building a Multiple Tower

The students in this class are building a tower of paper squares as tall as their teacher, using the multiples of 30. As students call out the multiples, one student lists them on the board and another writes them on self-stick notes and puts them on the wall next to their teacher. The tower is about knee-high.

Teacher: Right now we are at 240 and the tower is up to my knee. What number do you estimate we'll land on when the tower is as tall as I am? Write your estimate on a slip of paper.

Sabrina: I think maybe 554.

Teacher: Read out the multiples we have so far.

Bill: 30, 60, 90, 120, 150, 180, 210, 240.

Teacher: Does 554 fit the pattern?

Jake: No, because all the numbers end in a 0. So I don't think it could be 554.

Jill: But it could be 550 or 680.

Luke: If you look at these numbers (referring to the tens place), you add 3 each time.

Teacher: Let's think about which estimates are possibilities and which don't fit the pattern.

The students recheck their estimates, using the pattern as a guide. Some decide to alter their estimates, and the tower building continues until it reaches the teacher's height at 960.

Teacher: So we skip counted by 30s and I am 960. Can you figure out how many multiples are in my tower?

The teacher writes on the board: $\_\_\_\_ \times 30 = 960$

Amelia: Let's see. It's ten 30s to 300, so 20 to 600 and 30 to 900. Plus it's 2 more 30s to 60. So it's thirty-two 30s to 960.

Richard: I did it in the calculator and got 32, too.

Marisol: I broke it into 900 and then 60. Then I said, "How many times does 3 go into 9?" I know it's 3, so it's 30 into 900. Then it's 2 more to get to 960. So it's 32.

In this discussion, students use skip-counting patterns to help them make reasonable predictions about multiples of 30. They also consider what they already know about 30s—that there are 3 in 90 or 10 in 300—to help them solve the problem "How many 30s in 960?" Just as students can break multiplication problems into parts, they can also break division problems into parts that are easier to solve.

Students may not yet be thinking of their work on the multiple towers as division, but the question "How many 30s are in 960?" can be represented as $960 \div 30$. As they break up the dividend (960) into parts and divide each part by 30, they are developing strategies that they can apply to division problems.

Dialogue Box

What Does It Mean to "Add a Zero"?

Students have completed *Student Activity Book* pages 42–43. They have gathered to share their representations for 5×6 and 5×60. The teacher holds up a 5 by 6 rectangular array that one student made with connecting cubes.

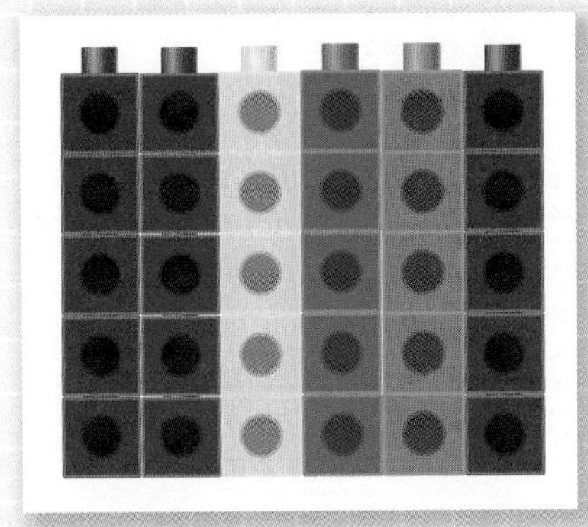

Teacher: How many more of these (the 5 by 6 array) do you need to make 5×60?

The class decides to skip count together by 30s.

Anna: We need 10 of those.

Teacher: It seems that many people say "add a zero" to explain what the relationship is. Can anyone explain what that really means?

Benson: You're adding a 10.

Derek: No, times 10.

Teacher: You decided that we need 10 of these 5×6 arrays to make a 5×60 array. Does this make sense then?

The teacher writes on the board: $(5 \times 6) \times 10 = 5 \times 60$

The students puzzle over it for a bit but then decide that both parts of the equation are equal to 300.

Steve: You know $5 \times 6 = 30$, so if you multiply 30×10 you get 300.

Teacher: Instead of 5×6 and 5×60, what if I have 6×5 and 6×50? You know that $6 \times 5 = 30$, so what should the answer be for 6×50?

Helena: I think the relationship is the same. This time you're making the 5 ten times bigger.

Andrew: They're in groups. First they're in groups of 5 and then they're in groups of 50.

Teacher: What do you mean?

Lucy: The zero really means 10. It's 5×10.

Teacher: Damian, you had a sketch of a story problem that might help us see what Andrew is saying about groups. Can you explain it?

The teacher continues to have students share representations, which include ten 5×6 arrays cut from graph paper and put together to make a 5×60 array and a cube construction with the dimensions of $5 \times 6 \times 10$. Kimberly points to one of the 5×6 faces of her 3-D cube construction.

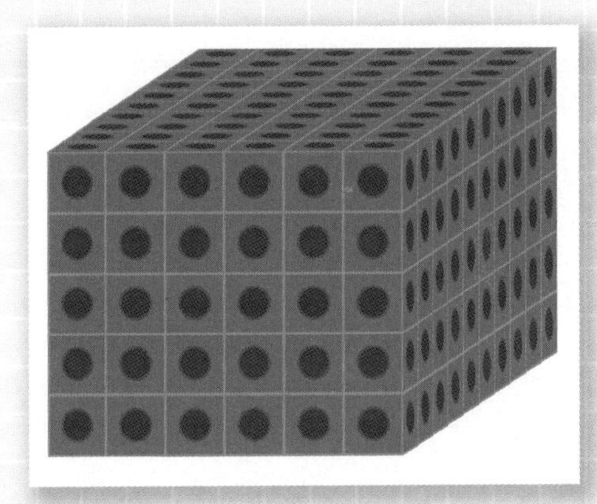

Kimberly: See, this is 5×6, but if you want to do 5×60, you can see that there's really 10 in back of every one of these, so it's ten 30s, which makes 300.

At this point, not all students can articulate the idea behind "adding a zero" as clearly as some of the students in this discussion, so the teacher decides to leave the representations on display. He will continue to ask students to explain what the zero represents as students use this pattern in their problem solving. See **Teacher Note:** Multiplying by Multiples of 10, page 167.

The *Student Math Handbook* pages related to this unit are pictured on the following pages. This book is designed to be used flexibly: as a resource for students doing classwork, as a book students can take home for reference while doing homework and playing math games with their families, and as a reference for families to better understand the work their children are doing in class.

When students take the *Student Math Handbook* home, they and their families can discuss these pages together to reinforce or enhance students' understanding of the mathematical concepts and games in this unit.

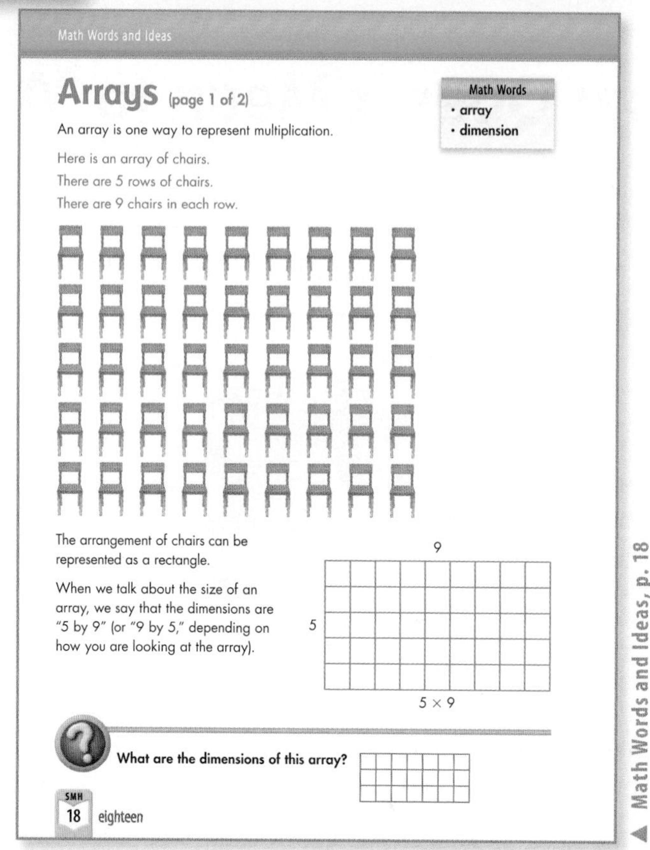

Math Words and Ideas

Arrays (page 1 of 2)

Math Words
- array
- dimension

An array is one way to represent multiplication.

Here is an array of chairs.
There are 5 rows of chairs.
There are 9 chairs in each row.

The arrangement of chairs can be represented as a rectangle.

When we talk about the size of an array, we say that the dimensions are "5 by 9" (or "9 by 5," depending on how you are looking at the array).

What are the dimensions of this array?

SMH 18 eighteen

Math Words and Ideas, p. 18

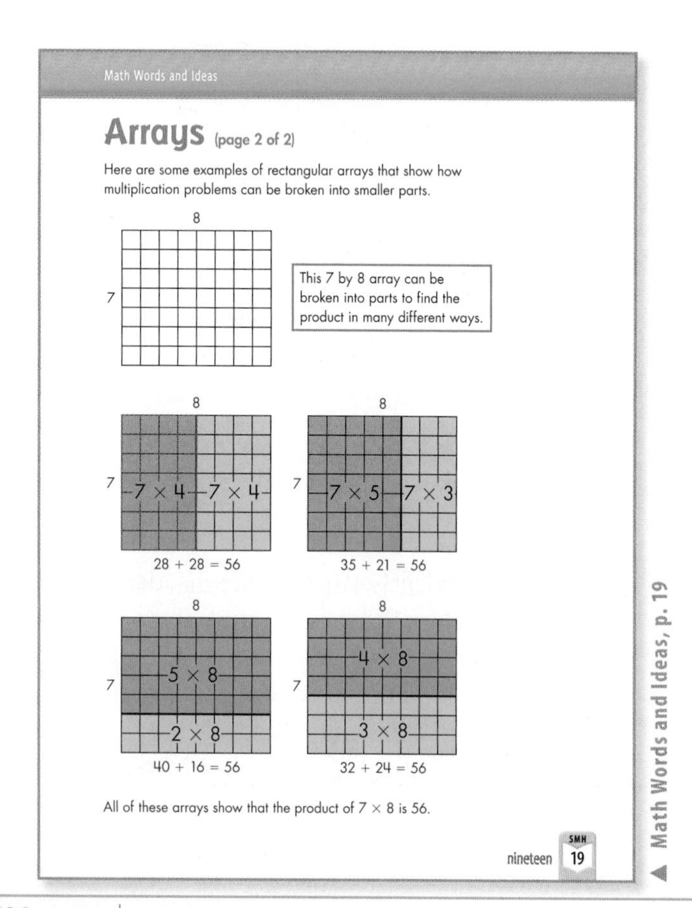

Math Words and Ideas

Arrays (page 2 of 2)

Here are some examples of rectangular arrays that show how multiplication problems can be broken into smaller parts.

This 7 by 8 array can be broken into parts to find the product in many different ways.

28 + 28 = 56

35 + 21 = 56

40 + 16 = 56

32 + 24 = 56

All of these arrays show that the product of 7 × 8 is 56.

nineteen SMH 19

Math Words and Ideas, p. 19

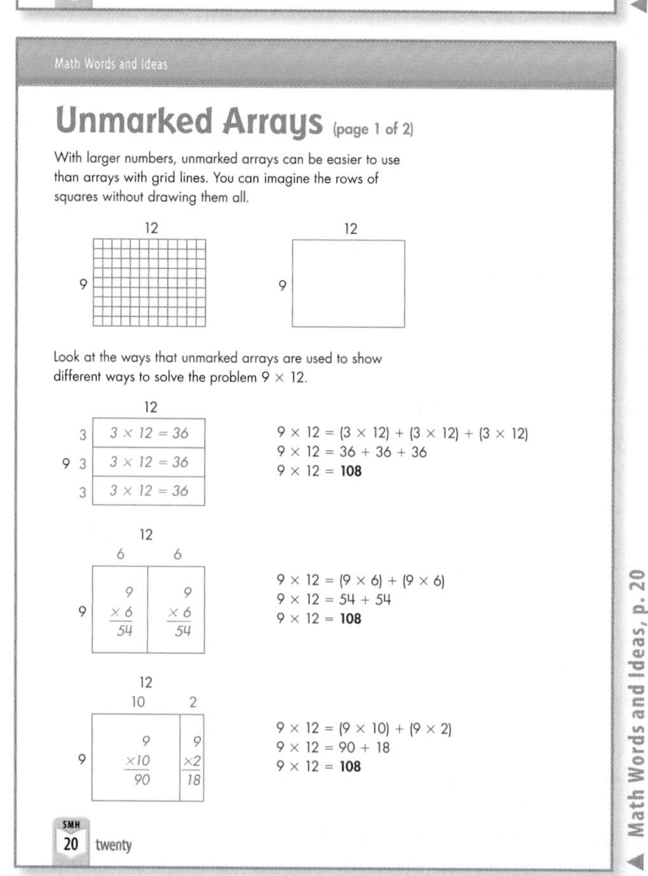

Math Words and Ideas

Unmarked Arrays (page 1 of 2)

With larger numbers, unmarked arrays can be easier to use than arrays with grid lines. You can imagine the rows of squares without drawing them all.

Look at the ways that unmarked arrays are used to show different ways to solve the problem 9 × 12.

9 × 12 = (3 × 12) + (3 × 12) + (3 × 12)
9 × 12 = 36 + 36 + 36
9 × 12 = **108**

9 × 12 = (9 × 6) + (9 × 6)
9 × 12 = 54 + 54
9 × 12 = **108**

9 × 12 = (9 × 10) + (9 × 2)
9 × 12 = 90 + 18
9 × 12 = **108**

SMH 20 twenty

Math Words and Ideas, p. 20

Math Words and Ideas

Unmarked Arrays (page 2 of 2)

These unmarked arrays show different ways to solve the problem 14×20.

20: 10 | 10; 14: $14 \times 10 = 140$ | $14 \times 10 = 140$

$140 + 140 = \mathbf{280}$

20; 14: 7 — $7 \times 20 = 140$; 7 — $7 \times 20 = 140$

$140 + 140 = \mathbf{280}$

20; 14: 10 — $10 \times 20 = 200$; 4 — $4 \times 20 = 80$

$200 + 80 = \mathbf{280}$

This unmarked array shows a solution for 34×45.

45: 40 | 5; 34: 30 | 4

$30 \times 40 = \mathbf{1{,}200}$

$30 \times 5 = \mathbf{150}$

$4 \times 40 = \mathbf{160}$

$4 \times 5 = \mathbf{20}$

$$\begin{array}{r} 1{,}200 \\ 160 \\ 150 \\ +\ 20 \\ \hline 1{,}530 \end{array}$$

$34 \times 45 = \mathbf{1{,}530}$

Use unmarked arrays to show some ways to solve 8×14.

twenty-one SMH 21

Math Words and Ideas, p. 21

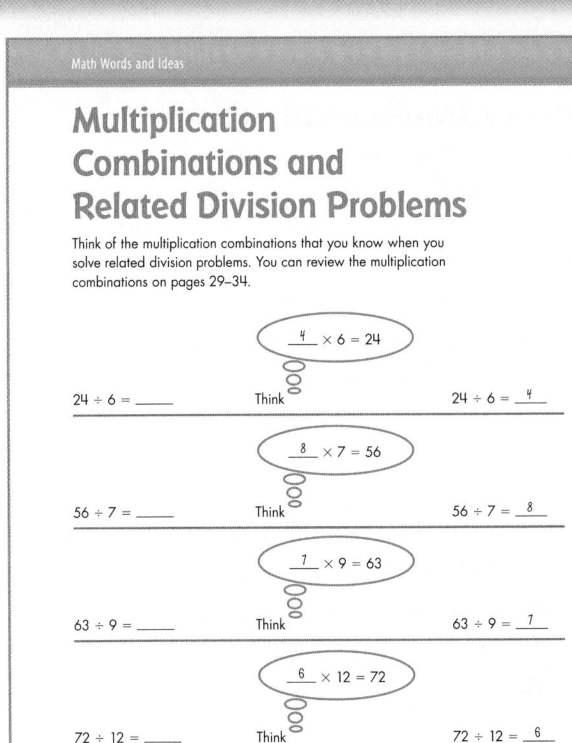

Math Words and Ideas

Multiplication Combinations and Related Division Problems

Think of the multiplication combinations that you know when you solve related division problems. You can review the multiplication combinations on pages 29–34.

	Think	
$24 \div 6 =$ ____	$\underline{4} \times 6 = 24$	$24 \div 6 = \underline{4}$
$56 \div 7 =$ ____	$\underline{8} \times 7 = 56$	$56 \div 7 = \underline{8}$
$63 \div 9 =$ ____	$\underline{7} \times 9 = 63$	$63 \div 9 = \underline{7}$
$72 \div 12 =$ ____	$\underline{6} \times 12 = 72$	$72 \div 12 = \underline{6}$

What multiplication combination could help you solve this problem?
$45 \div 5 =$ ____

thirty-five SMH 35

Math Words and Ideas, p. 35

Math Words and Ideas

Multiple Towers

Math Words
- multiple

When you skip count by a certain number, you are finding multiples of that number.

Tonya's class made a multiple tower for the number 16. They recorded the multiples of 16 on a paper strip, starting at the bottom.

They circled every 10th multiple of 16 and used them as landmark multiples to solve the following problems.

$\underline{21} \times 16 = 336$

Tonya's solution
We know $20 \times 16 = 320$. 336 is next on the tower after 320, so it is one more 16.

$30 \times 16 = \underline{480}$

Venetta's solution
30×16 would be the next landmark multiple on our tower. Since $3 \times 16 = 48$, then $30 \times 16 = 48 \times 10$.

$208 \div 16 = \underline{13}$

Nadeem's solution
Ten 16s land on 160. Three more 16s will go to 208.

336, 320, 304, 288, 272, 256, 240, 224, 208, 192, 176, 160, 144, 128, 112, 96, 80, 64, 48, 32, 16

10 X 16

How would you use this multiple tower to solve this problem?
$11 \times 16 =$ ____

SMH 36 thirty-six

Math Words and Ideas, p. 36

Math Words and Ideas

Multiplying Groups of 10

(page 1 of 2)

Each of these models helps show the relationship between these two multiplication equations.

$3 \times 4 = 12$

$3 \times 40 = 120$

Cubes

3 groups of 4 cubes

3 groups of 40 cubes

Arrays

4; 3 — a 3 by 4 array

40; 3 — a 3 by 40 array

Skip Counting Patterns

This pattern of multiples increases by 4.

Multiples of 4: 4 8 (12) 16 20 24 28 32 36 40 . . .

This pattern of multiples increases by 4 tens.

Multiples of 40: 40 80 (120) 160 200 240 280 320 360 400 . . .

thirty-seven SMH 37

Math Words and Ideas, p. 37

Math Words and Ideas

Multiplying Groups of 10

(page 2 of 2)

Consider the relationship among these three equations.

$3 \times 4 = 12$
$3 \times 40 = 120$
$30 \times 40 = 1{,}200$

$3 \times 4 = 12$	$3 \times 4 = 12$
$3 \times 40 = 120$	$(3 \times 4) \times 10 = 12 \times 10$
$30 \times 40 = 1{,}200$	$(3 \times 4) \times (10 \times 10) = 12 \times 100$

Solve these related problems.
5 × 7 = ______ 5 × 70 ______ 50 × 70 = ______

Math Words and Ideas, p. 38

Math Words and Ideas

Multiplication Cluster Problems

Multiplication cluster problems are sets of multiplication problems that help you use what you know about easier problems to solve harder problems.

1. Solve the problems in each cluster.
2. Use one or more of the problems in the cluster to solve the final problem, along with other problems if you need them.

Solve these cluster problems.	How did you solve the final problem?
$2 \times 3 =$ 6 $5 \times 3 =$ 15 $50 \times 3 =$ 150 Now solve this problem. $52 \times 3 =$ **156**	*I multiplied 50 by 3 and then the 2 by 3, and then I added.* *50 × 3 = 150* *2 × 3 = 6* ***156***

Solve these cluster problems.	How did you solve the final problem?
$4 \times 8 =$ 32 $20 \times 8 =$ 160 $25 \times 4 =$ 100 Now solve this problem. $24 \times 8 =$ **192**	*I know that 25 × 4 = 100.* *Then I know that 25 × 8 = 200 because it is double.* *I need to subtract 8 because it is really 24 × 8.* *200 − 8 =* ***192***

Math Words and Ideas, p. 39

Math Words and Ideas

Strategies for Solving Multiplication Problems

(page 1 of 4)

Breaking Numbers Apart

In Grade 4, you are learning how to solve multiplication problems with a 2-digit factor. In the examples on this page and page 41, students broke a multiplication problem with large numbers into smaller parts that made it easier to solve.

Steve and Kimberly solved the problem 28×4 by breaking the factor 28 into parts. Notice that the two students had two different ways to break apart 28.

Steve's solution

$28 = 20 + 8$ — *I broke 28 into 20 and 8.*

$20 \times 4 = 80$ — *I used the 20 and multiplied 20 × 4. I know that 20 × 2 = 40 and 40 + 40 = 80.*

$8 \times 4 = 32$ — *Next I needed to multiply 8 × 4. I know that multiplication combination.*

$80 + 32 =$ **112** — *For the last step I added 80 and 32.*

Kimberly's solution

$28 = 25 + 3$ — *I broke 28 into 25 and 3.*

$25 \times 4 = 100$ — *I used the 25 and multiplied 25 × 4. I know that 25 × 4 = 100 because 4 quarters equal $1.00.*

$3 \times 4 = 12$ — *Next I needed to multiply 3 × 4. I know that multiplication combination.*

$100 + 12 =$ **112** — *For the last step, I added 100 and 12.*

Math Words and Ideas, p. 40

Math Words and Ideas

Strategies for Solving Multiplication Problems

(page 2 of 4)

Richard solved the problem 38×26 by breaking apart both factors.

There are 38 rows in the auditorium with 26 chairs in each row. How many people can sit in the auditorium?

Richard's solution

How many people are in the first 30 rows?

30 × 20 = 600 That's the first 30 rows, with 20 people in each row.

30 × 6 = 180 That's 6 more people in each of those 30 rows, so now I've filled up 30 rows.

How many people are in the last 8 rows?

8 × 20 = 160 That's 20 people in those last 8 rows.

8 × 6 = 48 Now I've filled up the last 8 rows with 6 more people in each row.

How many people can sit in the auditorium?

600 + 180 + 160 + 48 = ***988***

988 people can sit in the auditorium.

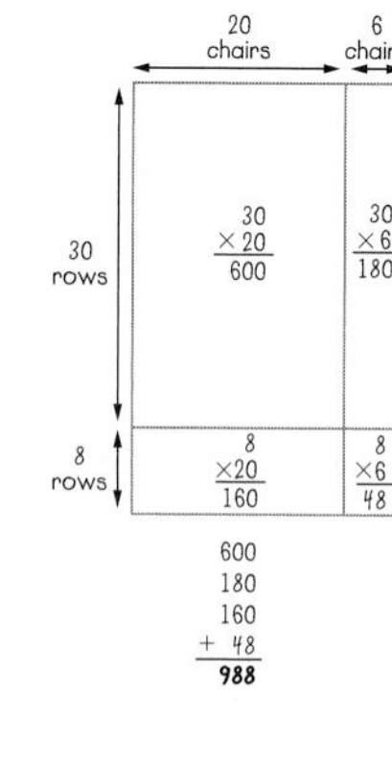

Math Words and Ideas, p. 41

Strategies for Solving Multiplication Problems

(page 3 of 4)

Changing One Number to Make an Easier Problem

Another way to solve multiplication problems is by changing one number to make the problem easier to solve. Amelia solved the auditorium problem, 38 × 26, by changing the 38 to 40 to make an easier problem.

Amelia's solution

I'll pretend that there are 40 rows in the auditorium instead of 38.

How many people could sit in 40 rows?

40 × 26 = 1,040 *I know that 10 × 26 = 260. I doubled that to get 520, and doubled that to get 1,040.*

26 chairs
40 rows
40 × 26 = 1,040

So, if there were 40 rows, 1,040 people could sit in the auditorium. But there are really only 38 rows, so I have 2 extra rows of 26 chairs. I need to subtract those.

2 × 26 = 52 *I need to subtract 52. I'll do that in two parts.*

1,040 − 40 = 1,000 *First I'll subtract 40.*

*1,000 − 12 = **988*** *Then I'll subtract 12.*

*So, **988** people can sit in the auditorium.*

26 chairs
38 rows
1,040 − 52 = 988

Math Words and Ideas, p. 42

Strategies for Solving Multiplication Problems

(page 4 of 4)

Creating an Equivalent Problem

One way to create an equivalent problem that is easier to solve is by "doubling and halving" the factors. Abdul solved the multiplication problem 6 × 35 by "doubling and halving" the factors to create the equivalent problem 70 × 3.

Abdul's solution

35 → 70
× 6 → × 3
210

I doubled 35 to get 70, and I took half of 6 to get 3.
My picture shows that 6 × 35 = 3 × 70.
For me, 3 × 70 is an easier problem to solve.

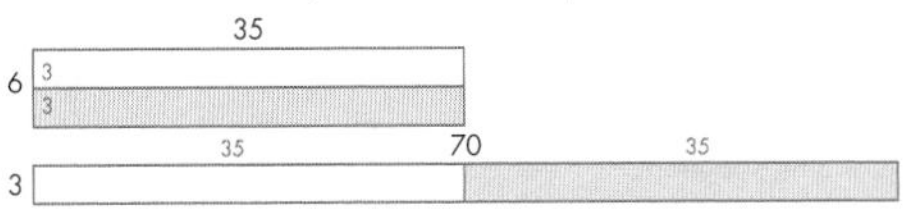

LaTanya solved the multiplication problem 4 × 36 by "tripling and thirding" the factors to create an equivalent problem.

LaTanya's solution

4 × 36 =
12 × 12 = **144**

I tripled 4 to get 12. (4 × 3 = 12)
I took a third of 36 to get 12. (36 ÷ 3 = 12)
My picture shows that 4 × 36 = 12 × 12.
For me, 12 × 12 is an easier problem to solve.

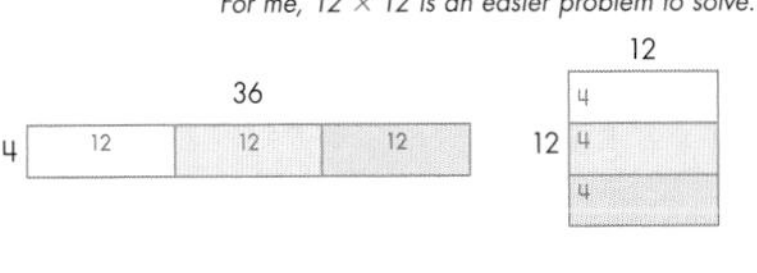

Math Words and Ideas, p. 43

Division

Math Words
- **division**

Use division when you want to separate a total into equal-sized groups.

Ms. Santos owns a souvenir store. She has 36 water bottles to arrange on 4 shelves. How many water bottles will there be on each shelf if each shelf has the same number of bottles?

WATER BOTTLES

There are 36 water bottles in all.

There are 4 shelves.

Ms. Santos can display 9 water bottles on each shelf.

36 ÷ 4 = 9

total number of water bottles — number of shelves — number of water bottles on each shelf

Math Words and Ideas, p. 44

Division and Multiplication

Division and multiplication are related operations that both involve equal-sized groups.

× Use multiplication when you want to combine groups that are the same size.

Number of groups	Size of group	Number in all the groups	Equation
22 teams	18 players on each team	*unknown*	22 × 18 = **396**

There are 22 youth soccer teams in our town, and there are 18 players on each team. How many players are on all of the teams?

Answer: There are **396** players in all.

÷ Use division when you want to separate a quantity into equal-sized groups.

Number of groups	Size of group	Number in all the groups	Equation
22 teams	*unknown*	396 players	396 ÷ 22 = **18**

There are 22 soccer teams in our town and 396 players altogether on all the teams. Each team has the same number of players. How many players are on each team?

Answer: Each team has **18** players.

Number of groups	Size of group	Number in all the groups	Equation
unknown	18 players on each team	396 players	396 ÷ 18 = **22**

There are 396 soccer players in our town, and there are 18 players on each team. How many teams are there?

Answer: There are **22** teams.

Math Words and Ideas, p. 45

Math Words and Ideas

Division Situations

Look at this division expression: 28 ÷ 7

There are two different kinds of division story problems we can think about.

The first type is a sharing situation.

There are 28 marbles being shared equally among 7 friends. How many marbles does each person get?

Each friend gets 4 marbles.

The second type is a grouping situation.

There are 28 marbles. I want to put 7 marbles in each bag. How many bags can I fill?

I can fill 4 bags.

Different symbols can be used to represent 28 divided by 7.

$28 \div 7$ $\quad 7\overline{)28}$ $\quad \frac{28}{7}$ $\quad 7 \times \underline{\ ?\ } = 28$

Write a story about 18 ÷ 3.

Math Words and Ideas, p. 46

Math Words and Ideas

Remainders

Math Words
- remainder

In some division problems the numbers do not divide evenly.

Look at this problem: 45 ÷ 6

My teacher has 45 pencils that she wants to tie together in groups of 6.

This problem has a remainder.

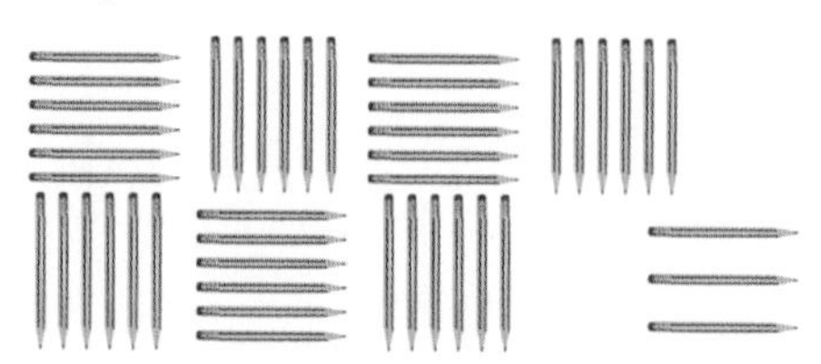

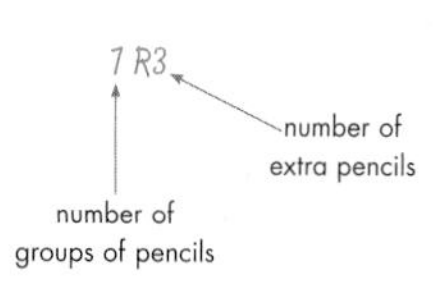

My teacher can make 7 groups of 6, and there are 3 pencils left over.

7 R3

number of extra pencils

number of groups of pencils

Steve has 22 apples. He wants to put them in bags with 4 to a bag. How many bags can he fill?

Math Words and Ideas, p. 47

Math Words and Ideas

Remainders: What Do You Do with the Extras? (page 1 of 2)

These two pages show some different story problems for the division problem 30 ÷ 4. The answer to each problem is different, even though you divided the same numbers.

There are 30 people who are taking a car trip. Each car holds 4 people. How many cars do they need?

7 cars will hold 28 people, but the other 2 people still need a ride, so they need 1 more car.

Answer: They need **8** cars.

There are 30 pencils and 4 students. The teacher wants to give the same number to each student. How many does each student get?

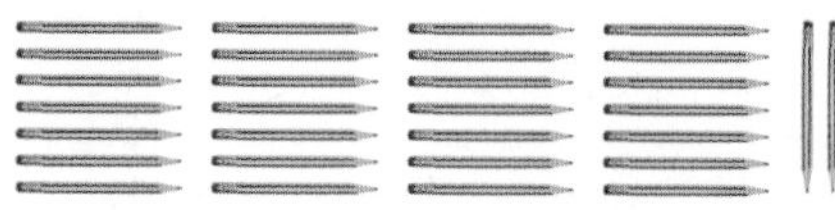

It does not make sense to break up the leftover pencils to give to the students, so the teacher can keep the remaining 2 pencils.

Answer: Each student gets **7** pencils.

Math Words and Ideas, p. 48

Math Words and Ideas

Remainders: What Do You Do with the Extras? (page 2 of 2)

Four friends earned $30 by washing people's cars. They want to share the money equally. How much does each person get?

Dollars can be split up into smaller amounts. Each person can get $7, and the $2 that are left can be divided evenly, so every person gets another 50¢.

Answer: Each person gets **$7.50.**

Four people are sharing 30 crackers evenly. How many crackers does each person get?

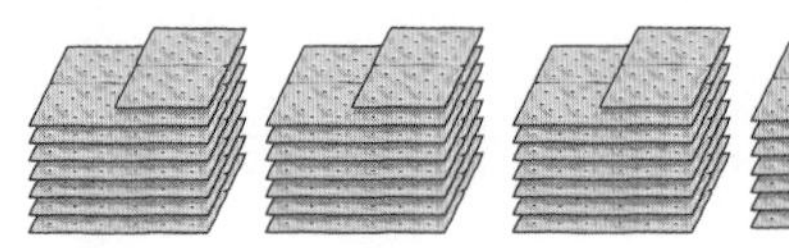

Each person gets 7 crackers. Then the last 2 crackers can be split in half. Each person gets another half cracker.

Answer: Each person gets $7\frac{1}{2}$ crackers.

What if the same problems involved these numbers? 186 ÷ 12 Write the new problems. Then tell what you would do with the extras.

Math Words and Ideas, p. 49

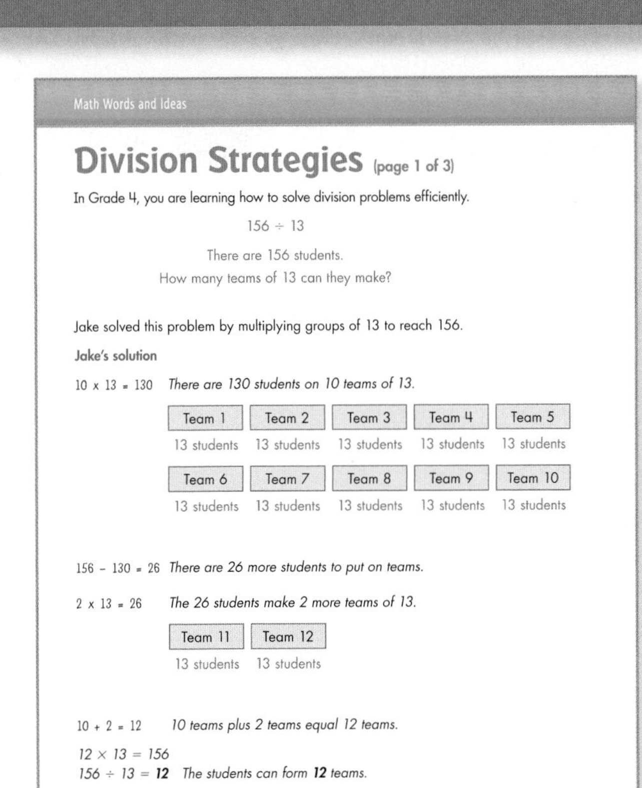

Math Words and Ideas

Division Strategies (page 1 of 3)

In Grade 4, you are learning how to solve division problems efficiently.

156 ÷ 13

There are 156 students.
How many teams of 13 can they make?

Jake solved this problem by multiplying groups of 13 to reach 156.

Jake's solution

10 x 13 = 130 *There are 130 students on 10 teams of 13.*

Team 1	Team 2	Team 3	Team 4	Team 5
13 students	13 students	13 students	13 students	13 students
Team 6	Team 7	Team 8	Team 9	Team 10
13 students	13 students	13 students	13 students	13 students

156 − 130 = 26 *There are 26 more students to put on teams.*

2 x 13 = 26 *The 26 students make 2 more teams of 13.*

Team 11	Team 12
13 students	13 students

10 + 2 = 12 *10 teams plus 2 teams equal 12 teams.*

12 × 13 = 156

*156 ÷ 13 = **12** The students can form **12** teams.*

SMH 50 fifty

Math Words and Ideas, p. 50

Math Words and Ideas

Division Strategies (page 2 of 3)

Here is another solution to 156 ÷ 13. Ursula solved the problem by breaking up 156 and dividing the parts by 13.

Ursula's solution

156 = 130 + 26 *I broke up 156 into two parts that are easier to divide by 13.*

130 ÷ 13 = 10 *130 students make 10 teams of 13.*

Team 1	Team 2	Team 3	Team 4	Team 5
13 students	13 students	13 students	13 students	13 students
Team 6	Team 7	Team 8	Team 9	Team 10
13 students	13 students	13 students	13 students	13 students

26 ÷ 13 = 2 *26 students make 2 teams of 13.*

Team 11	Team 12
13 students	13 students

10 + 2 = 12 *10 teams plus 2 teams equal 12 teams.*

*156 ÷ 13 = **12** The students can form **12** teams.*

fifty-one SMH 51

Math Words and Ideas, p. 51

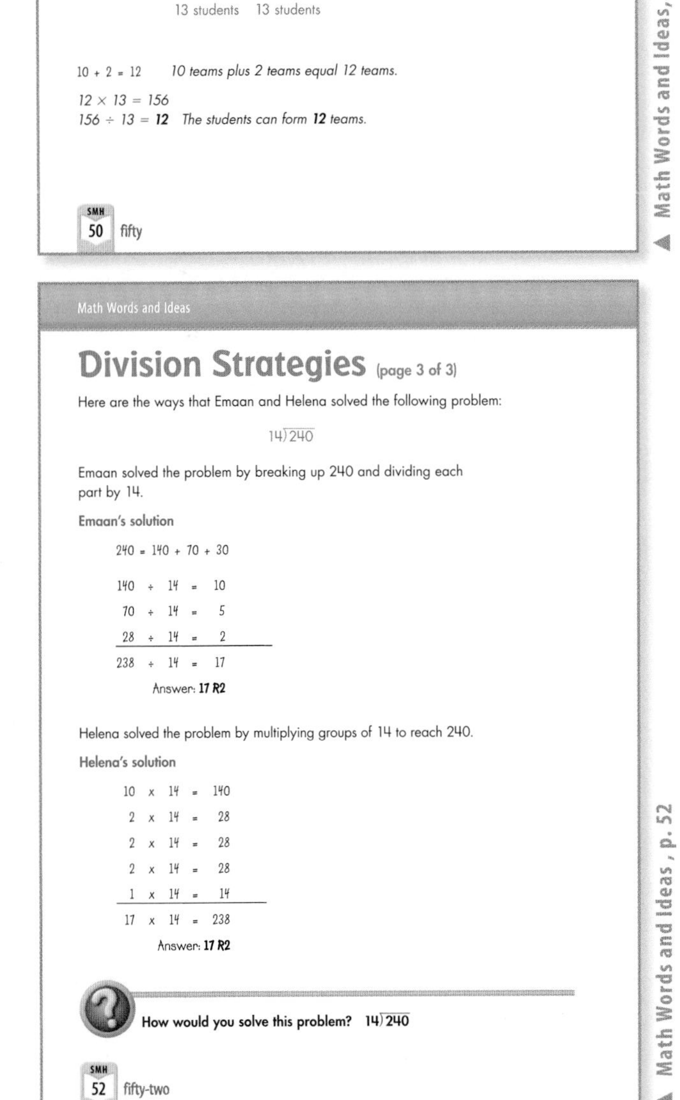

Math Words and Ideas

Division Strategies (page 3 of 3)

Here are the ways that Emaan and Helena solved the following problem:

$14\overline{)240}$

Emaan solved the problem by breaking up 240 and dividing each part by 14.

Emaan's solution

240 = 140 + 70 + 30

140 ÷ 14 = 10
70 ÷ 14 = 5
28 ÷ 14 = 2
238 ÷ 14 = 17

Answer: **17 R2**

Helena solved the problem by multiplying groups of 14 to reach 240.

Helena's solution

10 x 14 = 140
2 x 14 = 28
2 x 14 = 28
2 x 14 = 28
1 x 14 = 14
17 x 14 = 238

Answer: **17 R2**

How would you solve this problem? $14\overline{)240}$

SMH 52 fifty-two

Math Words and Ideas, p. 52

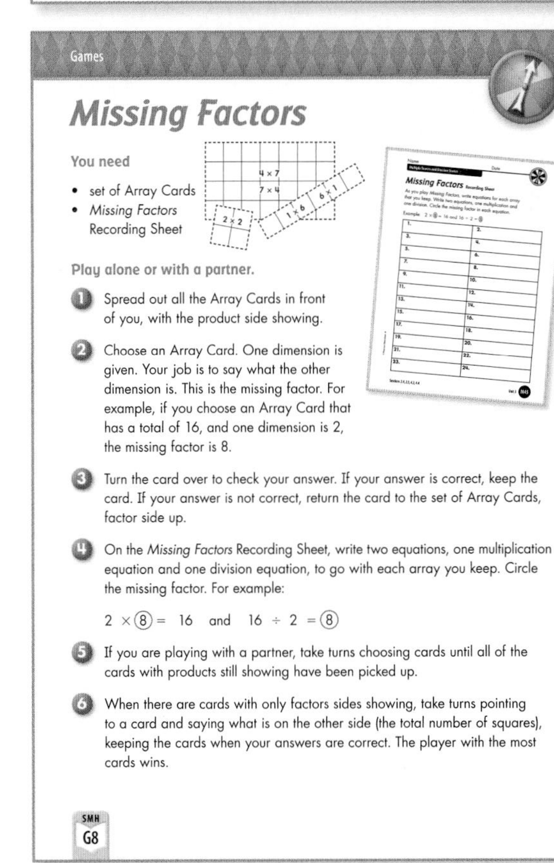

Games

Missing Factors

You need

- set of Array Cards
- *Missing Factors* Recording Sheet

Play alone or with a partner.

1. Spread out all the Array Cards in front of you, with the product side showing.
2. Choose an Array Card. One dimension is given. Your job is to say what the other dimension is. This is the missing factor. For example, if you choose an Array Card that has a total of 16, and one dimension is 2, the missing factor is 8.
3. Turn the card over to check your answer. If your answer is correct, keep the card. If your answer is not correct, return the card to the set of Array Cards, factor side up.
4. On the *Missing Factors* Recording Sheet, write two equations, one multiplication equation and one division equation, to go with each array you keep. Circle the missing factor. For example:

   2 × ⑧ = 16 and 16 ÷ 2 = ⑧
5. If you are playing with a partner, take turns choosing cards until all of the cards with products still showing have been picked up.
6. When there are cards with only factors sides showing, take turns pointing to a card and saying what is on the other side (the total number of squares), keeping the cards when your answers are correct. The player with the most cards wins.

SMH G8

Games, G8

Games

Small Array/Big Array

(page 1 of 2)

You need

- set of Array Cards
- *Small Array/Big Array* Recording Sheet
- construction paper

Play with a partner, or form 2-player teams and play each other.

1. Deal out 10 Array Cards to each player (or team) and spread them out, factor side up.
2. On a sheet of construction paper, spread out 6 more Array Cards, factor side up. These are the center cards. Place the remaining cards in a pile to one side.
3. Players take turns matching small arrays to big arrays. "Matching" means that both arrays have one dimension, or one whole side, that is the same. For example, 3 × 11 and 5 × 11 are a match.
4. On your turn, try to match one of your Array Cards to a center card. Place your card on top of the center card so that it covers part of the array. You may play only one array on a turn.

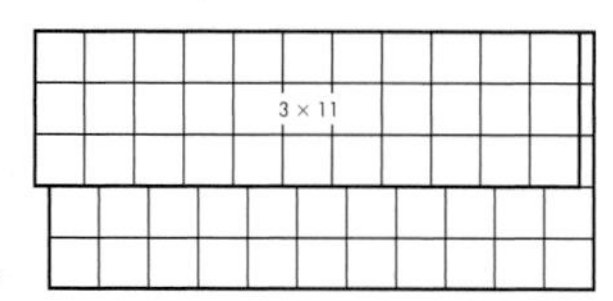

SMH G10

Games, G10

Games

Small Array/Big Array

(page 2 of 2)

5. If none of your Array Cards matches a center card, you may do one of these two things:
   (a) Draw a card from the pile. Play it if you can, or add it to your Array Cards if you cannot.
   (b) Choose one center array that matches another center array, and play that card. This is particularly useful when there are small arrays in the center.
6. If you use a center array to cover another center array, you must either
   (a) replace it with a card from the pile; or
   (b) put one of your own Array Cards in the center. There must always be 6 cards in the center.
7. The goal is to make a complete match by covering a big array with a combination of 2 or 3 smaller arrays. When you play a card that makes a complete match, you collect both the big array and the smaller arrays covering it. Then you replace the center card with one from the pile. On the *Small Array/Big Array* Recording Sheet, use equations to record the complete match, using parentheses to show the smaller arrays. For example:

   $5 \times 11 = (3 \times 11) + (2 \times 11)$

   $55 \quad = \quad 33 \quad + \quad 22$

8. Keep in mind that there is only one card for each array. Sometimes, to complete a match, you need an array that has already been used. When this happens, you may use your turn to say what the needed card is and complete the match.
9. The game is over when there are no more cards or no more matches can be made.

SMH G11

Games, G11

Index

IN THIS UNIT

I

J

K

L

M

N

O

P

Q

R